Editor in Chief
Sharon Coan, M.S. Ed.

Illustrators
Larry Bauer
Howard Chaney
Sue Fullam
Agi Palinay
Wendi Wright-Davis

Cover Artist
Chris Macabitas
Jeff Sutherland

Art Coordinator
Denice Adorno

Creative Director
Elayne Roberts

Imaging
James Edward Grace
Alfred Lau
Ralph Olmedo Jr.

Product Manager
Phil Garcia

Publishers
Rachelle Cracchiolo, M.S. Ed.
Mary Dupuy Smith, M.S. Ed.

Practice and Learn

for
8 to 12 Year Olds

Compiled and Written by

Karen Froloff
Dona Herweck Rice
Char-Lee L. Hill
Sheila Greenberg
Betty Weiss

Teacher Created Materials, Inc.
6421 Industry Way
Westminster, CA 92683
www.teachercreated.com
©2000 Teacher Created Materials, Inc.
Reprinted, 2000
Made in U.S.A.
ISBN-1-57690-971-9

Table of Contents

Introduction

Within this book are hundreds of pages designed to teach and reinforce the basic skills that are mandatory for success in school and life. The book is divided into sections by age level, but the pages can be used with any person who is ready to practice and learn the skills they contain. Research shows that skill mastery comes with exposure and drill. This book will provide a myriad of exercises to help learners attain mastery in the skills covered. We hope students will enjoy using these pages to "practice and learn."

Practice & Learn
for
8 Year Olds

Capitalize and Punctuate

Every sentence ends with a period (.), a question mark (?), or an exclamation point (!). Rewrite the sentences found below. Be sure to begin each one with a capital letter. End each one with the correct punctuation mark.

1. my cousin spent the night at my house

_____

_____

2. john said I could look at his snake

_____

_____

3. jim entered the bicycle race

_____

_____

4. what a race it was

_____

_____

5. did he wear a helmet

_____

_____

6. who won the race

_____

_____

What's My Ending?

Add a period (.), a question mark (?), or an exclamation point (!) to the end of each sentence.

1. He can go with him

2. Where are you

3. Help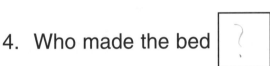

4. Who made the bed

5. Go to third base

6. I like to eat cookies

7. What a fine job

8. The tools are in the shed

9. How much do you want

10. What is your name

Scrambled Sentences

Unscramble the words to make a sentence. Be sure to add a capital letter at the beginning and punctuation at the end.

1. bird cat the chased the

   _____

   _____

2. letter friend I a wrote my to

   _____

   _____

3. puzzle the solved the family together

   _____

   _____

4. a baker cake baked the

   _____

   _____

5. sea jumped into penguin a the

   _____

   _____

6. frog the log over leaped the

   _____

   _____

What's a Noun?

Nouns are words that name a person, place, or thing. Write each word under the correct heading.

Adam	farmer	motor	scientist
attic	football	museum	state
comb	hoe	rainbow	zookeeper
Dr. Roberts	London	room	
door	mother	Russia	

Person	Place	Thing
ADam	attic	comB
Dr. RoBerts	London	door
farmer	museum	footBall
mother	room	hoe
scientist	Russia	moTor
zookeeper	state	rainBow

Person, Place, or Thing?

Complete each sentence with a noun from the word box. Then tell if the noun names a person, place, or thing.

dentist	sand	sister	truck
house	school	tire	

Person, Place, or Thing?

1. The ostrich buried its head in the

   _____.   _____

2. The man drove his

   _____ into town.   _____

3. My _____ had a cold so

   she stayed home.   _____

4. Our _____ reminded us

   to brush after eating.   _____

5. The new _____ has

   many classrooms.   _____

6. My bicycle got a flat

   _____ from the sharp

   pebble in the road.   _____

7. My parents are going to paint our

   _____.   _____

Naming More Than One

Add **s** or **es** to each word to make it more than one.

dog   dogs

1. cane _____

2. brush _____

3. duck _____

4. bear _____

5. fox _____

6. dress _____

7. glass _____

8. bag _____

9. bucket _____

10. sled _____

More Naming More Than One

Make each word more than one by **crossing out the y** and **adding ies.**

baby   **babies**

1. puppy _____

2. lady _____

3. baby _____

4. candy _____

5. pony _____

6. funny _____

7. kitty _____

8. daddy _____

9. jelly _____

10. ruby _____

Titles of People

Do you have an aunt or an uncle? If you do, write the name of your aunt or uncle here: _____

The word "aunt" or "uncle" is always capitalized when it is written with a name. It is called a title. Here are more titles:

Grandma	**President**	**Mister (Mr.)**	**Miss**	**Cousin**
Grandpa	**Captain**	**Mistress (Mrs.)**	**Coach**	**Doctor**

Sometimes titles are capitalized when they are written without a name, like Grandma or Grandpa. When titles are written with names, they are **always** capitalized.

Capitalize the titles of people when they are written with names.

Rewrite these names and titles with capitals where they are needed.

grandmother davis _____

mister hayes _____

captain jack _____

cousin jimmy _____

doctor morton _____

coach russell _____

Days of the Week

What day of the week is it today?_____

Did you use a capital letter to begin your answer? If you did, you know this capitalization rule:

Capitalize the days of the week.

Here are the days of the week. They are not in order, and they do not have capital letters. Write them in order with capitals on the lines inside the watch. Begin with Sunday.

friday   **sunday**

monday   **tuesday**

wednesday   **thursday**

saturday

When you have finished writing, color the strap. Cut it out, and cut out the slots marked A, B, and C. Put the strap around your wrist like a watch. Tuck the tab in the correct-fitting slot. Fold the tab over to hold the strap in place. You are wearing the days of the week now!

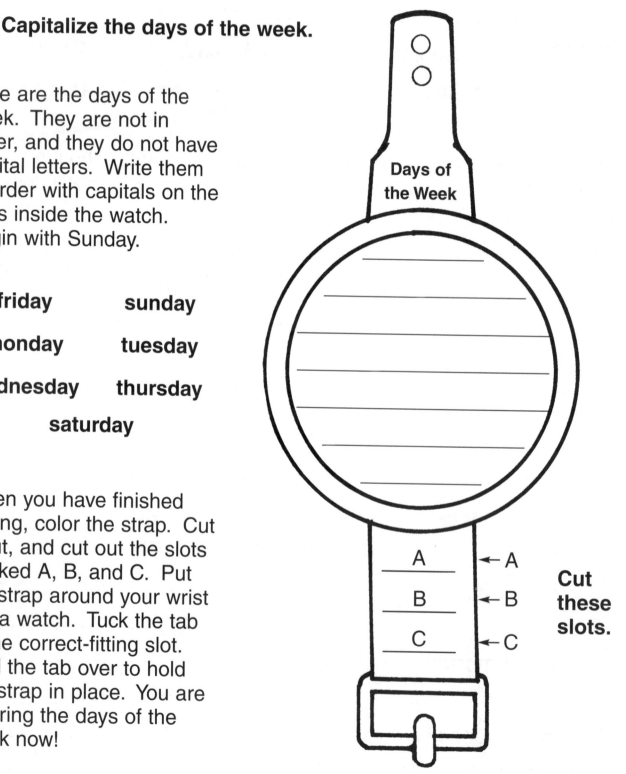

Days of
the Week

A ← A
B ← B
C ← C

Cut these slots.

Months of the Year

What month of the year is it today? _____

Did you use a capital letter to begin your answer? If you did, you know this capitalization rule:

Capitalize the months of the year.

The months of the year are written in order below, but they do not have capital letters. Rewrite them in order with capitals. Next to each month, write something that you like about that month. It could be a special holiday, a pretty time of year, or even your birthday! On the back of this paper, draw a picture of what you like about one month.

| **january** | **march** | **may** | **july** | **september** | **november** |
| **february** | **april** | **june** | **august** | **october** | **december** |

1. _____   _____

2. _____   _____

3. _____   _____

4. _____   _____

5. _____   _____

6. _____   _____

7. _____   _____

8. _____   _____

9. _____   _____

10. _____   _____

11. _____   _____

12. _____   _____

Holidays

What is your favorite holiday? _____

Did you start it with a capital letter? If you did, you know this capitalization rule:

Capitalize the names of holidays.

There are some names of holidays on this page. They are not capitalized correctly. Capitalize the holidays by changing a lowercase letter to a capital letter where it is needed. As you write each capital letter, color the same letter in the heart.

new year's Day

halloween

Fourth of july

hanukkah

father's day

mother's Day

easter

christmas

passover

valentine's Day

N O X F
D S B Y
P H E C
J W L M
V R A H

What letter did the colored hearts make? _____

Write the names of two holidays that begin with this letter.

　　1. _____

　　2. _____

Color the rest of the heart!

Vacation Time!

Do you like to go to museums, zoos, or parks?

Do you like to travel to a lake, ocean, river, or mountain?

These places and other places need capital letters when they are written with a name.

Capitalize the names of special places.

It is vacation time!

Here is a list of places that need capital letters. Correct the letters that need to be capitalized. Then choose three of the places you would like to visit!

1. pacific Ocean
2. Grand canyon
3. Mt. rushmore
4. amazon River

5. san diego Zoo
6. hyde park
7. sahara desert
8. lake Louise

9. disneyland
10. North pole
11. rocky Mountains
12. niagara falls

I would like to visit the following places:

1. _____

2. _____

3. _____

Name your favorite place to visit. Write something about this place.

_____

_____

_____

_____

Action Word Fill-In

A **verb** shows the **action** of the sentence.

The train sped along the tracks.

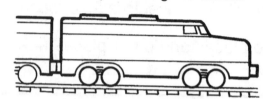

Write the word that shows what someone or something does.

1. The star twinkles in the sky. _____

2. The children watched the parade. _____

3. The dog chased the cat. _____

4. My brother set the table. _____

5. I swim like a fish. _____

6. The bird sings a pretty song. _____

7. You eat the last piece. _____

8. The player threw the ball. _____

More Action Word Fill-Ins

Write the word in the sentence. Add **s** or **es** if it is needed when the sentence is about one person or thing.

Jill **jumps** hurdles every day.

play   1. The cat _____ with the mouse.

win   2. The boxer _____ the match.

match   3. He _____ the opposites.

dance   4. We _____ to the music.

bark   5. My dog _____ at the birds.

eat   6. She _____ a hamburger.

like   7. Meg _____ to splash in the puddles.

shine   8. The sun _____ on the water.

watch   9. Jamie _____ the sunset.

walk   10. My uncle _____ five miles each day.

The Marching Band

Read the story. Then follow the directions below.

Marcus heard the music. "Listen!" he cried. "I hear it!" Marcus and his mother looked down the long street to their left. Only a moment later, they could see the band marching toward them. The bright red and blue uniforms sparkled almost as much as the shiny silver and gold instruments the musicians were playing.

As the band marched closer, Marcus looked at the instruments. He smiled when he saw the flutes. "Shawn should be coming by soon," he told his mother. After the flutes passed by, Marcus shouted, "There she is, Mom! There's Shawn!" He waved happily to his big sister.

When the parade was over, Marcus and his mother waited for Shawn to meet them. "You were great," he told Shawn.

"Thanks," Shawn answered. "I'm tired though. Let's go home!"

1. Circle the letter of the sentence that shows what happened first.
   - A. Marcus saw the band.
   - B. Marcus heard music.
   - C. Shawn went home.

2. Circle the letter of the sentence that shows what happened after Marcus saw the flutes.
   - A. He knew the trumpets would be next.
   - B. He hugged his mother.
   - C. He told his mother that he could see Shawn.

A Polar Bear's Day

Read the story. Then write the things that the polar bear does each day in order on the lines below.

The zookeeper at the Riverside Zoo was telling the children about the polar bear. "What does the polar bear do each day?" asked Paul.

"The polar bear swims, eats, plays, and sleeps," answered the zookeeper.

Paul thanked the zookeeper for his answer, but he was still curious. "When does the polar bear wake up? How many times does he eat each day? Does he take naps? Does he stay awake all night?" Paul's questions went on and on.

"Oh, I see. You want details about how the bear lives his day, right?" said the zookeeper. "Well, let me see. He gets up at dawn because the light and the heat wake him. He usually goes for a swim right away. He gets out of the water when we feed him, which is at about ten o'clock. He takes a nap after he eats. After his nap, he usually swims again. Then he plays until about six o'clock, when we feed him again. He swims and plays until bedtime, which is as soon as it gets dark. Now do you understand about a polar bear's day in the zoo?"

"Yes, thank you," answered Paul. Then he turned to watch the polar bear with interest.

List the things the polar bear does each day. The first has been done for you.

1. He gets up at dawn.

2. _____

3. _____

4. _____

5. _____

6. _____

7. _____

8. _____

9. _____

Kelly's Puppet

Read the story. Then follow the directions below.

Kelly was cleaning her room. She found three buttons and an old sock that had a hole in it. She decided to use the things she had found to make a puppet. After she finished cleaning her room, she carried the sock and buttons to her mother. "May I make a puppet with these?" she asked.

Her mother smiled and said, "Yes, and you can also use the yarn in the sewing basket."

Kelly got the yarn and some glue. She carefully glued the buttons onto the sock so that they looked like two eyes and a nose. After that, she added yarn for hair. Finally, she put the puppet on her hand. What a great toy! Kelly rushed to show her mother her new puppet.

1. Circle what Kelly did after she finished cleaning her room.
    A. Kelly put the puppet on her hand.
    B. Kelly found some buttons.
    C. Kelly took the buttons and sock to show her mother.

2. Circle what Kelly did last.
    A. Kelly showed the puppet to her mother.
    B. Kelly put the sock puppet on her hand.
    C. Kelly glued yarn on her puppet to make it look like hair.

Trip to the Zoo

Read each story and then answer the questions.

Miles and Robin wanted to go to the zoo. Their mother said they could go after they finished their chores. First, they cleaned their rooms. Next they mopped the kitchen floor. After that, they washed the family's car. Finally, they got ready to go to the zoo.

1. What did Miles and Robin do first? _____

_____

2. What did the boys do after they mopped the floor?_____

_____

Miles and Robin were on an imaginary safari. First, their mother gave them a map of the zoo. Then, the boys went to the shark pool. Next, they found the way to the tiger cage. After that, they visited the wolf den. Finally, they met their mother at the alligator exhibit. Miles and Robin had a busy afternoon!

1. Where did the boys go after they saw the tiger?

_____

2. What did the boys see last?_____

_____

3. What did the boys do last? _____

_____

Comprehension Fill-Ins

Complete each sentence with a word from the word box.

ate   knock

cough   laughed

cries   snore

delivers   wash

drove   wrote

1. Our mail carrier ___delivers___ our mail early each morning.

2. I forgot to ___wash___ the dishes after dinner.

3. My cold made me ___cough___ and sneeze all night.

4. Did you see how fast he ___drove___ his race car?

5. I have never heard anyone ___snore___ as loudly as that!

6. The family ___ate___ pizza for dinner.

7. My neighbor ___wrote___ a play for all of us to perform.

8. The doorbell is broken, so please ___knock___.

9. The children ___laughed___ at the circus clowns.

10. The puppy ___cries___ if we leave it alone.

Home Run!

Read the story. Then answer the questions.

Pow! Stacie stared in disbelief as the ball sailed over the pitcher, second base, and finally past the outfield fence. It was a home run, the first one she had ever hit! Dropping the bat at home plate, Stacie ran the bases one by one. Then she was home again, and the whole team rushed out to meet her.

1. What game is Stacie playing?

   SoftBall

2. How often does Stacie hit home runs?

   This was her first one

3. What does the team do when Stacie comes home?

   They all rushed out to meet
   her

Draw a picture from the story.

Pounce!

Read the story. Then answer the questions.

Kenny woke up on Saturday morning and looked out the window. "It's raining!" he moaned and pulled the covers over his head. Just then, he felt a pounce on his feet and then on his stomach. He peeked out, and there was Buttons, purring and peeking back.

"Maybe it won't be such a bad morning, after all," Kenny thought, and, petting Buttons, he jumped out of bed.

1. What kind of animal is Buttons?

_____

2. How does Kenny feel about the rain?

_____

3. What happens to cheer up Kenny?

_____

Draw a picture from the story.

Sing a Song of Sixpence

Read the poem. Then answer the questions.

> Sing a song of sixpence, a pocket full of rye;
>
> Four and twenty blackbirds baked in a pie.
>
> When the pie was opened, the birds began to sing;
>
> Now, was not that a dainty dish to
>   set before the king?
>
> The king was in his counting house,
>   counting out his money;
>
> The queen was in the parlor, eating
>   bread and honey.
>
> The maid was in the garden,
>   hanging out the clothes
>
> When down came a blackbird and
>   pecked off her nose.

1. How many blackbirds are in the pie? _____

   _____

2. What do the birds do when the pie is opened? _____

   _____

3. What is the king doing? _____

   _____

4. Where is the queen? _____

   _____

5. What happens to the maid? _____

   _____

There Was a Crooked Man

Read the poem. Then answer the questions.

There was a crooked man,

And he walked a crooked mile.

He found a crooked sixpence

Against a crooked stile.

He bought a crooked cat,

Which caught a crooked mouse.

And they all lived together

In a little crooked house.

1. Who walked a mile? _____

_____

2. What did he find? _____

_____

3. What did he buy? _____

_____

4. What did the cat do? _____

_____

5. What does everything in the poem have in common? _____

_____

Old King Cole

Read the poem. Then answer the questions.

Old King Cole
Was a merry old soul,
And a merry old soul was he.
He called for his pipe,
And he called for his bowl,
And he called for his fiddlers three.
Every fiddler, he had a fiddle,
And a very fine fiddle had he.
Oh, there is none so rare
As can compare
With King Cole and his fiddlers three.

1. What sort of person is old King Cole? _____

_____

2. What is the second thing King Cole calls for? _____

_____

3. How many fiddlers are there? _____

_____

4. What kind of fiddles do the fiddlers have? _____

_____

5. List two pairs of rhyming words from the poem._____

_____

Lemonade for Sale!

Read the story. Then answer the questions.

Amy and Melanie wanted to earn some
money to go to the movies. They tried
washing dogs, but it was too messy. They
tried babysitting, but it took too much time.
So they decided to have a lemonade
stand in front of their apartment building.

On a hot, dry, Saturday morning in June,
the girls mixed the cold drinks in a plastic pitcher. They
sold the lemonade drinks for one quarter each. Ten
children and two adults bought the cold lemonade. Amy
and Melanie each needed one dollar to get into the
movies. Hooray! They were on their way!

1. Who is this story about?

_____

2. What two ways do they try to make money without any success?

_____

3. When do they open their lemonade stand?

_____

4. How much is a glass of lemonade?

_____

5. Do they get to go to the movies?

_____

Adding Palm Trees

There are several ways to add numbers in a column. One way is to add the top two numbers first. Then add the bottom number to the sum of the first two numbers. Add the numbers on each tree.

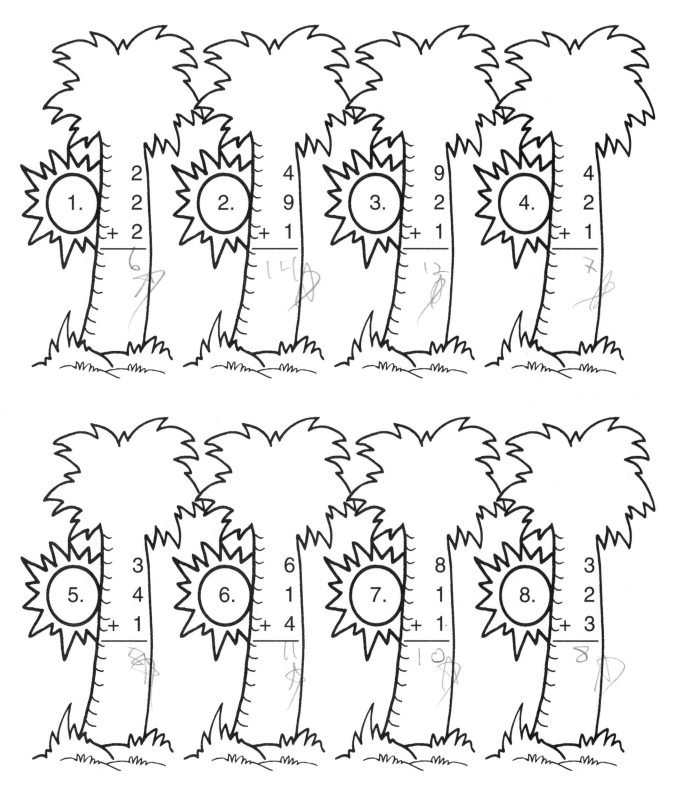

1.
$$\begin{array}{r} 2 \\ 2 \\ +\ 2 \\ \hline \end{array}$$

2.
$$\begin{array}{r} 4 \\ 9 \\ +\ 1 \\ \hline \end{array}$$

3.
$$\begin{array}{r} 9 \\ 2 \\ +\ 1 \\ \hline \end{array}$$

4.
$$\begin{array}{r} 4 \\ 2 \\ +\ 1 \\ \hline \end{array}$$

5.
$$\begin{array}{r} 3 \\ 4 \\ +\ 1 \\ \hline \end{array}$$

6.
$$\begin{array}{r} 6 \\ 1 \\ +\ 4 \\ \hline \end{array}$$

7.
$$\begin{array}{r} 8 \\ 1 \\ +\ 1 \\ \hline \end{array}$$

8.
$$\begin{array}{r} 3 \\ 2 \\ +\ 3 \\ \hline \end{array}$$

Skyscrapers Touch the Sky!

Skyscrapers stand very tall. Add the numbers on each one. Start by adding the top two numbers together and the bottom two numbers together. Then add the sums of each of those pairs to each other.

1.
3
4
3
+ 2

2.
4
3
2
+ 1

3.
2
5
2
+ 2

4.
4
1
2
+ 1

5.
1
3
1
+ 1

6.
2
1
3
+ 1

7.
3
2
1
+ 3

Add Them All Up!

To discover a secret message, find the sums. Then place each letter in the matching numbered space.

A.	B.	C.	D.	E.	G.
21	23	51	15	10	26
+ 21	+ 12	+ 10	+ 14	+ 10	+ 11

I.	L.	M.	N.	O.	R.
31	42	51	53	24	21
+ 20	+ 11	+ 41	+ 31	+ 43	+ 10

S.	T.	U.	W.	Y.
33	13	24	34	62
+ 33	+ 12	+ 15	+ 14	+ 10

___ ___ ___ ___ ___ ___ ___ ___ ___ ___ ___ ___ ___ ___ ___!
61 67 84 37 31 42 25 39 53 42 25 51 67 84 66

___ ___ ___   ___ ___ ___   ___ ___ ___ ___ ___ ___
72 67 39   42 31 20   42 29 29 51 84 37

___ ___ ___ — ___ ___ ___ ___ ___
25 48 67   29 51 37 51 25

___ ___ ___ ___ ___ ___ ___.
84 39 92 35 20 31 66

Learning to Regroup

You've come a long way. You can now add

$$11 + 5 \quad \text{or} \quad 10 + 15$$

Here's a problem for you: Sandy has 15 marbles. George also has 15 marbles. All together, how many marbles do Sandy and George have?

Simple! You just add.

tens	ones
1	5
+1	5
21	0

tens	ones
[1] 1	5
+1	5
3	0

Which answer do you think is correct? If you said 30, you are right.

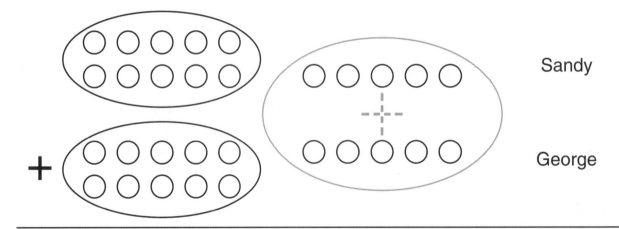

Sandy

George

2 tens + 1 more group = 3 tens, or 30 of tens

Adding in this way is called regrouping. When you add the two numbers in the ones column and your answer is 10, 11, 12, 13, 14, 15, 16, 17, 18, or 19, you must place the 1, which is in the tens column, on top of the two numbers in the tens column. Then you add those three numbers to find the correct answer.

32

The Champion Egg Layer

Gertie's chickens are the champion egg layers of Cameron County. Add the numbers on the eggs to learn how many eggs her chickens lay each day.

$$14 + 18$$

Sunday

$$15 + 15$$

Monday

$$19 + 17$$

Tuesday

$$15 + 19$$

Wednesday

$$19 + 12$$

Thursday

$$16 + 17$$

Friday

$$19 + 19$$

Saturday

#2971 Practice and Learn

Reveal the Message

To discover the special secret message, find the sums. Then place the letters in the correct spaces.

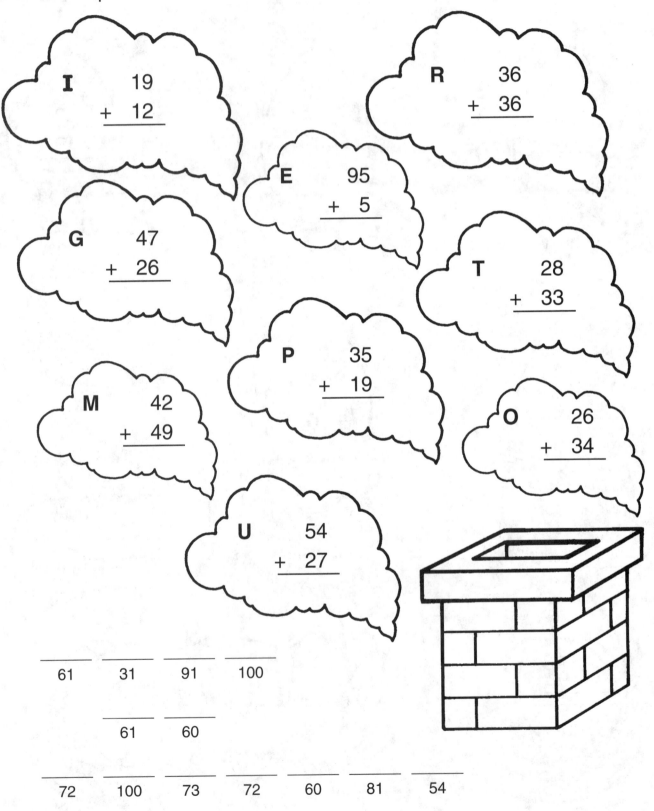

I   19
  + 12

R   36
  + 36

E   95
  + 5

G   47
  + 26

T   28
  + 33

M   42
  + 49

P   35
  + 19

O   26
  + 34

U   54
  + 27

___ ___ ___ ___
61 31 91 100

    ___ ___
    61 60

___ ___ ___ ___ ___ ___ ___
72 100 73 72 60 81 54

Pick a Hat

Find each sum. Draw a circle around the hat with the smallest sum.

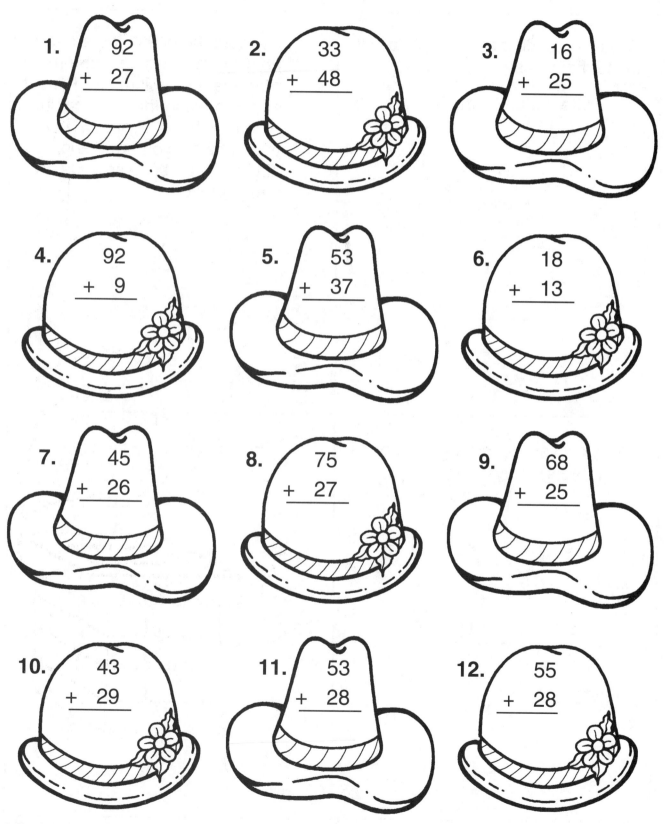

1. 92 + 27

2. 33 + 48

3. 16 + 25

4. 92 + 9

5. 53 + 37

6. 18 + 13

7. 45 + 26

8. 75 + 27

9. 68 + 25

10. 43 + 29

11. 53 + 28

12. 55 + 28

Subtracting Two-Digit Numbers (with Regrouping)

When regrouping to subtract, follow these directions:

1. Write the problem.

$$\begin{array}{r} 53 \\ -\ 14 \\ \hline \end{array}$$

2. Subtract the ones. If there are not enough ones, take a ten from the tens column and add it as ten ones to the ones column (you now have 13 ones). Keep track of what you are doing above the problem so you can see your work.

$$\begin{array}{r} {\scriptstyle 4\ 1} \\ \cancel{5}3 \\ -\ 14 \\ \hline \end{array}$$

3. Now you can subtract the ones (13 – 4).

$$\begin{array}{r} {\scriptstyle 4\ 1} \\ \cancel{5}3 \\ -\ 14 \\ \hline 9 \end{array}$$

4. Then subtract the tens (4 – 1).

$$\begin{array}{r} {\scriptstyle 4\ 1} \\ \cancel{5}3 \\ -\ 14 \\ \hline 39 \end{array}$$

Color the Picture Frames

What color frame should each animal picture have? Solve the subtraction problem in each frame. Then use the code to color the frame the appropriate color.

22 = brown   25 = black   28 = red   29 = purple   51 = pink
74 = green   77 = blue   78 = orange   89 = yellow

1.
$$\begin{array}{r} 7\,8\,1^{11} \\ -\quad 3 \\ \hline 7\,8 \end{array}$$

2.
$$\begin{array}{r} 7\,8\,0^{10} \\ -\quad 6 \\ \hline 7\,4 \end{array}$$

3.
$$\begin{array}{r} 7\,8\,0^{10} \\ -\quad 3 \\ \hline 7\,7 \end{array}$$
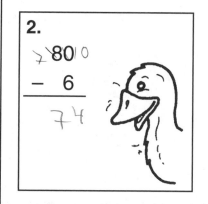

4.
$$\begin{array}{r} 2\,3\,0^{10} \\ -\quad 8 \\ \hline 2\,2 \end{array}$$
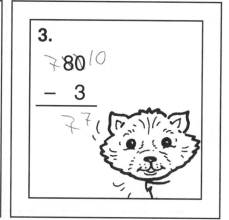

5.
$$\begin{array}{r} 2\,3\,5^{15} \\ -\quad 7 \\ \hline 2\,8 \end{array}$$

6.
$$\begin{array}{r} 5\,6\,0^{10} \\ -\quad 9 \\ \hline 5\,1 \end{array}$$

7.
$$\begin{array}{r} 2\,3\,7^{17} \\ -\quad 8 \\ \hline 2\,9 \end{array}$$

8.
$$\begin{array}{r} 8\,9\,7^{17} \\ -\quad 8 \\ \hline 8\,9 \end{array}$$

9.
$$\begin{array}{r} 2\,3\,1^{11} \\ -\quad 6 \\ \hline 2\,5 \end{array}$$

#2971 Practice and Learn

Three in a Row

Solve each subtraction problem. To win this tic-tac-toe game, draw a line through the three squares that have a 7 in their answers.

66 − 39	97 − 28	37 − 19
58 − 19	85 − 68	73 − 18
72 − 19	39 − 18	95 − 18

6/21/01

Who Took the Cookies?

To find out which bear ate the cookies, solve each subtraction problem. The bear with the numeral 6 in the difference took the cookies.

Who ate the cookies?

1.
$$72 - 59 = 13$$

2.
$$92 - 88 = 4$$

3.
$$37 - 19 = 18$$

4.
$$82 - 25 = 57$$

5.
$$52 - 36 = 16$$

6.
$$65 - 28 = 37$$

#2971 Practice and Learn

Catching Baseballs

Cross out each answer in the mitt as you solve the problems.

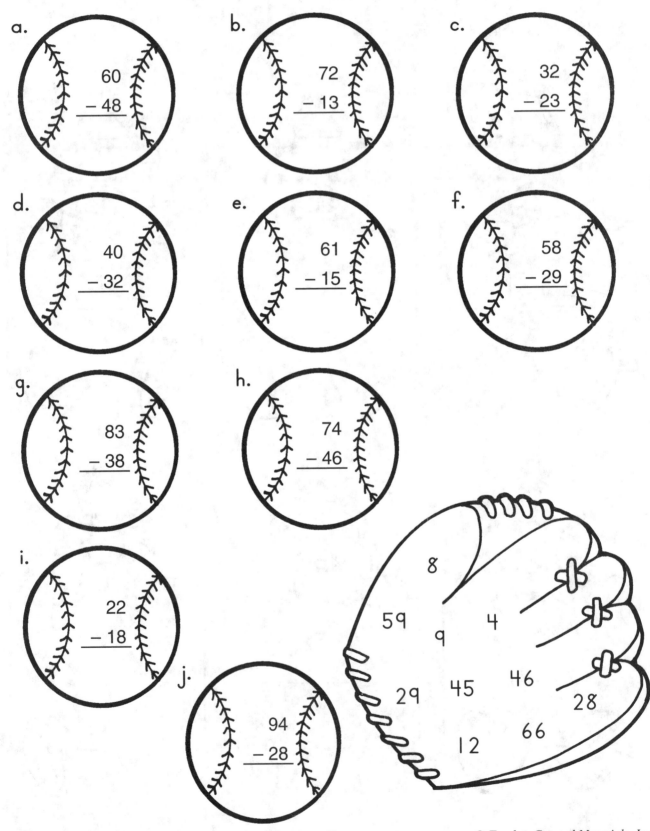

a.
$$\begin{array}{r} 60 \\ -\ 48 \\ \hline \end{array}$$

b.
$$\begin{array}{r} 72 \\ -\ 13 \\ \hline \end{array}$$

c.
$$\begin{array}{r} 32 \\ -\ 23 \\ \hline \end{array}$$

d.
$$\begin{array}{r} 40 \\ -\ 32 \\ \hline \end{array}$$

e.
$$\begin{array}{r} 61 \\ -\ 15 \\ \hline \end{array}$$

f.
$$\begin{array}{r} 58 \\ -\ 29 \\ \hline \end{array}$$

g.
$$\begin{array}{r} 83 \\ -\ 38 \\ \hline \end{array}$$

h.
$$\begin{array}{r} 74 \\ -\ 46 \\ \hline \end{array}$$

i.
$$\begin{array}{r} 22 \\ -\ 18 \\ \hline \end{array}$$

j.
$$\begin{array}{r} 94 \\ -\ 28 \\ \hline \end{array}$$

8   59   4   9   29   45   46   28   12   66

Practice & Learn

for
9 Year Olds

Find the Noun

A noun names

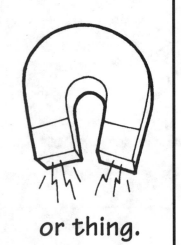

a person,   place,   or thing.

Underline each noun.

1. The dancer jumped in the air.

2. The boy watched television.

3. Mr. Smith teaches our class.

4. The baby cried for her mother.

5. The sisters walked to the store.

6. My school has two stories.

7. The teenagers rode their skateboards through the park.

8. The dentist treated a new patient.

9. A little dog picked a fight with a big cat.

10. There were presents, cake, and candles at my birthday party.

Common and Proper Nouns

Proper nouns begin with capital letters, and common nouns are just regular nouns. The word **cat** is a common noun, but **Boots**, the cat's name, is a proper noun.

I have a **cat**.

His name is **Boots**.

Circle each word used as a common noun in the sentences below. Underline the words used as proper nouns. *opposite*

1. I live in the green house on Elm Street.

2. My dog, Max, and I went for a walk.

3. There are three Ryans in my class.

4. My family is planning a trip to the Grand Canyon.

5. "Mom, where is my yellow shirt?" Jenny asked her mother.

6. Where is Primrose Park?

7. The only vegetable I like is broccoli.

8. Our neighbor's cat is named Sylvester.

9. My teacher is Mrs. Simms.

10. Ricky, Sam, and Tim are going to play football in the park.

Plural Nouns

In most cases, an *s* is added to a noun to name more than one.

If the noun ends in **s**, **x**, **ch**, or **sh**, *es* is added.

fox  foxes

Write the plural form of each noun.

1. cat _____

2. dog _____

3. house _____

4. gate _____

5. church _____

6. monkey_____

7. tree _____

8. class_____

9. door _____

10. chair _____

11. lunch_____

12. box _____

13. bush _____

14. glass_____

15. truck _____

16. brush _____

Plural Nouns Ending in Y

When a noun ends in **y**, change the **y** to **i** and add *es*.

bunny

bunnies

Write the plural forms of the nouns below.

1. penny _pennie_

2. pony _ponies_

3. berry _berries_

4. family _families_

5. factory _factories_

6. candy _candies_

7. party _patties_

8. cherry _cherries_

9. baby _babies_

10. filly _fillies_

11. jelly _jellies_

12. lily _lilies_

13. lady _ladies_

14. patty _patties_

15. fly _flies_

16. story _stories_

Unusual Plural Nouns

Some nouns do not follow the normal rules when they become plurals.

leaf   leaves

In the blanks, write the plural form of each underlined word.

1. The <u>woman</u> next door invited several _____ to tea.

2. Although one baby <u>tooth</u> fell out, many more must fall out before I have all my adult _____.

3. One <u>man</u> on my father's bowling team is much taller than the other _____.

4. I saw only one <u>child</u>, but I could hear many more _____ playing.

5. It is much more difficult to hop on one <u>foot</u> than it is to hop on both _____.

6. We caught one <u>mouse</u> in the trap, but we suspected there were other _____ in the attic as well.

7. The pioneer knew that one <u>ox</u> could not pull his wagon so he would need a team of _____.

8. One <u>wife</u> suggested that all of the _____ should meet for a morning walk.

9. The large <u>goose</u> bossed all the other _____ in the barnyard.

10. I added the hot <u>loaf</u> of bread to the other _____ I had baked in the morning.

Possessives

Possessives show who or what owns something. Singular nouns are made possessive by adding an apostrophe and then an *s*. Plural possessives are formed by adding an apostrophe after the *s*. However, when a plural noun does not end with an *s*, an apostrophe and then an *s* are added.

The **boy's kite** flew high in the sky.

Rewrite the underlined nouns in the sentences below to make them possessive.

1. The <u>baby</u> rattle fell to the ground. _____

2. <u>Mary</u> doll has brown hair. _____

3. Those <u>boys</u> skates are in the locker. _____

4. The <u>tree</u> leaves have turned red and gold. _____

5. <u>Ken</u> mother brought his lunch to school. _____

6. The lost <u>dogs</u> owner was very glad to see them again. _____

7. The <u>children</u> balloons flew away. _____

8. The <u>kitten</u> ball rolled under the couch. _____

9. Some <u>woman</u> hair was blowing in the wind. _____

10. The <u>pan</u> handle was very hot. _____

Linking Verbs

You have learned that all sentences have verbs. A verb can be a word that tells what a subject does. When a verb tells what a subject does, it is called an **action verb**. However, a verb can also be a word that tells us what the subject is. When a verb describes what a subject is, it is called a **linking verb**.

Examples:

My friend **is** the owner of a dog. The linking verb is *is*.

The dog **is** nice. The linking verb is *is*.

We **were** on the boat with the dog. The linking verb is *were*.

Find the linking verbs in the following sentences. Underline them in the sentences. Then write them on the lines. The first one is done for you.

1. The turtle <u>seems</u> hungry.

1. _____ *seems* _____

2. The turtle is very small.

2. _____

3. My cat Fluffy is furry.

3. _____

4. My cat looks very sleepy.

4. _____

5. My brothers are tall.

5. _____

6. They are always busy.

6. _____

7. The turtle and the cat were in the wagon.

7. _____

8. My brothers are in trouble.

8. _____

9. My cousins are taller than my brothers.

9. _____

10. My sister is older than my brother.

10. _____

Past and Present

Verbs in the **present tense** show action that is happening now. In the **past tense**, verbs show action that already happened.

Today the bird **sings.**

Yesterday the bird **sang.**

Change each of these present-tense verbs to the past tense by adding *d* or *ed*.

1. walk _____

2. climb _____

3. jump _____

4. play _____

5. comb _____

6. roar _____

7. smile _____

8. fold _____

9. close _____

10. paint _____

Change each of the past-tense verbs to the present tense by removing the *d* or *ed*.

11. colored _____

12. scribbled _____

13. turned _____

14. cooked _____

15. washed _____

16. shared _____

17. stacked _____

18. typed _____

19. laughed _____

20. delivered _____

Irregular Verbs

Irregular verbs do not change from present to past tense by adding *d* or *ed*. Other letters of the verb change to make the past tense. Draw lines to connect the present-tense and past-tense of each irregular verb.

run	gave
see	brought
eat	saw
come	ate
make	built
build	ran
sleep	made
give	slept
take	took
bring	came
sing	sang

Singular and Plural Verbs

When subjects and verbs are together in a sentence, they must agree in number.

The sandal (fit, (fits)) well.

A **singular subject** (only one) takes a singular verb.

A **plural subject** (more than one) takes a plural verb.

Circle the correct singular or plural verb. Write the word **singular** or **plural** after each sentence.

1. The rabbit (hops, hop). _plural_____

2. The sun (shines, shine). _plural_____

3. The cakes (was, were) delicious. _____

4. Angry tigers (roars, roar) loudly. _____

5. The man (rides, ride) his bike to work. _____

6. Winter vacation (is, are) coming soon. _____

7. The boys (has, have) red shirts. _____

8. The flowers (is, are) blooming. _____

9. Karen (dances, dance) very well. _____

10. The tomatoes (is, are) ripe. _____

Which Verb?

6/29/01

Circle the correct verb for each sentence.

The runners **race** to the finish line.

1. We _____ the book.   **read**   **reads**

2. They _____ the kite.   **fly**   **flies**

3. Mr. Kim _____ across the pool.   **swim**   **swims**

4. Lucky _____ the ball.   **chase**   **chases**

5. The panda _____ the tree.   **climb**   **climbs**

6. I _____ a mile.   **run**   **runs**

7. You _____ up the mountain.   **hike**   **hikes**

8. They _____ to 100.   **count**   **counts**

9. She _____ the violin.   **play**   **plays**

10. We _____ the circus.   **watch**   **watches**

Was/Were and Does/Do

was? were? does? do?

He **was** playing.   She **does** her chores.

They **were** playing.   They **do** their chores.

Write **was** or **were** in each sentence.

1. Where_____Were_____we supposed to meet?

2. Who_____was_____with you?

3. I_____was_____at school when the siren sounded.

4. We_____were_____watching a play.

5. She_____was_____confused about the homework.

6. They_____were_____wondering where to go.

Write **do** or **does** in each sentence.

7. Where_____do_____you keep the sugar?

8. I will_____do_____the dishes.

9. They will_____do_____the laundry after we leave.

10. She_____does_____her best on all her work.

11. Kevin_____does_____a good job when he hoes the garden.

12. Who_____does_____the paperwork in the office?

Adjectives

Adjectives are words that describe. Write an adjective for each word.

(tall) building

1. _____stairs

2. _____windows

3. _____stories

4. _____chimney

5. _____hallway

6. _____apartment

7. _____families

8. _____neighbor

9. _____room

10. _____street

11. _____door

12. _____friend

Choose the Adjectives

Adjectives describe people, places, and things.

a **diamond** ring

many   **loose**   **funny**   **large**   **striped**

Use the words in boldface to add an adjective to each sentence.

1. The_____zebra is a beautiful animal.

2. My clothes are baggy and_____.

3. _____people watch television each day.

4. We laughed at the_____movie.

5. The giant was so_____he blocked the sun when he stood.

Add an adjective to each sentence below. Write the new sentences.

6. The monkeys swing from the trees.

_____

7. The owl hooted in the night.

_____

8. The farmer plants his crops.

_____

9. Have you seen my shoes?

_____

10. A hummingbird flew past the window.

_____

Pronouns

Pronouns are words that are used in the place of nouns. Some pronouns are *I, we, you, it, he, she,* and *they.* There are other pronouns as well.

Read the sentences below. In each blank, write a pronoun to replace the bold noun.

1. The **boy** played baseball. _____

2. The **girl** swam across the pool. _____

3. The **children** climbed the trees. _____

4. **Mary and Frank** rode their bikes to school. _____

5. The team surprised **Lily** with a trophy. _____

6. Kim saw the **dog** run across the street. _____

7. **Mom** read the new bestseller. _____

8. **Gary** saw a strange shadow. _____

9. The girls walked to **Mary**'s house. _____

10. The family found **kittens** in a basket on their porch. _____

11. Where should I put the **presents**? _____

12. My **dad** put gas in the car. _____

13. The **players** won the championship! _____

14. Where is the **key**? _____

15. Please, give that to **Rick**. _____

He, She, or They

Maria whispered, "We don't want to wake the sleeping babies."

She whispered, "We don't want to wake the sleeping babies."

SH

Read the sentences below. Decide who is the speaker. Write **he**, **she**, or **they** on the line after each statement.

1. "Wow, ice cream for dessert!" yelled the students in 2-B. _they_ ✗

2. "Who wants to play soccer today?" asked Diana. _she_ ✗

3. "That is my favorite song!" shouted Grandfather. _he_ ✗

4. "We're lost in the woods!" cried Hansel and Gretel. _they_ ✗

5. "I wish I had a fairy godmother," sighed Cinderella. _she_ ✗

6. "Line up for recess," said Mrs. Johnson with a smile. _she_ ✗

7. "You need to do your homework after supper," said Father. _he_ ✗

8. "Let's order pizza for dinner," suggested Mother. _she_ ✗

I and We, Me and Us

I and *we* are used when the person or people are doing the action. *Me* and *us* are used when something is happening to the person or people.

Examples

I am going to have a party.

We are going to have a party.

Mom is having a party for *me*.

Mom is having a party for *us*.

Circle the correct pronoun in each sentence.

1. (We, Us) are going to the store.

2. Would you like to come with (with, us)?

3. (I, Me) played baseball after school.

4. Karen threw the ball to (I, me).

5. Our parents are taking (we, us) out to dinner tonight.

6. Did you hear that (I, me) won first prize?

7. Jim and (I, me) are neighbors.

8. When do you think (we, us) will go?

9. That secret is between Jose and (I, me).

10. Jill told (we, us) about the party.

The Same Thing

Read each sentence. Write the word from the word box that means the same thing as the underlined word.

Let's **gather** some leaves for our art project.

Let's **collect** some leaves for our art project.

asked	bucket	eat	shore	small
big	decorate	quiet	slept	watched

_____ 1. The Martians <u>observed</u> the people of Earth.

_____ 2. The waves roll upon the <u>beach</u>.

_____ 3. We will <u>dine</u> at a nearby restaurant.

_____ 4. The children filled the <u>pail</u> with sand.

_____ 5. After playing, we all <u>napped</u> for awhile.

_____ 6. The teacher <u>questioned</u> the students about their homework.

_____ 7. In December some people <u>trim</u> a tree.

_____ 8. The insects were <u>tiny</u>.

_____ 9. A <u>large</u> storm is coming our way.

_____ 10. Everyone was <u>silent</u>.

Synonyms

When comparing and contrasting objects and ideas, it is helpful to use special words called synonyms. **Synonyms** are words that mean nearly the same thing. Look at the list of synonyms below.

good, helpful   big, large
fast, quick   gentle, mild
little, small   bad, evil
strong, powerful   tired, sleepy
sour, tart   bright, shiny

Circle the synonyms in each row.

1. busy	tired	active	bad
2. nibble	chew	hit	play
3. cook	flavorful	tasty	show
4. joyful	happy	sad	angry
5. fall	walk	stand	trip
6. huge	pretty	anxious	enormous
7. worried	anxious	smart	angry
8. mad	angry	funny	disappointed
9. talk	kick	chat	sing
10. rush	slow	hurry	mild

Antonym Match-Up

Antonyms are words with opposite meanings.

large   small

Draw a line to connect the antonyms.

1. happy   young

2. brave   far

3. right   afraid

4. fast   weak

5. big   little

6. rude   tame

7. old   sad

8. strong   answer

9. crowded   ugly

10. smile   frown

11. close   slow

12. loud   wrong

13. ask   easy

14. wild   quiet

15. beautiful   empty

16. hard   polite

Antonyms

Read each sentence. Write the word from the word box that means the opposite of the underlined word.

The lady **laughed** as she watched the movie.

The lady **cried** as she watched the movie.

bad	difficult	empty	few	no one
calm	down	everybody	low	white

_____ 1. The leaf was too <u>high</u> to reach.

_____ 2. The bag was <u>full</u>.

_____ 3. The sun was <u>up</u> when we left.

_____ 4. <u>Many</u> people listen to the radio.

_____ 5. The drill team was dressed all in <u>black</u>.

_____ 6. The students thought the test was <u>easy</u>.

_____ 7. <u>Nobody</u> came to the play.

_____ 8. <u>Someone</u> is coming to the party.

_____ 9. The sea was <u>wild</u>.

_____ 10. Everyone had a <u>good</u> time at the show.

Homophones

Homophones are words that sound the same but are spelled differently and have different meanings.

Jim **ate eight** slices of pizza today!

Choose the correct homophone to use in each sentence.

pail   pale   1. They collected sea shells in the_____.

Two   To   2. _____friends went to the concert.

here   hear   3. Do you_____that noise?

wear   where   4. I am going to_____my new sweater.

so   sew   5. He will have to_____his button onto his
shirt.

hi   high   6. The snow fell_____in the mountains.

wood   would   7. Collect some_____for the fire.

be   bee   8. A honey_____flew to the hive.

blew   blue   9. The wind_____across the water.

knew   new   10. I_____you would come!

Which Word Shall I Use?

Circle the correct word on the right that matches the word or phrase on the left. An example has been done for you.

listen = (hear)/here

1. relative — ant/(aunt)

2. cry — (tear)/tier

3. moisture — (dew)/do/due

4. jewel — purl/(pearl)

5. evening — (night)/knight

6. forbidden — band/(banned)

7. transparent — shear/(sheer)

8. character — roll/(role)

9. company — (guest)/guessed

10. small — we/(wee)

11. female deer — (doe)/dough

12. cold — (chilly)/chili

13. smash — brake/(break)

14. tree — (fir)/fur

Wally the Word Worm

Look carefully at the paragraph below. It has some incorrectly used homophones. How many incorrectly used homophones can you find in the paragraph below? Circle each one. Over each of the words that you circle, write the correct homophone. The first one has been done for you.

one

Wally Worm woke up early (won) knight. He stretched and started down the rode in search of food. Just then too of his friends met hymn. They new wear sum red apples had fallen from the trees knot two far away. They offered too show hymn where he could find them. So together they inched there weigh two the orchard and dove inn. They eight until they could eat know more.

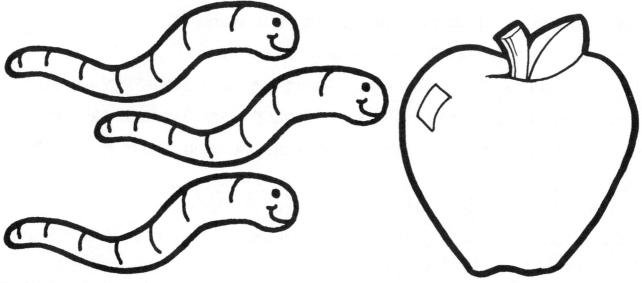

That's Capital!

Some words need to be capitalized. This means they start with capital letters. You should always capitalize . . .

- the first word in a sentence.
- the word *I.*
- titles of people (such as *Dr.* Martin and *Mrs.* Garcia).
- the special names of people and places (such as *France* and the *Grand Canyon*).
- titles or family names when they are used in place of a person's name (such as "Good morning, *General*" and "Give the list to *Mom.*").
- the days of the week and months of the year.
- titles of books, movies, songs, plays, magazines, newspapers, and television shows.
- holidays.
- school subjects when they are the names of languages or subject titles (such as *English* or *Modern Art in America*).

The following sentences have some words that need to be capitalized. Cross out each letter that needs to be changed to a capital. Write the capital above the crossed out letter. The first letter is done for you.

    W

1. When i went to the store, i saw my teacher, mrs. roe, buying strawberries.

2. my family will go to disneyland in july.

3. i am reading *old yeller* this week.

4. my sister, sarah, says her favorite subject is spanish.

5. on wednesday, we will celebrate groundhog day.

6. my brother said that mom was a cheerleader at roosevelt high school.

7. in august, we're going to visit aunt margaret in san francisco, california.

8. benjie, my little brother, had a birthday, and we sang, "happy birthday to you."

9. my friend, rosa, speaks spanish, and i speak english.

10. my neighbor, julia, is going to be an exchange student in paris, france, next august.

Capitalization

Proper nouns are the specific names of people, places, and things (including days, months, and holidays). All proper nouns must be capitalized. Put the proper nouns from the word box in their correct columns below. Be sure to add the capital letters!

rocky mountains	november	alexander	christmas	monday
mr. peterson	plum street	thursday	south america	sandy
saturday	august	thanksgiving	russia	february
mardi gras	spot	fluffy	colorado river	march

Names (*people and pets*)   **Places**

_____   _____

_____   _____

_____   _____

_____   _____

_____   _____

Days   **Months**   **Holidays**

_____   _____   _____

_____   _____   _____

_____   _____   _____

_____   _____   _____

#2971 Practice and Learn

Capital Review

It is time to see how much you have learned about capitalization. Circle all the letters below that should be capitals. *(Hint:* There are 64 of them.)

1. the first day of school is exciting.

2. freddy wilson's frog, peepers, hopped into mrs. woolsey's purse.

3. as i walked outside, i smelled smoke.

4. in the play, robin hood was played by lieutenant bronksy.

5. the fourth thursday in november is thanksgiving.

6. i like halloween best when it is on a saturday.

7. aunt susan went to yellowstone national park.

8. connie lives on maple street in bismarck, north dakota.

9. brazil, argentina, and peru are in south america.

10. the mediterranean sea and the atlantic ocean touch spain.

11. the letter was signed, "love always, esther."

12. davis medical center opened in january last year.

13. one of the religions practiced by many african people is islam.

14. italians and germans belong to the caucasian race.

15. last tuesday ruben walked his dog, spotty, down tulip street to central park.

Matching

Contractions are made by bringing two words together into one. Draw a line to match the contractions to the words.

she'll	they will
it's	you are
won't	I am
you'll	it is
you're	is not
isn't	she will
we're	he is
I'll	we are
they'll	can not
weren't	will not
I'm	you will
he's	they are
can't	are not
aren't	I will
they're	were not

Correct Contractions

The turtle **is not** moving quickly.

The turtle **isn't** moving quickly.

Read each sentence and circle the correct contraction that fills in the blank.

1. We _____ be late for the party.

   aren't   won't   isn't

2. _____ feed his pet at dinner time.

   He'll   He's   I'm

3. _____ fun to build a snowman.

   Isn't   Wouldn't   It's

4. _____ the library?

   Where's   We're   Weren't

5. She _____ know the answer.

   don't   didn't   isn't

6. _____ go to the movies.

   He's   She's   Let's

7. I _____ come to soccer practice.

   can't   aren't   isn't

8. _____ be happy to help you.

   I'd   I'm   I've

End Marks

How many blocks do you see [?]

I see 18 blocks [.]

Add a period (.), a question mark (?), or an exclamation point (!) to the end of each sentence.

1. I will go with you ☐

2. Where is it ☐

3. Help me ☐

4. Who ate the cookies ☐

5. Go to the third house ☐

6. I like to play basketball ☐

7. What a great day ☐

8. The children are in the yard ☐

9. How many are there ☐

10. What is happening here ☐

11. When are we going to the game ☐

12. I would like the sugar cookie, please ☐

13. Is it time for bed ☐

14. I'm so happy to see you ☐

15. It's over there ☐

#2971 Practice and Learn

Rules for Commas

Here are three rules for using commas in sentences.

   A. Commas should be used to separate words in a series.

     Example: Joe and his sister love marshmallows, graham crackers, and chocolate.

   B. A comma should be used after the words *yes*, *no*, and *well*.

     Example: Yes, I love s'mores.

   C. When a person is spoken to, a comma should be used to set off that person's name.

     Example: Pedro, do you want a graham cracker?

Use the three comma rules to place commas in the sentences below.

1. No Mary does not like marshmallows.

2. Well maybe Bernard will try the s'mores.

3. Bobby would you like to try a s'more?

4. Alice wants a hot dog potato chips and a pickle.

5. We played baseball basketball and volleyball.

6. Harry would you like to dance?

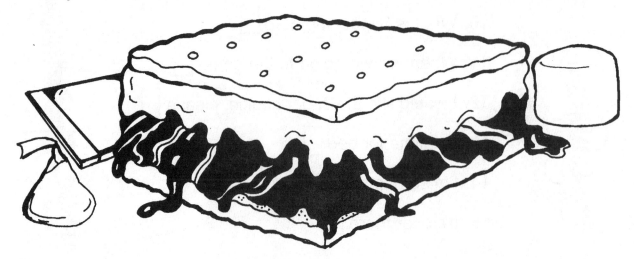

More Rules for Commas

Here are three more rules for using commas in sentences.
- A. An appositive is a group of words that tells more about another word. Use commas to set off an appositive from the rest of the sentence.
  - **Example:** Dr. Lee, David's father, is my dentist.

- B. The day and the year in dates should be separated by commas.
  - **Example:** My dental appointment is for January 16, 2000, the day after my birthday.

- C. The names of cities and states should be separated by commas.
  - **Example:** Dr. Lee will move his office from San Diego, California, to Oceanside next month.

Use the comma rules to place commas in the sentences that follow.

1. Jack my brother does not like to go to the dentist.

2. I like my dentist Dr. Lee.

3. Dr. Payce the dentist in the next office is also a good dentist.

4. On March 2 1999 Dr. Lee took David and me camping.

5. My first visit to Dr. Lee was on February 27 1994.

6. By June 30 2012 I will have become a dentist myself.

7. I was born in Brooklyn New York and so was Dr. Lee.

8. He visits Chicago Illinois every summer.

9. David wishes they would go to Orlando Florida each year instead.

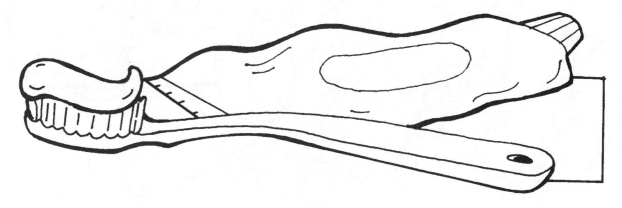

Compound Sentences

A **comma** should be placed before *and*, *but*, and *or* when they join two complete sentences to make a compound sentence.

Read the sentences and place the commas where they belong.

1. You wear your blue jeans and I'll wear my black jeans.

2. Your white T-shirt fits better but your red T-shirt is more colorful.

3. Do you want yellow patches on your jeans or do you want pink patches?

4. Jill's T-shirt looks great and Amy's jeans are terrific.

5. I have three pairs of blue jeans but I want another pair of green jeans.

6. You need to wash your old jeans and you should iron your new jeans.

7. This white T-shirt is mine but that white T-shirt is yours.

8. Let's all wear our blue jeans today and let's wear our red jeans tomorrow.

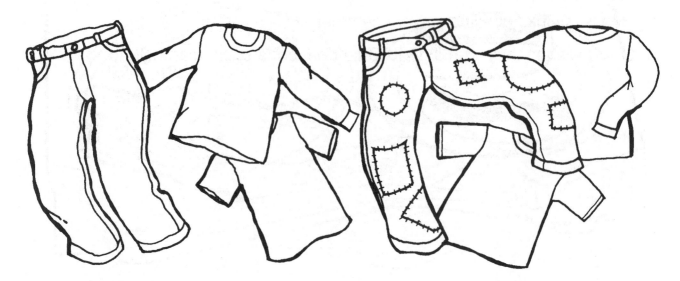

Commas Review

Add the commas where they belong.

1. Yes I would love to go to the movie.

2. We have potato chips cheese and chili.

3. Grandma could we please spend the night?

4. This red car belongs to my mom and this blue car belongs to my dad.

5. John may I borrow your football?

6. We saw swans ducks and an ostrich.

7. Invite Casey Jackie and Toby to go with us.

8. No we can't go to the zoo today.

9. My sister likes hot dogs and I like pizza.

10. Aunt Irene my mom's sister liked the book but I liked the movie.

More Commas Review

Add commas where they belong.

1. Tasha's birthday is March 4 1981.

2. Dennis my best friend lives in San Francisco California but he is moving to Oakland.

3. Our teacher Mr. Hill took us on a field trip to Boston Massachusetts.

4. July 16 1973 is my parents' anniversary.

5. The Davis family is moving to Orlando Florida on July 13 2001.

6. My friend Mrs. Allen is a nurse.

7. The airplane will land in Paris France after taking off from London England.

8. He visits Chicago Illinois every summer but this year he will go to Montreal Canada.

Apostrophes

An **apostrophe** is used to show ownership (possession) in writing. For example, another way to write **toy belonging to baby** is **baby's toy**.

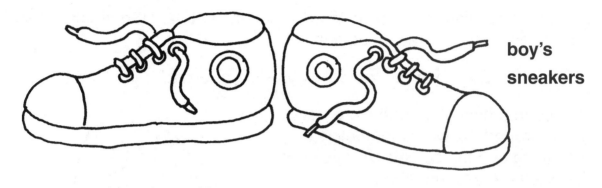

boy's sneakers

Rewrite the phrases below using an **'s**. (**Note:** If the word ends in **s**, only add an apostrophe.)

1. food belonging to a dog _____

2. cage belonging to a bird _____

3. bike belonging to Kenny _____

4. store belonging to Mr. Stout _____

5. radio belonging to Janie _____

6. book belonging to Don _____

7. baseball belonging to the coach _____

8. desk belonging to the student _____

9. closet belonging to the class _____

10. pencil belonging to Mrs. Davis _____

Quotation in Conversation

When two or more people speak to each other in conversation, use quotation marks to show exactly what they are saying.

A direct quotation is the exact words spoken. Quotation marks are used before and after a direct quotation.

Example: "Thank you for the delicious slice of pizza," said Jim.

Notice that quotation marks are never used around the words that tell who is speaking and the comma always goes before the quotation mark.

Sometimes we write what a person says without showing exact words. When this happens, we do not use quotation marks. Never use quotation marks unless you are showing a speaker's exact words.

Example:
Janet thought that her tent was too small.

Place quotation marks around only what is said.

1. Yes, Ryan, Mom answered, Matt can come over after lunch.

2. Thanks, Mom, Ryan answered.

3. Ryan said that he and Matt would play basketball after school.

4. Mom said, While you play basketball, I'll bake cookies.

5. Ryan asked when Matt could come over to play.

6. Mom answered that Matt could come over after lunch.

Quotation Marks Review

Add the correct punctuation to complete the quotations.

1. Bobby yelled Mom where are my blue jeans?

2. A plane is flying overhead said Jim's dad.

3. Mindy said Look at the turtles.

4. Watch out yelled Sara The dog will get out!

5. Dad said that the boys could play all afternoon.

6. Grandma cried Joey will you tie my shoe?

7. The boys yelled Come out and play!

8. Mother said Change the channel, boys.

9. Amanda asked if her friend could come with her.

10. Can you ride a bicycle? asked Joseph.

Punctuation Review

Read the story below. Add the missing punctuation.

Have you ever been on a farm

Mrs Young took her third grade class to Mr Frank s

farm on Tuesday morning They saw cows chickens

and horses Mr Frank wanted to know if any students

would like to ride a horse Leslie screamed I do Also

John and Carl wanted to ride Mrs Young s class will

never forget the special day on the farm

Are You a Good Sentence Detective?

A **sentence** is a group of words that tells us something or asks us a question. It is always a complete thought.

Example: John cooks dinner.

What does the sentence tell us?

It tells us who it is about. *John*

It tells us what John does. *cooks dinner*

There are only 10 complete sentences shown in the magnifying glass. Write these 10 sentences on a separate paper.

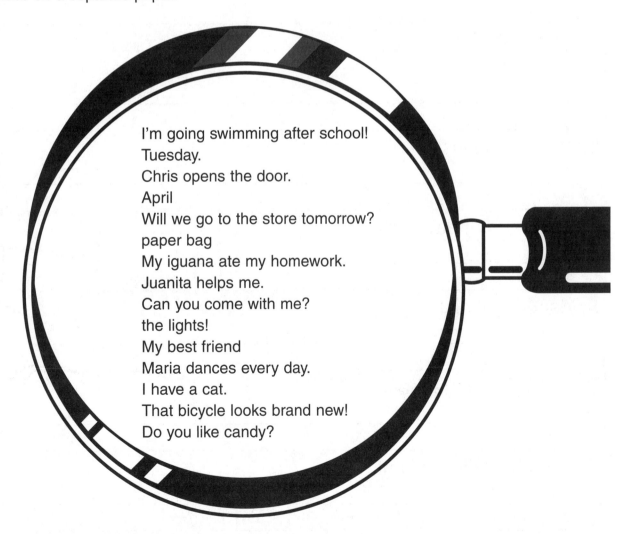

I'm going swimming after school!
Tuesday.
Chris opens the door.
April
Will we go to the store tomorrow?
paper bag
My iguana ate my homework.
Juanita helps me.
Can you come with me?
the lights!
My best friend
Maria dances every day.
I have a cat.
That bicycle looks brand new!
Do you like candy?

Sentence Fragments

A **sentence fragment** is an incomplete sentence. It is missing either the subject or the predicate, and it does not make sense by itself.

The tired horse **(fragment)**

The tired horse moved slowly across the meadow. **(sentence)**

Make the fragments below into complete sentences.

1. the hungry bear

_____

_____

2. chews gum loudly

_____

_____

3. the mountains

_____

_____

4. my first birthday party

_____

_____

5. danced all night

_____

_____

6. the gigantic elephant

_____

_____

7. is my favorite present

_____

_____

Fragment or Sentence?

In the box there are four complete sentences and three sentences fragments. Rewrite the sentences, adding capitals and ending punctuations. Rewrite the fragments, adding either subjects or predicates.

1. i have many things in my room
2. there is a box of clothes under the bed
3. a rug is in front of the closet
4. two stuffed rabbits
5. i can see trees from my window
6. the bedspread and curtains
7. a large poster of

1. _____

_____

2. _____

_____

3. _____

_____

4. _____

_____

5. _____

_____

6. _____

_____

7. _____

_____

Sentence Run-Ons

You have learned that each sentence is a complete thought. What about sentences that do not stop when they should? A sentence that runs on to the next thought is called a run-on sentence.

Run-on: My birthday is tomorrow I hope I get a bike.

Correct: My birthday is tomorrow. I hope I get a bike.

Each of the following is a run-on sentence. Write each run-on as two complete sentences.

1. It is windy today I should fly my kite.

   _____

2. I like to read *James and the Giant Peach* is my favorite book.

   _____

3. Where are you going when will you be home?

   _____

4. The boy ran home after school then he did his homework.

   _____

5. The clown danced in the parade he gave balloons to all the children.

   _____

6. My sister really enjoys camping I do, too.

   _____

7. The puppies cried for their mother they were hungry.

   _____

8. I don't feel like going to bed I want to stay up to watch my show!

   _____

9. Who is there what do you want?

   _____

10. They wanted to climb the tree the branches were too high to reach.

   _____

Run-On or Sentence?

In the box there are four complete sentences and three run-ons. Rewrite the sentences, adding capitals and ending punctuations. Rewrite the run-ons to make them complete sentences.

1. the monkeys danced to the peddler's music
2. my sister cried for my mother she wouldn't stop
3. my favorite game to play is Chinese checkers
4. the students wondered what the teacher had planned for the day
5. they were late to the party everyone was worried about them
6. the birds were singing in the trees the flowers looked colorful in the sun
7. he knew that it would be an exciting day the moment he saw the pony

1. _____

_____

2. _____

_____

3. _____

_____

4. _____

_____

5. _____

_____

6. _____

_____

7. _____

_____

Compound Words

A compound word is made up of two smaller words. For example, **honeymoon** consists of two words, **honey** and **moon**. See how many compound words you can make from the single words below.

honey	road	rail	sail	person
play	boat	wood	snake	over
head	rattle	ply	sales	light
moon	rain	take	ground	bow

1. _____

2. _____

3. _____

4. _____

5. _____

6. _____

7. _____

8. _____

9. _____

10. _____

11. _____

12. _____

More Compound Words

Write a word in the blank between each set of words. The trick is that the new word must complete a compound word both to the left and to the right of it. The first one has been done for you.

1. dug   _____out_____ side

2. foot   _____ ladder

3. arrow   _____ line

4. country _____ walk

5. tea   _____ belly

6. camp   _____ place

7. basket   _____ room

8. touch   _____ stairs

9. drug   _____ keeper

10. base   _____ park

11. flash   _____ house

12. hill   _____ ways

13. look   _____ doors

14. quarter _____ bone

15. some   _____ ever

Getting to the Root of It

Sometimes a word has letters added to the beginning or end of it that change the meaning of the word. The main word is called the **root word**, and the added letters are **prefixes** or **suffixes**. For example, in the word **soundless**, the root word is **sound**, and in the word **unusual** the root word is **usual**. Notice how the meanings of these two words change with the added letters.

Read the words below. Circle the root words.

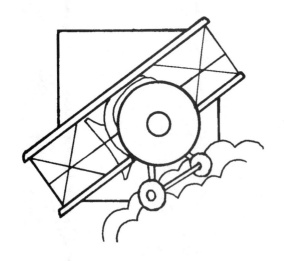

1. irregular

2. misspell

3. prideful

4. useless

5. impossible

6. disloyal

7. unknown

8. prearrange

9. mermaid

10. biplane

11. joyous

12. uniform

13. tricycle

14. nonstop

15. royalty

Brush Up on Root Words

On each brush is the name of a person who does an action. Find the root word in each and write it on the tooth.

Example: farmer, farm

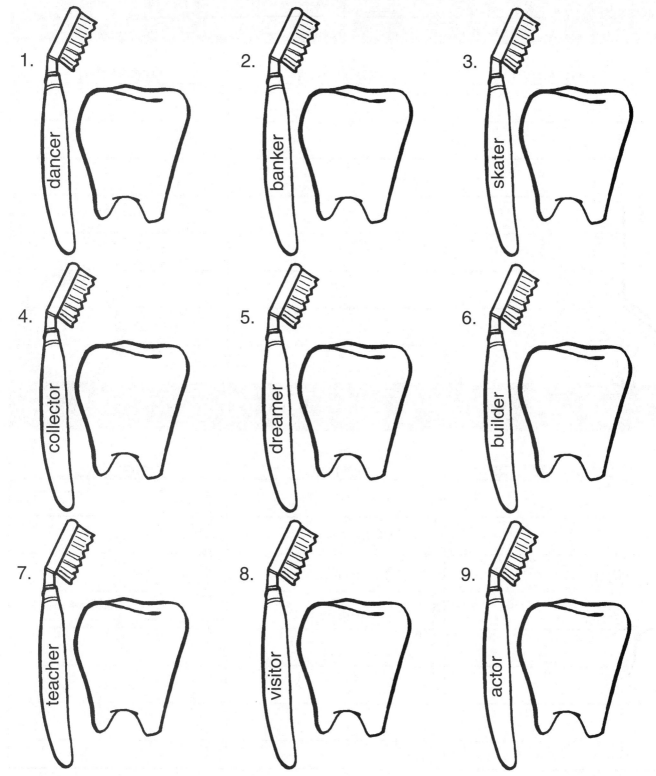

1. dancer

2. banker

3. skater

4. collector

5. dreamer

6. builder

7. teacher

8. visitor

9. actor

Prepare for Prefixes

Here are six common prefixes. How many words can you find that begin with these prefixes? Write them in the columns. One word in each column has been done for you.

un	dis	pre
unusual	discover	preorder

under	re	mis
understand	remake	mistake

90

Prefix Practice

Find the words with prefixes in the following sentences and underline them. Write the prefix, root word, and definition in the correct column. Use a dictionary to help you if you need it.

Sentence	Prefix	Root	Definition
1. John reread the book because it was good.			
2. Ann came to class unprepared.			
3. Did you go to preschool?			
4. Bob misspelled California.			
5. The plant was underwatered.			
6. Joe felt overjoyed when he won.			
7. The students misjudged her.			
8. In health class, we learned not to overeat.			

Surfing with Suffixes

A **suffix** is one or more syllables at the end of a root word. When a word has a suffix, the syllable division is between the suffix and the root word. Circle the suffixes in the waves and then write the word on the wave with a hyphen to divide it into syllables.

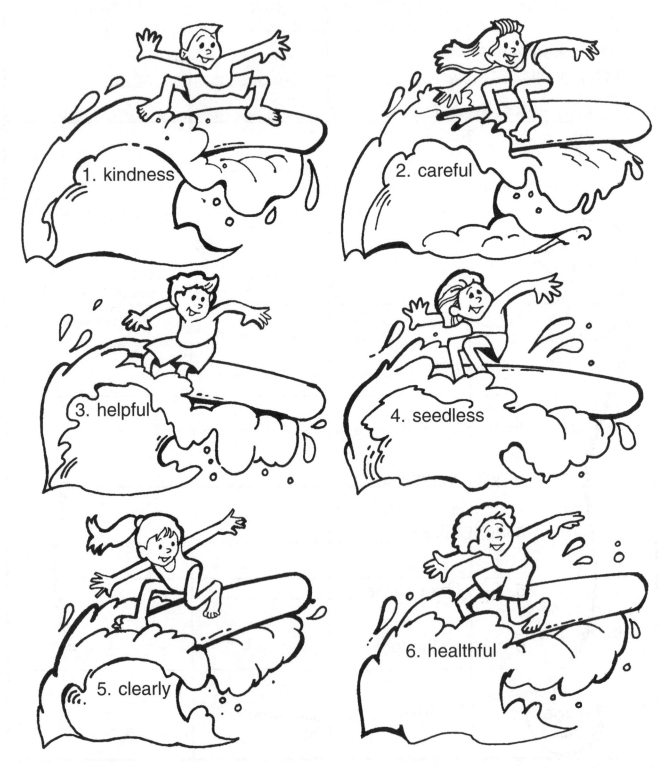

1. kindness

2. careful

3. helpful

4. seedless

5. clearly

6. healthful

Bubbling Over with Suffixes

The suffix **less** can mean *without*. The suffix **ous** can mean *full of*. Circle the suffix in each bubble. Read the clues in the bubble box. Find the word in the bubbles that goes with the meaning. Color each bubble when you use the word.

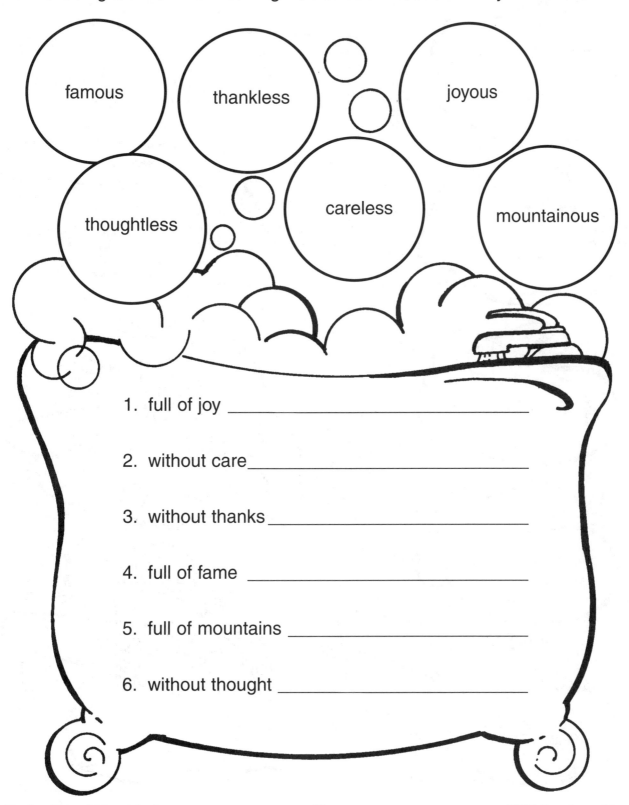

famous

thankless

joyous

thoughtless

careless

mountainous

1. full of joy _____

2. without care _____

3. without thanks _____

4. full of fame _____

5. full of mountains _____

6. without thought _____

Titles Tell the Main Idea

If you read the title of a story, poem, or book, you will find a clue about the main idea. Read each title and description below. Draw a line to connect the pairs of mittens.

1. "The Snow Sunday"

A. Animals and plants are still alive, even though the pond is frozen.

2. "Ice Is Nice"

B. One very cold day, Sue learned that pets need special winter care.

3. "Winter at the Pond"

C. Every Sunday the aunts visited May Lie's house, except for the day that it snowed.

4. "The Coldest Day of the Year"

D. Ice has many important uses.

5. "Disaster at the Ice Skating Party"

E. Skating on the ice can be very dangerous.

About Barn Owls

Read the paragraph below. Color the owl that has the main idea.

Barn owls learn to fly before they leave their nests.

Barn owls can hunt for food by 12 weeks of age.

Barn owls are fully grown by about 12 weeks of age.

Barn owls are fully grown by about 12 weeks of age. First, they hatch from eggs. At three weeks, their eyes are open, and they can jump and walk. Three weeks later, their feathers begin to grow. By eight weeks, they are practicing flight and are ready to leave their nests. Two weeks later, they begin to explore on their own. Finally, by 12 weeks they are grown and can hunt for food on their own.

Practicing Similes

Similes compare two different things, using *like* or *as*. "The cat was as still as a statue," is an example of a simile.

To write similes, complete each comparison found below.

1. An orange is as ___Bright___ as ___the sun___.

2. A puppy is as ___happy___ as ___a clown___.

3. A star is as ___small___ as ___a eye___.

4. Ice is as ___cold___ as ___a snowflake___.

5. The water is as ___clear___ as ___crystal___.

6. The rock is as ___still___ as ___a statue___.

7. The color is as ___Dark___ as ___night___.

8. The clouds are as ___fluffy___ as ___cotton candy___.

9. Snow is as ___white___ as ___paper___.

10. My kitten is as ~~as~~ ___stupid___ as ___a dumB Ban___.

Similes

A **simile** is a figure of speech in which two things are compared with the words _like_ or _as_.

Example: He moved as quick as a wink.

Complete the following similes.

1. As blind as _a bat_

2. As cool as _a coke_

3. As mad as _a bull_ _a wet hen._

4. As happy as _a kid_ _(can be)_

5. As busy as _a bee_

6. As neat as _a pin_

7. As flat as _a pancake_

8. As pale as _a ghost_

9. As easy as _abc_ _or 123_ _or pie_

10. As proud as _a mom_ _a peacock_

11. As fresh as _clean_ _a daisy_

12. As hard as _you_ _a brick_

13. As light as _day ?_

14. As sharp as _a knive_ _(a tack)_

15. As wise as _an owl_

Creating Metaphors

Metaphors compare two different things without using *like* or *as*. Use comparison words to complete the metaphors below.

1. The cloud is a _____ .

2. The tree is a _____ .

3. The eagle is _____ .

4. The ice was _____ .

5. The moon was _____ .

6. The wolf was _____ .

7. The rain is _____ .

8. The rock is _____ .

9. The baby is _____ .

10. The ocean is _____ .

Simile and Metaphor Review

6/26/01

A **simile** is a way of comparing two things by using the words *like* or *as*.

A **metaphor** describes by comparing one thing to another without using the words *like* or *as*.

Read the sentences below. Put an **S** in the box if it is a simile. Put an **M** in the box if it is a metaphor.

[S] 1. The wall was as hard as a rock.

[S] 2. The ice was as slick as glass.

[M] 3. The moon was a bright diamond in the sky.

[S] 4. The cat is as soft as velvet.

[M] 5. The flock of birds made a rainbow in the sky.

[S] 6. The lake was as smooth as a fine piece of china.

[S] 7. The puffy clouds are like cotton balls hanging in the sky.

[M] 8. The star is a beacon lighting the way.

[S] 9. The small child playing in the garden was as playful as a puppy.

[S] 10. The earth is like a round marble.

Understanding Place Value

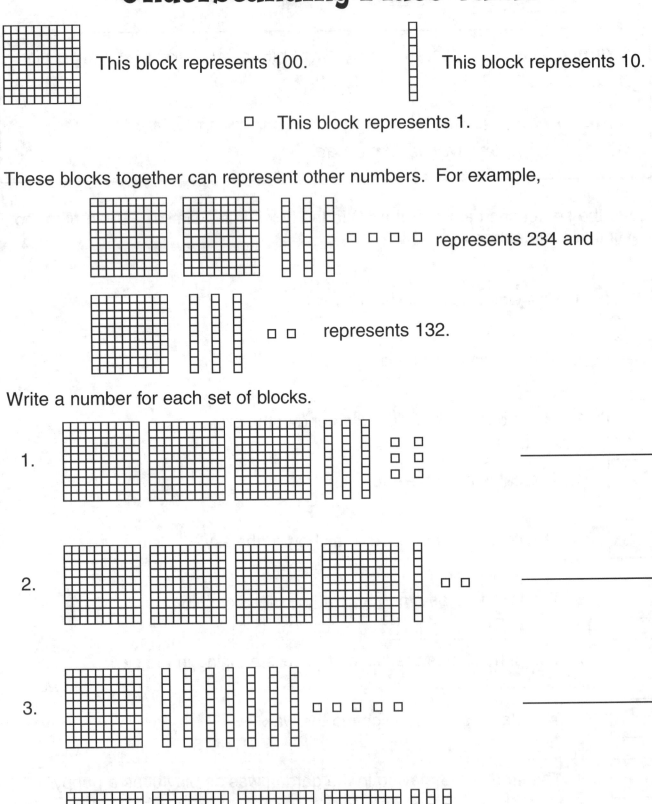

This block represents 100.

This block represents 10.

This block represents 1.

These blocks together can represent other numbers. For example,

represents 234 and

represents 132.

Write a number for each set of blocks.

1. _____

2. _____

3. _____

4. _____

Ones, Tens, and Hundreds

Look at the number blocks. Complete the place value charts.

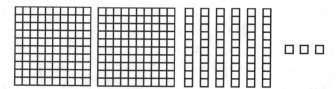

1.

hundreds	tens	ones

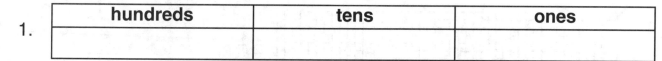

2.

hundreds	tens	ones

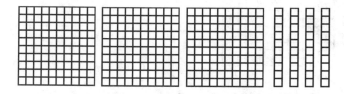

3.

hundreds	tens	ones

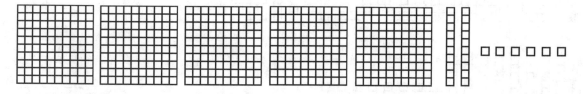

4.

hundreds	tens	ones

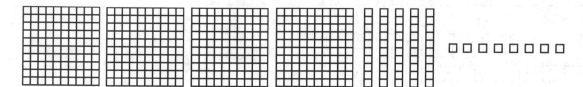

5.

hundreds	tens	ones

Which Is It?

Write the number that each set of blocks represents.

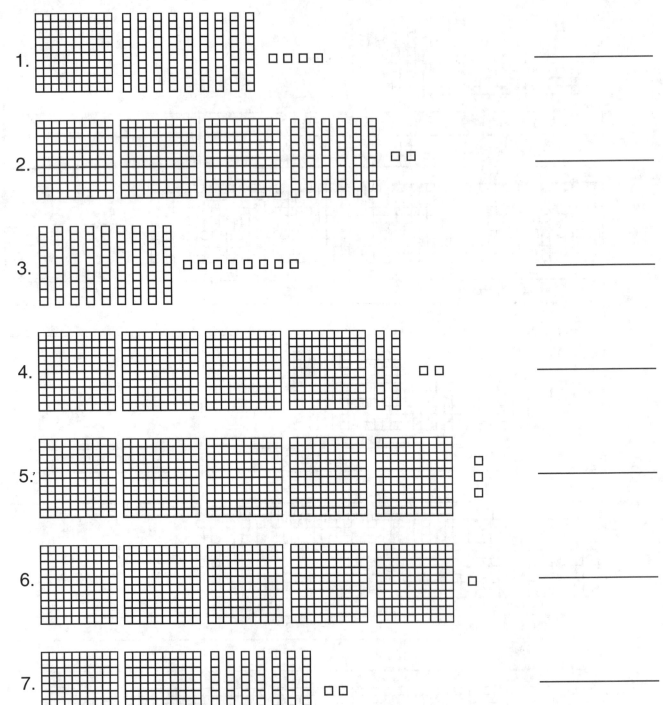

1. _____

2. _____

3. _____

4. _____

5. _____

6. _____

7. _____

8. _____

Rounding

Sometimes you will just need the general value of a number. To get it, you will round. Rounding is not the exact number, but it is close.

There are some basic rules for rounding.

- ✦ If the number is 5 or above, round up to the next tens place. For example, 26 is rounded to 30.
- ✦ If the number is less than 5, round down to the last tens. For example, 13 is rounded to 10.
- ✦ If the number is more than 100, round up to the nearest hundreds place for numbers bigger than 50. For example, 162 is rounded to 200.
- ✦ If the number is more than 100, round down to the last hundreds place for numbers less than 50. For example, 123 is rounded to 100.

Now it is your turn. For each number given, circle the correct rounded number.

1. 48 → 40 or 50?

2. 62 → 60 or 70?

3. 93 → 90 or 100?

4. 15 → 10 or 20?

5. 67 → 60 or 70?

6. 11 → 10 or 20?

7. 19 → 10 or 20?

8. 408 → 400 or 500?

9. 559 → 500 or 600?

10. 232 → 200 or 300?

11. 875 → 800 or 900?

12. 845 → 800 or 900?

13. 341 → 300 or 400?

14. 633 → 600 or 700?

15. 196 → 100 or 200?

16. 255 → 250 or 260?

The Cat's Meow

Cross out each answer on the cat as you solve the problems.

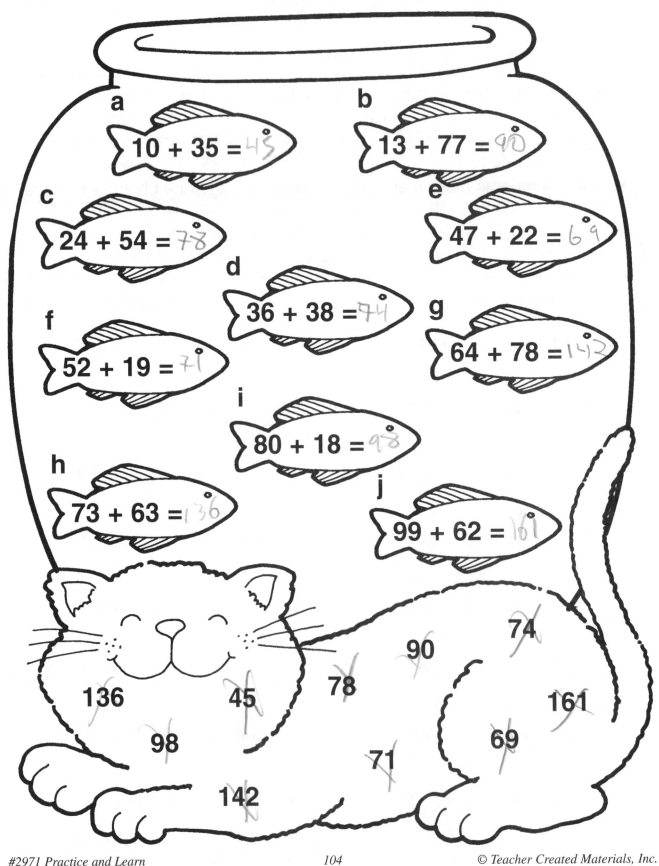

a. 10 + 35 = 45

b. 13 + 77 = 90

c. 24 + 54 = 78

e. 47 + 22 = 69

d. 36 + 38 = 74

f. 52 + 19 = 71

g. 64 + 78 = 142

i. 80 + 18 = 98

h. 73 + 63 = 136

j. 99 + 62 = 161

74
90
78
136   45   161
98   71   69
142

Lightning Quick

Solve the problems. Draw a line from the lightning to the cloud with the sum of 43. Color the lightning bolt.

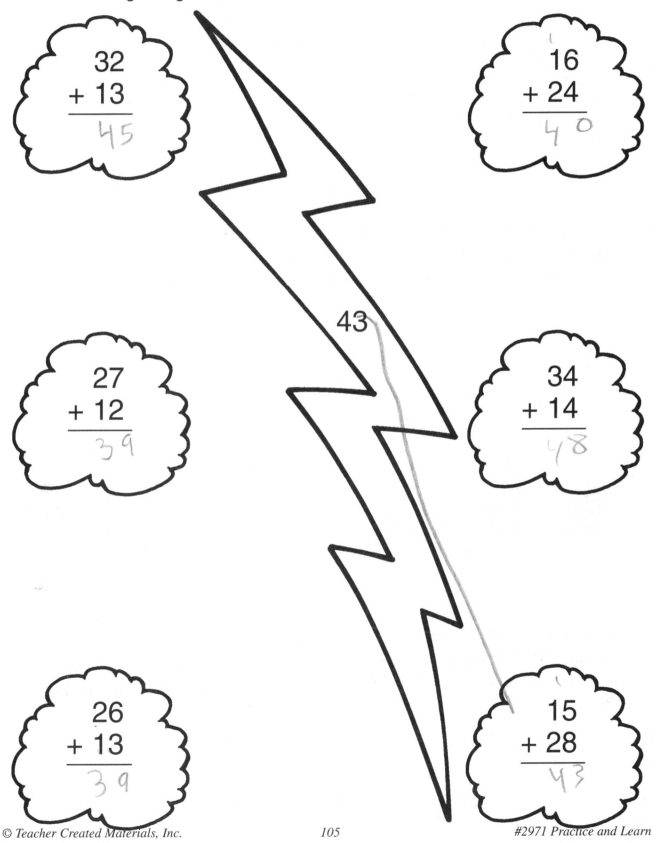

$$\begin{array}{r} 32 \\ + 13 \\ \hline 45 \end{array}$$

$$\begin{array}{r} 16 \\ + 24 \\ \hline 40 \end{array}$$

$$\begin{array}{r} 27 \\ + 12 \\ \hline 39 \end{array}$$

43

$$\begin{array}{r} 34 \\ + 14 \\ \hline 48 \end{array}$$

$$\begin{array}{r} 26 \\ + 13 \\ \hline 39 \end{array}$$

$$\begin{array}{r} 15 \\ + 28 \\ \hline 43 \end{array}$$

 #2971 Practice and Learn

Addition Word Problems

Read each word problem. In the box, write the number sentence it shows. Find the sum.

a

At the circus, Kenny saw 12 tigers, 14 horses, and 22 monkeys. How many animals did he see in all?

b

When Sandra went to the tidepools, she counted 28 starfish, 32 fish, and 46 shells. How many things did she see in all?

c

During one month, Jared ate 27 sandwiches, 23 apples, and 52 cookies. How many things did he eat in all?

d

Emily did 14 addition problems and 33 subtraction problems at school. At home, her mother gave her 21 more. How many problems did she solve in all?

Find the Sums

Find the sums.

a. 29 + 48	**g.** 14 + 75	**m.** 74 + 68	**s.** 97 + 50
b. 37 + 95	**h.** 20 + 52	**n.** 38 + 15	**t.** 45 + 29
c. 10 + 36	**i.** 41 + 52	**o.** 25 + 49	**u.** 34 + 17
d. 56 + 26	**j.** 27 + 30	**p.** 39 + 27	**v.** 74 + 19
e. 40 + 33	**k.** 52 + 73	**q.** 10 + 64	**w.** 27 + 28
f. 86 + 56	**l.** 67 + 70	**r.** 86 + 16	**x.** 55 + 54

Oh, Nuts!

Cross out each answer on the squirrel as you solve the problems.

a.
$$35 - 11$$

b.
$$77 - 13$$

c.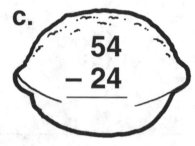
$$54 - 24$$

d.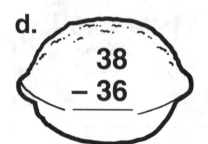
$$38 - 36$$

e.
$$47 - 22$$

f.
$$52 - 19$$

g.
$$74 - 68$$

h.
$$73 - 63$$

i.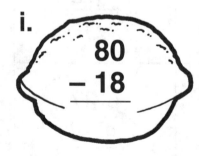
$$80 - 18$$

j.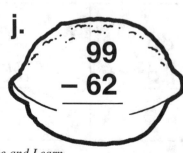
$$99 - 62$$

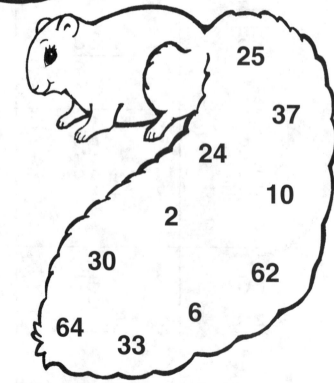

25

37

24

10

2

30

62

64

6

33

Home Run!

Cross out each answer in the mitt as you solve the problems.

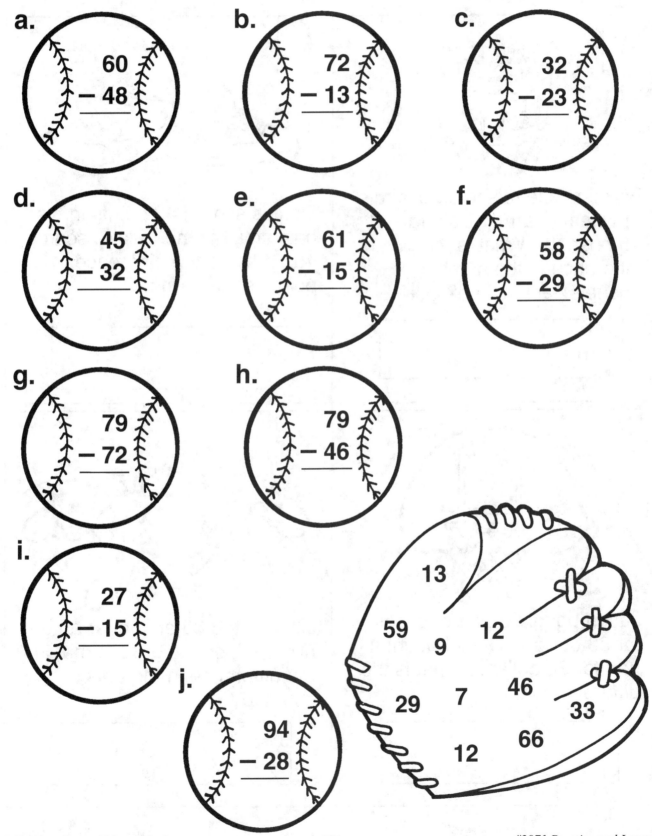

a.
$$60 - 48$$

b.
$$72 - 13$$

c.
$$32 - 23$$

d.
$$45 - 32$$

e.
$$61 - 15$$

f.
$$58 - 29$$

g.
$$79 - 72$$

h.
$$79 - 46$$

i.
$$27 - 15$$

j.
$$94 - 28$$

13

59   12

9

29   7   46

33

12   66

Subtraction Word Problems

Read each word problem. Write the number sentence it shows. Find the difference.

a

Farmer Cole raised 93 bushels of wheat. Farmer Dale raised 68 bushels. What is the difference in the number of bushels each raised?

b

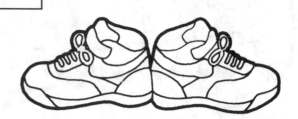

Dennis scored 43 points in his basketball game. Claire scored 40. What is the difference in points each earned?

c

Jason bought a pair of shoes for 53 dollars. Clark bought a pair for 28 dollars. What is the difference paid?

d

Jill counted 83 ants near an ant hill. Jack counted 62. What is the difference in the ants counted?

Find the Differences

Find the differences.

a. $\begin{array}{r} 49 \\ -28 \\ \hline \end{array}$	**g.** $\begin{array}{r} 74 \\ -72 \\ \hline \end{array}$	**m.** $\begin{array}{r} 74 \\ -68 \\ \hline \end{array}$	**s.** $\begin{array}{r} 97 \\ -50 \\ \hline \end{array}$
b. $\begin{array}{r} 97 \\ -35 \\ \hline \end{array}$	**h.** $\begin{array}{r} 50 \\ -22 \\ \hline \end{array}$	**n.** $\begin{array}{r} 38 \\ -15 \\ \hline \end{array}$	**t.** $\begin{array}{r} 45 \\ -29 \\ \hline \end{array}$
c. $\begin{array}{r} 30 \\ -16 \\ \hline \end{array}$	**i.** $\begin{array}{r} 41 \\ -32 \\ \hline \end{array}$	**o.** $\begin{array}{r} 45 \\ -29 \\ \hline \end{array}$	**u.** $\begin{array}{r} 34 \\ -17 \\ \hline \end{array}$
d. $\begin{array}{r} 56 \\ -26 \\ \hline \end{array}$	**j.** $\begin{array}{r} 37 \\ -30 \\ \hline \end{array}$	**p.** $\begin{array}{r} 79 \\ -32 \\ \hline \end{array}$	**v.** $\begin{array}{r} 74 \\ -19 \\ \hline \end{array}$
e. $\begin{array}{r} 40 \\ -33 \\ \hline \end{array}$	**k.** $\begin{array}{r} 72 \\ -53 \\ \hline \end{array}$	**q.** $\begin{array}{r} 60 \\ -14 \\ \hline \end{array}$	**w.** $\begin{array}{r} 28 \\ -28 \\ \hline \end{array}$
f. $\begin{array}{r} 86 \\ -56 \\ \hline \end{array}$	**l.** $\begin{array}{r} 77 \\ -70 \\ \hline \end{array}$	**r.** $\begin{array}{r} 86 \\ -16 \\ \hline \end{array}$	**x.** $\begin{array}{r} 55 \\ -54 \\ \hline \end{array}$

What's the Difference?

Find the differences.

a. $\begin{array}{r}57\\-47\\\hline\end{array}$	**g.** $\begin{array}{r}72\\-12\\\hline\end{array}$	**m.** $\begin{array}{r}71\\-59\\\hline\end{array}$	**s.** $\begin{array}{r}79\\-54\\\hline\end{array}$
b. $\begin{array}{r}75\\-23\\\hline\end{array}$	**h.** $\begin{array}{r}88\\-24\\\hline\end{array}$	**n.** $\begin{array}{r}30\\-18\\\hline\end{array}$	**t.** $\begin{array}{r}95\\-48\\\hline\end{array}$
c. $\begin{array}{r}53\\-17\\\hline\end{array}$	**i.** $\begin{array}{r}84\\-19\\\hline\end{array}$	**o.** $\begin{array}{r}42\\-38\\\hline\end{array}$	**u.** $\begin{array}{r}77\\-70\\\hline\end{array}$
d. $\begin{array}{r}49\\-26\\\hline\end{array}$	**j.** $\begin{array}{r}92\\-14\\\hline\end{array}$	**p.** $\begin{array}{r}86\\-63\\\hline\end{array}$	**v.** $\begin{array}{r}44\\-16\\\hline\end{array}$
e. $\begin{array}{r}62\\-56\\\hline\end{array}$	**k.** $\begin{array}{r}65\\-36\\\hline\end{array}$	**q.** $\begin{array}{r}96\\-45\\\hline\end{array}$	**w.** $\begin{array}{r}36\\-24\\\hline\end{array}$
f. $\begin{array}{r}63\\-33\\\hline\end{array}$	**l.** $\begin{array}{r}42\\-30\\\hline\end{array}$	**r.** $\begin{array}{r}61\\-15\\\hline\end{array}$	**x.** $\begin{array}{r}73\\-30\\\hline\end{array}$

Times Tables

Complete the times tables.

0 x 0 = _____	1 x 6 = _____	2 x 12 = _____	4 x 5 = _____
0 x 1 = _____	1 x 7 = _____	3 x 0 = _____	4 x 6 = _____
0 x 2 = _____	1 x 8 = _____	3 x 1 = _____	4 x 7 = _____
0 x 3 = _____	1 x 9 = _____	3 x 2 = _____	4 x 8 = _____
0 x 4 = _____	1 x 10 = _____	3 x 3 = _____	4 x 9 = _____
0 x 5 = _____	1 x 11 = _____	3 x 4 = _____	4 x 10 = _____
0 x 6 = _____	1 x 12 = _____	3 x 5 = _____	4 x 11 = _____
0 x 7 = _____	2 x 0 = _____	3 x 6 = _____	4 x 12 = _____
0 x 8 = _____	2 x 1 = _____	3 x 7 = _____	5 x 0 = _____
0 x 9 = _____	2 x 2 = _____	3 x 8 = _____	5 x 1 = _____
0 x 10 = _____	2 x 3 = _____	3 x 9 = _____	5 x 2 = _____
0 x 11 = _____	2 x 4 = _____	3 x 10 = _____	5 x 3 = _____
0 x 12 = _____	2 x 5 = _____	3 x 11 = _____	5 x 4 = _____
1 x 0 = _____	2 x 6 = _____	3 x 12 = _____	5 x 5 = _____
1 x 1 = _____	2 x 7 = _____	4 x 0 = _____	5 x 6 = _____
1 x 2 = _____	2 x 8 = _____	4 x 1 = _____	5 x 7 = _____
1 x 3 = _____	2 x 9 = _____	4 x 2 = _____	5 x 8 = _____
1 x 4 = _____	2 x 10 = _____	4 x 3 = _____	5 x 9 = _____
1 x 5 = _____	2 x 11 = _____	4 x 4 = _____	5 x 10 = _____

Times Tables (cont.)

Complete the times tables.

5 x 11 = _____	7 x 4 = _____	8 x 10 = _____	10 x 3 = _____	11 x 9 = _____
5 x 12 = _____	7 x 5 = _____	8 x 11 = _____	10 x 4 = _____	11 x 10 = _____
6 x 0 = _____	7 x 6 = _____	8 x 12 = _____	10 x 5 = _____	11 x 11 = _____
6 x 1 = _____	7 x 7 = _____	9 x 0 = _____	10 x 6 = _____	11 x 12 = _____
6 x 2 = _____	7 x 8 = _____	9 x 1 = _____	10 x 7 = _____	12 x 0 = _____
6 x 3 = _____	7 x 9 = _____	9 x 2 = _____	10 x 8 = _____	12 x 1 = _____
6 x 4 = _____	7 x 10 = _____	9 x 3 = _____	10 x 9 = _____	12 x 2 = _____
6 x 5 = _____	7 x 11 = _____	9 x 4 = _____	10 x 10 = _____	12 x 3 = _____
6 x 6 = _____	7 x 12 = _____	9 x 5 = _____	10 x 11 = _____	12 x 4 = _____
6 x 7 = _____	8 x 0 = _____	9 x 6 = _____	10 x 12 = _____	12 x 5 = _____
6 x 8 = _____	8 x 1 = _____	9 x 7 = _____	11 x 0 = _____	12 x 6 = _____
6 x 9 = _____	8 x 2 = _____	9 x 8 = _____	11 x 1 = _____	12 x 7 = _____
6 x 10 = _____	8 x 3 = _____	9 x 9 = _____	11 x 2 = _____	12 x 8 = _____
6 x 11 = _____	8 x 4 = _____	9 x 10 = _____	11 x 3 = _____	12 x 9 = _____
6 x 12 = _____	8 x 5 = _____	9 x 11 = _____	11 x 4 = _____	12 x 10 = _____
7 x 0 = _____	8 x 6 = _____	9 x 12 = _____	11 x 5 = _____	12 x 11 = _____
7 x 1 = _____	8 x 7 = _____	10 x 0 = _____	11 x 6 = _____	12 x 12 = _____
7 x 2 = _____	8 x 8 = _____	10 x 1 = _____	11 x 7 = _____	
7 x 3 = _____	8 x 9 = _____	10 x 2 = _____	11 x 8 = _____	

Single-Digit Multiplication

Solve the problems.

6 x 6 = _____   9 x 5 = _____   6 x 7 = _____   8 x 0 = _____

3 x 1 = _____   4 x 7 = _____   7 x 3 = _____   8 x 9 = _____

9 x 6 = _____   6 x 8 = _____   8 x 1 = _____   9 x 7 = _____

9 x 9 = _____   8 x 4 = _____   0 x 3 = _____   1 x 9 = _____

3 x 2 = _____   4 x 8 = _____   0 x 4 = _____   3 x 3 = _____

4 x 9 = _____   0 x 5 = _____   7 x 2 = _____   8 x 8 = _____

3 x 4 = _____   0 x 6 = _____   3 x 5 = _____   0 x 7 = _____

2 x 0 = _____   3 x 6 = _____   0 x 8 = _____   0 x 0 = _____

1 x 6 = _____   4 x 5 = _____   0 x 1 = _____   1 x 7 = _____

2 x 9 = _____   4 x 2 = _____   5 x 8 = _____   1 x 4 = _____

4 x 3 = _____   5 x 9 = _____   1 x 5 = _____   4 x 6 = _____

5 x 0 = _____   0 x 9 = _____   8 x 5 = _____   5 x 7 = _____

Single- and Double-Digit Multiplication

Solve the problems.

2 x 2	3 x 8	5 x 1	10 x 0
2 x 3	11 x 5	7 x 4	10 x 8
10 x 3	11 x 9	12 x 5	7 x 5
11 x 8	10 x 4	11 x 10	6 x 0
7 x 6	12 x 8	10 x 5	11 x 11
6 x 1	7 x 7	9 x 0	10 x 6
11 x 12	6 x 2	7 x 8	9 x 1
10 x 7	12 x 0	6 x 3	7 x 9
9 x 2	10 x 8	12 x 1	6 x 4
10 x 7	9 x 3	10 x 9	12 x 2

Column Multiplication

Solve the problems.

96	90	47	25	16
x 6	x 3	x 9	x 1	x 6

40	82	60	71	32
x 8	x 5	x 2	x 7	x 4

68	33	20	24	41
x 8	x 1	x 6	x 9	x 4

46	49	38	24	27
x 2	x 7	x 4	x 3	x 3

56	84	70	58	50
x 7	x 2	x 9	x 7	x 1

21	77	79	86	13
x 2	x 6	x 4	x 3	x 2

22	74	26	14	48
x 6	x 1	x 9	x 7	x 3

42	88	69	43	19
x 4	x 5	x 8	x 3	x 2

Division Facts

Solve the problems.

$0 \div 0 = $ _____ $6 \div 1 = $ _____ $24 \div 2 = $ _____ $24 \div 4 = $ _____

$1 \div 0 = $ _____ $7 \div 1 = $ _____ $3 \div 3 = $ _____ $28 \div 4 = $ _____

$2 \div 0 = $ _____ $8 \div 1 = $ _____ $6 \div 3 = $ _____ $32 \div 4 = $ _____

$3 \div 0 = $ _____ $9 \div 1 = $ _____ $9 \div 3 = $ _____ $36 \div 4 = $ _____

$4 \div 0 = $ _____ $10 \div 1 = $ _____ $12 \div 3 = $ _____ $40 \div 4 = $ _____

$5 \div 0 = $ _____ $11 \div 1 = $ _____ $15 \div 3 = $ _____ $44 \div 4 = $ _____

$6 \div 0 = $ _____ $12 \div 1 = $ _____ $18 \div 3 = $ _____ $48 \div 4 = $ _____

$7 \div 0 = $ _____ $2 \div 2 = $ _____ $21 \div 3 = $ _____ $5 \div 5 = $ _____

$8 \div 0 = $ _____ $4 \div 2 = $ _____ $24 \div 3 = $ _____ $10 \div 5 = $ _____

$9 \div 0 = $ _____ $6 \div 2 = $ _____ $27 \div 3 = $ _____ $15 \div 5 = $ _____

$10 \div 0 = $ _____ $8 \div 2 = $ _____ $30 \div 3$ _____ $20 \div 5 = $ _____

$11 \div 0 = $ _____ $10 \div 2 = $ _____ $33 \div 3 = $ _____ $25 \div 5 = $ _____

$12 \div 0 = $ _____ $12 \div 2 = $ _____ $36 \div 3 = $ _____ $30 \div 5 = $ _____

$1 \div 1 = $ _____ $14 \div 2 = $ _____ $4 \div 4 = $ _____ $35 \div 5 = $ _____

$2 \div 1 = $ _____ $16 \div 2 = $ _____ $8 \div 4 = $ _____ $40 \div 5 = $ _____

$3 \div 1 = $ _____ $18 \div 2 = $ _____ $12 \div 4 = $ _____ $45 \div 5 = $ _____

$4 \div 1 = $ _____ $20 \div 2 = $ _____ $16 \div 4 = $ _____ $50 \div 5 = $ _____

$5 \div 1 = $ _____ $22 \div 2 = $ _____ $20 \div 4 = $ _____ $55 \div 5 = $ _____

Division Facts (cont.)

Solve the problems.

60 ÷ 5 = ___	42 ÷ 7 = ___	96 ÷ 8 = ___	60 ÷ 10 = ___	132 ÷ 11 = ___
6 ÷ 6 = ___	49 ÷ 7 = ___	9 ÷ 9 = ___	70 ÷ 10 = ___	12 ÷ 12 = ___
12 ÷ 6 = ___	56 ÷ 7 = ___	18 ÷ 9 = ___	80 ÷ 10 = ___	24 ÷ 12 = ___
18 ÷ 6 = ___	63 ÷ 7 = ___	27 ÷ 9 = ___	90 ÷ 10 = ___	36 ÷ 12 = ___
24 ÷ 6 = ___	70 ÷ 7 = ___	36 ÷ 9 = ___	100 ÷ 10 = ___	48 ÷ 12 = ___
30 ÷ 6 = ___	77 ÷ 7 = ___	45 ÷ 9 = ___	110 ÷ 10 = ___	60 ÷ 12 = ___
36 ÷ 6 = ___	84 ÷ 7 = ___	54 ÷ 9 = ___	120 ÷ 10 = ___	72 ÷ 12 = ___
42 ÷ 6 = ___	8 ÷ 8 = ___	63 ÷ 9 = ___	11 ÷ 11 = ___	84 ÷ 12 = ___
48 ÷ 6 = ___	16 ÷ 8 = ___	72 ÷ 9 = ___	22 ÷ 11 = ___	96 ÷ 12 = ___
54 ÷ 6 = ___	24 ÷ 8 = ___	81 ÷ 9 = ___	33 ÷ 11 = ___	108 ÷ 12 = ___
60 ÷ 6 = ___	32 ÷ 8 = ___	90 ÷ 9 = ___	44 ÷ 11 = ___	120 ÷ 12 = ___
66 ÷ 6 = ___	40 ÷ 8 = ___	99 ÷ 9 = ___	55 ÷ 11 = ___	132 ÷ 12 = ___
72 ÷ 6 = ___	48 ÷ 8 = ___	108 ÷ 9 = ___	66 ÷ 11 = ___	144 ÷ 12 = ___
7 ÷ 7 = ___	56 ÷ 8 = ___	10 ÷ 10 = ___	77 ÷ 11 = ___	
14 ÷ 7 = ___	64 ÷ 8 = ___	20 ÷ 10 = ___	88 ÷ 11 = ___	
21 ÷ 7 = ___	72 ÷ 8 = ___	30 ÷ 10 = ___	99 ÷ 11 = ___	
28 ÷ 7 = ___	80 ÷ 8 = ___	40 ÷ 10 = ___	110 ÷ 11 = ___	
35 ÷ 7 = ___	88 ÷ 8 = ___	50 ÷ 10 = ___	121 ÷ 11 = ___	

6/21/0/

What Time Is It?

Read the time on the clocks. Write the time on the lines.

1.
3:45

6.
4:15

11.
10:50

2.
6:05

7.
1:30

12.
6:00

3.
5:55

8.
12:45

13.
2:35

4.
4:25

9.
7:20

14.
1:00

5.
2:10

10.
8:35

15.
11:50

A.M. and P.M.

A.M. is the time after 12 o'clock midnight and before 12 o'clock noon. **P.M.** is the time after 12 o'clock noon and before 12 o'clock midnight. (Midnight itself is **A.M.** and noon itself is **P.M.**) Write **A.M.** or **P.M.** after each of these events to say what time it usually falls in.

1. dinnertime _____

2. getting up _____

3. afternoon nap _____

4. after-school baseball game _____

5. before-school dance class _____

6. breakfast _____

7. evening movie _____

8. evening bath _____

9. after-dinner dessert _____

10. sunrise _____

11. going to school _____

12. sunset _____

13. lunch _____

14. morning cartoons _____

15. going to bed _____

16. after-school piano lessons _____

17. morning exercises _____

18. homework _____

19. afternoon reading _____

20. morning snack _____

21. early recess _____

22. after-school bike ride _____

23. afternoon computer games _____

24. dawn _____

Practice & Learn
for
10 Year Olds

On the Go with Plurals

To form the plural of a noun ending with a consonant and a **y**, change the **y** to **i** and add *es*. Change these singular nouns to plural nouns by using this rule.

1. party _____

2. company _____

3. army _____

4. country _____

5. spy _____

6. puppy _____

7. liberty _____

8. fly _____

9. berry _____

10. factory _____

11. flurry _____

12. family _____

13. story _____

14. victory _____

15. baby _____

16. lady _____

17. monopoly _____

18. body _____

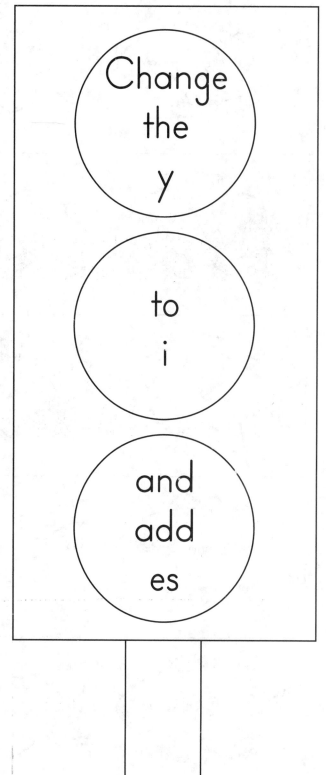

Change the y

to i

and add es

School of Fish

Nouns that end in **ch**, **sh**, **ss**, **x**, or **z** can be made plural by adding *es.* Color the fish below that use this rule. Write the plural form of each word.

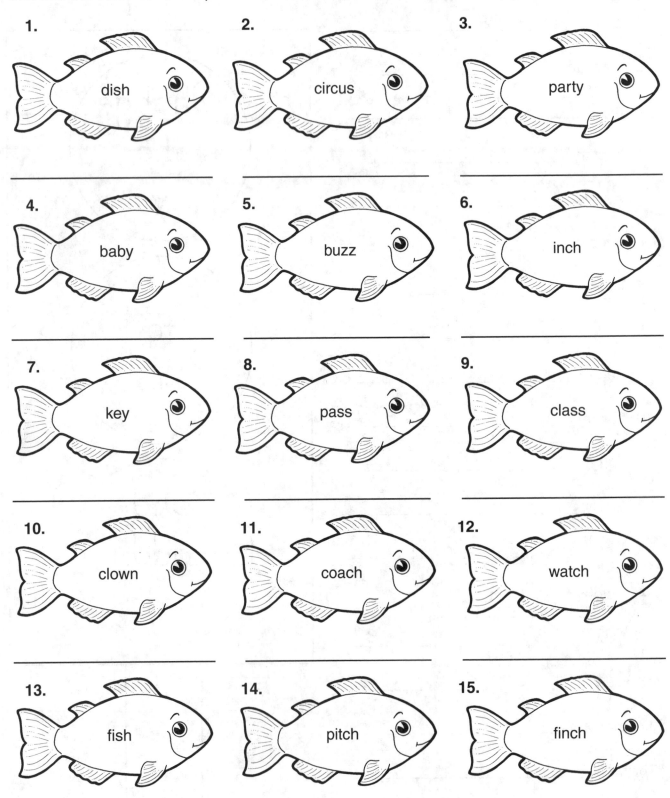

1. dish

2. circus

3. party

4. baby

5. buzz

6. inch

7. key

8. pass

9. class

10. clown

11. coach

12. watch

13. fish

14. pitch

15. finch

124

"Stepping Up" with Plurals

The first ladder is for singular words. The other ladder is for the plural form of each singular word. Climb each ladder by filling in the blanks with the matching singular or plural word.

Example: The plural for *pen* is *pens.* Write it on the second ladder step.

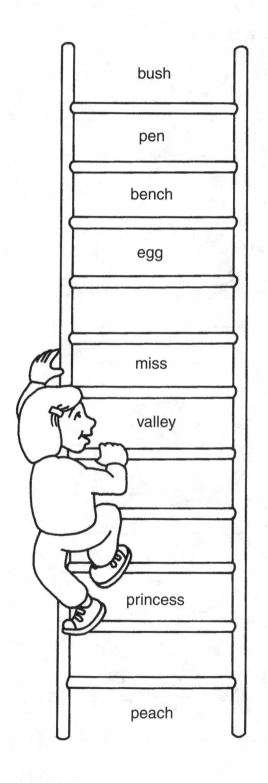

bush

pen

bench

egg

miss

valley

princess

peach

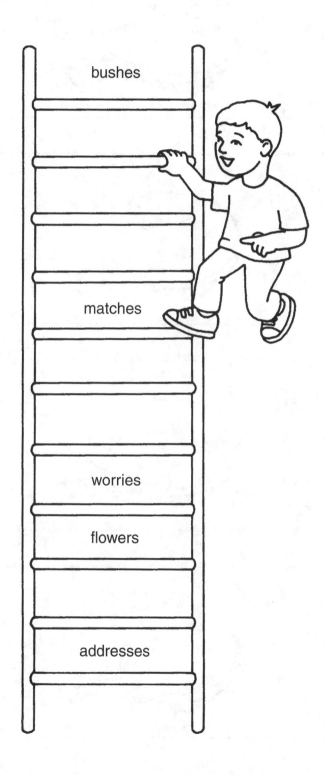

bushes

matches

worries

flowers

addresses

Predicting Plurals

Have fun predicting plurals. On each fortune cookie there is a noun. Write the plural form of the word on the fortune cookie. On the lines under the fortune cookies, write sentences using the plural words.

1.

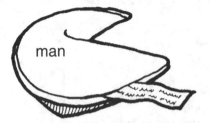

2.

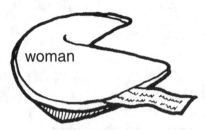

_____

_____

3.

4.

_____

_____

5.

6.

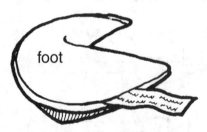

_____

_____

7.

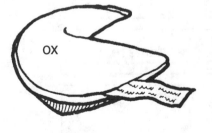

8.

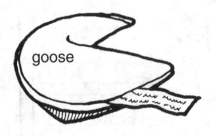

_____

_____

Possessives

Possessive nouns show who or what owns something. Singular possessive nouns are made by adding an apostrophe and then an *s*. Plural possessive nouns are formed by adding an apostrophe after the *s*. However, when a plural noun does not end with an *s*, an apostrophe and then an *s* are added. Rewrite the underlined nouns in the sentences to make them possessive. (Possessive nouns function in sentences as adjectives. They describe other nouns.)

1. The <u>doll</u> dress tore on the carriage. _____

2. <u>Lena</u> ball went over the fence. _____

3. Those <u>girls</u> jumping rope was tangled. _____

4. The <u>turtle</u> shell is like a home. _____

5. <u>Kate</u> mother brought her skates to the party. _____

6. The lost <u>child</u> father was relieved to find him. _____

7. The <u>boys</u> kites flew away. _____

8. The <u>penguin</u> baby cuddled against its mother. _____

9. The <u>blouse</u> button came loose. _____

10. The <u>pan</u> handle was very hot. _____

11. That <u>man</u> car is parked in the wrong place! _____

12. <u>Jen</u> homework is late. _____

13. The <u>lions</u> cage is near the tigers. _____

14. My <u>toys</u> cupboard needs to be cleaned. _____

15. The <u>play</u> cast was ready for opening night. _____

Action Verbs

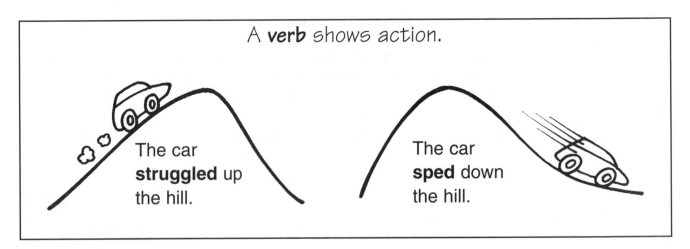

A **verb** shows action.

The car **struggled** up the hill.

The car **sped** down the hill.

Write the words used as verbs on the lines.

1. Barbara plays basketball well. _____

2. The bird flies over my head. _____

3. The bicycle makes Frank happy. _____

4. The children ran to the playground. _____

5. The balloon popped in front of me. _____

6. The pen ran out of ink. _____

7. I fell on the sidewalk. _____

8. I eat a piece of fruit each day. _____

9. The old horse stood quietly in the field. _____

10. Our teacher reads a story to us each day. _____

Take Action!

An **action verb** tells what the subject does. It shows action.

Examples: run, swing, jump, laugh, see, hit, leap

What are some of your favorite action verbs? Write them here:_____

_____

In the following paragraph, there are 50 action verbs. Can you find at least 40 of them?
When you find one, underline it in the paragraph and then write it on another sheet of paper.

In the morning, Benjamin woke up and jumped out of bed. He landed on his brother, Timothy, who was asleep in the bottom bunk. Timothy sat up and rubbed his eyes. He grumbled at Benjamin and then fell back on his bed. Benjamin looked at Timothy for a long time. He wanted to see if Timothy was asleep. Then Benjamin ran to the corner and grabbed his horn. Benjamin blew into his horn and played some musical notes. He liked the way his horn sounded. But he heard another sound. He stopped and listened. A moaning sound came from Timothy. Benjamin didn't like that sound. He grabbed his horn and ran out the door. He sat on the front lawn and played some more music. The notes floated in the air. He felt happy until he heard another sound. He stopped and listened. A groaning sound came from his next door neighbor. Benjamin ran into the backyard. He played his horn some more. He liked the notes. Then he heard another sound. It was his mother. She called his name again. He went inside. His mother took his horn and put it away. Then she put Benjamin back in his bed. She told him it was too early to get up. Benjamin's mother went back to bed, too. Benjamin tried to imagine the sounds of his horn. Suddenly, he heard another sound. He stopped and listened. Timothy snored again and again. Benjamin moaned. He stuck his fingers in his ears, but he still heard Timothy. So he covered his ears with his pillow. Soon he fell fast asleep.

We're Here to Help!

Some **non-action verbs** help action verbs do their work. They work together in a sentence, like a team. These non-action verbs are called **helping verbs**.

Example: People **can travel** in many ways.

The non-action helping verb is *can*.

The action verb is *travel*.

The complete verb is *can travel*.

Find the helping and action verbs in sentences shown below. Use the following list of verbs to help you. Then fill in the chart at the bottom of the page by writing the helping and action verbs from the sentences.

Helping Verbs:	am	is	should	are	were	has	have	had	can	will
Action Verbs:	drink	ridden	pushed	driven	move	pulled	going	ride	seen	go

1. Jimmy should ride his bicycle.
2. An elephant is ridden in India.
3. The scooters were pushed by the children.
4. An airplane can move quickly.
5. Amy has driven a bus.

6. Sled dogs have pulled the children across the snow.
7. I have seen a bear.
8. You will go to a birthday party.
9. Henry is going to eat all the cake.
10. We will drink all the punch.

Helping Verbs

1. _____
2. _____
3. _____
4. _____
5. _____
6. _____
7. _____
8. _____
9. _____
10. _____

Action Verbs

1. _____
2. _____
3. _____
4. _____
5. _____
6. _____
7. _____
8. _____
9. _____
10. _____

Verb Tenses

The words below are written in the **present tense** (today). On the blank after each word, write its form in the **past tense** (before today). The first one has been done for you.

present tense

past tense

paint

painted

1. paint _painted_

2. climb _____

3. play _____

4. laugh _____

5. shout _____

6. jump _____

7. run _____

8. see _____

9. eat _____

10. come _____

11. make _____

12. build _____

13. sleep _____

14. give _____

15. take _____

16. bring _____

17. sing _____

18. hold _____

19. go _____

20. write _____

Past and Present

Verbs in the **present tense** show action that is happening now. In the **past tense**, verbs show action that already happened.

Change each of these present tense verbs to the past tense by adding *d* or *ed*.	Change each of the past tense verbs to the present tense by removing the *d* or *ed*.
1. turn _____	11. smiled _____
2. cook _____	12. folded _____
3. roll _____	13. closed _____
4. watch _____	14. painted _____
5. park _____	15. climbed _____
6. fill _____	16. shared _____
7. color _____	17. joked _____
8. fold _____	18. matched _____
9. close _____	19. laughed _____
10. look _____	20. played _____

7/8/61

Changing Irregular Verbs

Change the following irregular verbs from present to past tense.	Change the irregular verbs from past to present tense.
1. blow _blown_	11. caught _catch_
2. come _came_	12. read _read_
3. sing _sang_	13. rode _ride_
4. wear _wore_	14. drank _drink_
5. take _tooke_	15. swung _swing_
6. cry _cried_	16. shone _shine_
7. make _made_	17. paid _pay_
8. give _gave_	18. wrote _write_
9. fall _fell_	19. swept _sweep_
10. fly _flew_	20. tore _tear_

Was and Were

Write **was** or **were** in each sentence.

Four little birds **were** chirping a song.

1. What _____ that?

2. Where _____ you going?

3. I _____ at the movies.

4. We _____ cleaning the room.

5. She _____ very helpful today.

6. They _____ afraid of the big dog.

7. Jan and Laura _____ playing in the sand.

8. Tim _____ in the kitchen.

9. My friend and I _____ just about to leave.

10. Who _____ in charge of the show?

Is, Am, and Are

Write **is**, **am**, or **are** in each sentence.

Today **is** Marc's birthday.
How old **is** he?

1. Who _____ you waiting for?

2. Where _____ we going tomorrow?

3. I _____ very hungry.

4. The boy _____ a good reader.

5. The children _____ playing in the park.

6. We _____ having a good time.

7. They _____ having some trouble with their car.

8. Terry _____ a good friend.

9. How _____ I going to get there?

10. I _____ feeling very tired.

Just One or More?

Subjects and verbs are very important parts of a sentence. They need to get along well. If they do not agree with each other, your sentence will not sound right. It is important that they agree in number. A **singular subject** tells about one person, place, or thing. It needs a singular verb. A **plural subject** tells about more than one person, place, or thing. It needs a plural verb.

Examples

Singular Subjects		Plural Subjects	
dress	rabbit	dresses	rabbits
car	Michael	cars	Michael and Jason
boy	house	boys	houses
Singular Verbs		**Plural Verbs**	
has	jumps	have	jump
is	hops	are	hop
runs	sings	run	sing

In the following sentences, circle the correct verb. On the line before each number, write an **S** if you circled a singular verb or a **P** if you circled a plural verb.

_____ 1. The dress (has, have) a big bow in back.

_____ 2. These cars (runs, run) funny.

_____ 3. The boys (jumps, jump) from the tree.

_____ 4. The rabbit (hops, hop) around the yard.

_____ 5. Michael and Jason (sing, sings) this morning.

_____ 6. My house (are, is) yellow and white.

_____ 7. All the houses on our street (are, is) one story.

_____ 8. Michael (hop, hops) on one foot.

_____ 9. My old toy car (are, is) rusty.

_____ 10. Our rabbit (has, have) a large cage.

Now write your own sentences on the lines below. Write one sentence with a singular subject and verb and another sentence with a plural subject and verb. Make your sentences as interesting as you can.

1. Singular: _____

2. Plural: _____

Adjectives

Adjectives are words that describe people, places, and things. Circle the adjectives in the following sentences that are descriptive words.

1. The unusual man came to our front door.

2. A playful puppy ran through our yard.

3. I like the green bike with the long seat.

4. We can play with this funny, old toy.

5. I am wearing a new pair of gray shoes.

6. My mother is tall and pretty.

7. My teacher is smart and funny.

8. I saw a silly show on television.

9. The happy pig rolled in the mud in the large barnyard.

10. There was a small, black spider hanging from the shiny web.

11. The choir members wore colorful robes during their lively performance.

12. My grandfather is kind and generous.

13. Should I wear my orange shirt or my yellow one?

14. The little girls pretended to have tea at their imaginary party.

15. The night was quiet when the barn owl began to hoot.

Enchanted Enhancements

Sometimes a simple, complete sentence is all that is needed. However, at other times it is a good idea to give more details.

Descriptive language and additional information about the subject are very useful and make the sentence more interesting.

A word that helps describe something is an **adjective**. There are three types of adjectives.

- **Demonstrative Adjectives:** These point things out. They answer the question, "Which one(s)?"

  Examples: this, that, these, those

  I like this dress. Those cookies look delicious.

- **Common Adjectives:** These describe the subject in a general way. They answer the question, "What kind of?" or "How many?"

  Examples: soft, warm, six, blue, sunny, tired, tall

  The building is tall. The kitten is soft.

- **Proper Adjectives:** These are made from proper nouns and are always capitalized. They answer the question, "What kind of?"

  Examples: Irish, Martian, African American, Native American

  I love French cheese! There are many Japanese cars.

In the following sentences, circle the adjectives. Then, on the lines, write the questions (*What kind of? How many? Which one?*) that the adjectives answer.

1. I don't like this sandwich. _____

2. The old man came to the door. _____

3. Most French students speak English. _____

4. We're learning a Scottish dance tomorrow. _____

5. The yellow flowers are wilting. _____

6. I have three brothers. _____

7. For dinner tonight, they're serving a delicious, spinach casserole. _____

8. Give me your dollar, and I'll give you my comic book. _____

9. Tim doesn't want that soft pear. _____

10. Watch out for the mean dog down the street. _____

11. My clueless brother threw away my homework. _____

12. Those black shoes are too small. _____

More Enhancements

Now it is your turn to enhance the sentences in the following story. Fill in the blanks with descriptive words or phrases. You may use demonstrative adjectives (such as *this, that, these,* and *those*), common adjectives (such as *birthday, large, frozen, lovely, three),* and proper adjectives (such as *British, German,* and *Jurassic*). You may also wish to use descriptive phrases (such as *weather-beaten* or *pocket-sized*). Have fun with this activity but remember to try for interesting images with descriptive language rather than choosing words or phrases that will make the sentences sound silly.

It was my _____ birthday so I ran home from school. When I got to my _____ house it looked like no one was home. "Hello!" I shouted. "Where is my _____ family? Your _____ son and brother is home now!" No one answered. I went to our _____ kitchen to see if there was a note. No note. Not even a _____ note. I went into the _____ room and turned on the _____ television. There was a _____ show on. I turned the television off. I went back into the kitchen to get something to eat. "I want something that's _____ to eat," I said to myself. I saw yogurt, but it was pineapple flavored. "I don't want _____ yogurt. I want _____ yogurt," I said, grabbing a _____ yogurt. I sat down to eat the _____ yogurt. Then I looked for something else. I found _____ candy. I was just about to eat it when the _____ telephone rang. "Hello?" It was my _____ mom. She told me she would be home soon but needed me to go into the _____ basement to get a _____ chicken from the _____ freezer. "Okay," I said. Then I ate some _____ candy.

The telephone rang again. "Honey," my mom said, "please get the _____ chicken from the basement now!"

"Okay!" I said again. As I walked toward the _____ basement stairs, I started wondering how she knew I hadn't gone down to the basement yet. I opened the _____ door. I slowly crept down the _____ steps into the _____ basement. I was getting the creeps. How did she know? Why was it so dark? The _____ stairs made creaking noises. Finally, I got to the bottom and waved my hand around to try to find the _____ light switch. I felt some _____ cobwebs and shrieked just a little. Just then, the _____ lights came on, and I heard _____ voices screaming, "Happy birthday!" I nearly ran all the way back up the _____ steps. My heart was pounding so hard I thought it would break right through my _____ chest! I saw the _____ basement was full of _____ people. They were holding _____ balloons and _____ gifts. Everyone I knew was there—my _____ mom, my _____ Aunt Amelia, my _____ sister Lindsay, all our _____ neighbors, and all of my _____ friends.

So _____ is where everyone was, and _____ was how my _____ mom knew I hadn't come downstairs yet. The _____ chicken, I just remembered! I went to the _____ freezer and opened the door to grab a _____ chicken. Everyone stared at me. Then they all started to laugh. "No, honey," my mom said, "we don't need a chicken after all. Tonight we're having _____ pizza and _____ birthday cake with _____ candles!" We went upstairs and had a party!

Articles: A and An

Articles are a kind of adjective. The three most common articles are *the, a,* and *an*. *A* is used before words that begin with a consonant sound while *an* is used before words that begin with a vowel sound. Write **a** or **an** in the blanks below.

1. _____crayon

2. _____ape

3. _____saucer

4. _____egg

5. _____monkey

6. _____pill

7. _____itch

8. _____orange

9. _____house

10. _____leaf

11. _____ ant crawled across the leaf.

12. Have you seen _____ purple butterfly?

13. I would like to eat _____ sandwich for lunch.

14. _____ apple a day keeps the doctor away.

15. _____ goat chewed on my pant leg!

Comparison Suffixes

Some adjectives end in *er* or *est*. These endings are used to show how people, places, or things compare to each other. The suffix **er** compares two nouns or pronouns and the ending **est** compares more than two nouns.

Examples: December is *cold.*   Mary is *young.*

January is *colder* than December.   Jane is *younger* than Mary.

February is the *coldest* month of the year.   Micheal is the *youngest* of the family.

Use adjectives that end in *er* or *est* to complete the following sentences.

1. Chris is tall, but Marcos is _____ than Chris. Carey is the

    _____ of the three boys.

2. Cookies are sweet, but cakes are _____ than cookies. Candy is the

    _____ of all three desserts.

3. An orange is small. A plum is _____ than an orange. A grape is the

    _____ fruit of them all.

4. Joe's room is messy, but Tom's room is _____. Of all the rooms in

    the house, the kitchen is the _____.

5. A rock is big. A hill is _____ than a rock. A mountain is

    the _____ of all.

6. A flower is pretty. A bouquet is _____. A garden is the

    _____ of them all.

7. Pearls are hard. Rubies are _____, but a diamond is the

    _____ gem of all.

8. This magazine is thick. That book is _____. The dictionary is the

    _____.

Adverbs

Adverbs are describing words that tell **when** (a time), **where** (a place), or **how** (how something is done).

The monkey eats his banana **quietly**.

(How)

Underline the adverbs. On the lines, write **how, where,** or **when** to show the way in which the adverb is used.

_____ 1. I walked quietly.

_____ 2. We will go tomorrow.

_____ 3. We can play later.

_____ 4. My cousins will come here.

_____ 5. The cheetah growled fiercely.

_____ 6. The mother sang softly.

_____ 7. The ballerina dances gracefully.

_____ 8. Yesterday I played baseball.

_____ 9. The orchestra played well.

_____ 10. He completed his homework quickly.

Pronouns

Pronouns are words that are used in place of nouns. Some pronouns are *I, we, you, it, he, she,* and *them*. There are other pronouns as well. Read the sentences below. Rewrite the sentences using the correct pronoun to replace the noun in bold print.

1. **The boy** played baseball. _____

2. **The girl** swam across the pool. _____

3. **The children** climbed the trees. _____

4. **Mary and Frank** rode their bikes to school. _____

5. The team surprised **Lily** with a trophy. _____

6. Kim saw **the dog** run across the street. _____

7. **Mom** read the new best seller. _____

8. **Gary** saw a strange shadow. _____

9. The girls walked to **Mary's** house. _____

10. The family found **kittens** in a basket on their porch. _____

11. Where should I put **the presents**? _____

12. **My dad** put gas in the car. _____

13. **The players** won the championship! _____

14. Where is **the key**? _____

15. Please, give that to **Rick**. _____

Synonyms

When comparing and contrasting objects and ideas, it is helpful to use special words called synonyms. **Synonyms** are words that mean nearly the same thing. See the examples in the box below.

good, helpful	strong, powerful	gentle, mild
fast, quick	sour, tart	bad, evil
little, small	big, large	tired, sleepy

Circle the synonyms in each row.

1. busy   tired   active   bad

2. nibble   chew   hit   play

3. cook   flavorful   tasty   show

4. joyful   happy   sad   angry

5. walk   fall   stand   trip

6. pretty   huge   anxious   enormous

7. worried   anxious   smart   angry

8. mad   angry   funny   disappointed

9. talk   kick   chat   sing

10. laugh   sneeze   cry   weep

More Synonyms

Draw a line to connect synonym pairs.

1.	neat		see
2.	sad		calm
3.	thin		chilly
4.	look		skinny
5.	plain		powerful
6.	strong		stingy
7.	cold		large
8.	big		small
9.	cheap		wealthy
10.	quiet		pointed
11.	poor		simple
12.	little		unhappy
13.	sharp		spotless
14.	loud		needy
15.	rich		noisy

Synonyms and the Thesaurus

A **thesaurus** is a book that provides a list of words with the same, or nearly the same, meaning. Locate each word in a thesaurus. Draw a line to connect the synonyms.

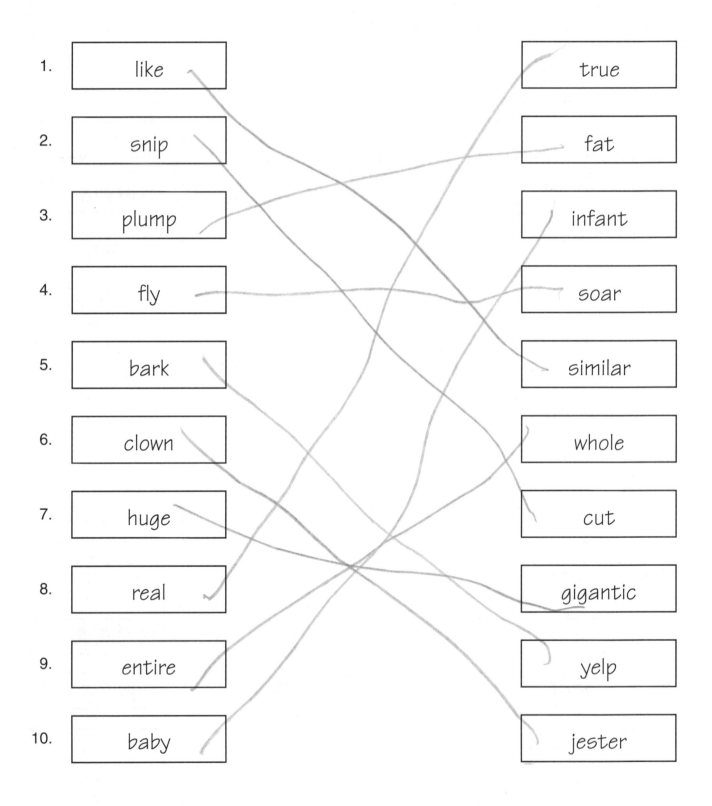

1. like

2. snip

3. plump

4. fly

5. bark

6. clown

7. huge

8. real

9. entire

10. baby

true

fat

infant

soar

similar

whole

cut

gigantic

yelp

jester

Antonyms

When comparing and contrasting objects and ideas, another kind of word that is helpful to use is called an antonym. **Antonyms** are words that have opposite meanings. See the examples in the box below.

night, day	up, down	bad, good
sad, happy	fresh, spoiled	clean, dirty
dark, bright	cool, warm	large, small

Circle the antonyms in each row.

1. laugh   smile   cry   run

2. even   fast   slow   easy

3. hurt   heal   harmful   sad

4. shiny   sea   dull   air

5. wake   sleep   rest   cat

6. girl   bird   boy   enormous

7. coffee   fire   water   tea

8. truth   confess   fly   lie

9. smart   lively   ugly   pretty

10. furry   hard   light   soft

Find the Antonyms

Complete each sentence with an antonym. You may choose to use a dictionary or a thesaurus to help you find the best antonym. There are many correct answers.

1. A flower is soft, but a rock is _____.

2. Sugar is sweet, but a lemon is _____.

3. Fire is hot, but ice is _____.

4. Let's do the work now and not wait until _____.

5. Tell the truth. Don't _____.

6. Try to be kind and not _____.

7. The water is clear and not at all _____.

8. The sun rises in the east and sets in the _____.

I Spy Homophones

Homonyms are words that sound alike but are spelled differently. Use the clues below to supply the missing homophone pairs.

Example: *Hare* and *hair* are homophones.

You can use them to solve the first problem.

1. a rabbit and something on your head

   _____   _____

2. belongs to us and a measurement of time

   _____   _____

3. used to make bread and a female deer

   _____   _____

4. opposite of yes and to understand

   _____   _____

5. past tense of read and a color

   _____   _____

6. a story and the end of a dog

   _____   _____

Which Word?

Words that sound or sometimes look similar often have meanings that are not alike at all. Decide which of the two word choices on the right is the correct one to correspond with the word or phrase on the left and then circle it.

1. strength	*mite/might*
2. in no way	*not/knot*
3. well liked	*popular/poplar*
4. fruit	*plumb/plum*
5. without covering	*bare/bear*
6. cry	*ball/bawl*
7. forbidden	*band/banned*
8. French money	*frank/franc*
9. musical instrument	*symbol/cymbal*
10. cold	*chilly/chili*
11. odor	*scent/sent*
12. religious song	*hymn/him*
13. market	*bazaar/bizarre*
14. color	*blew/blue*
15. breakfast food	*cereal/serial*

Tune In to Homophones

Written on each television screen is a message. The messages are full of misused homophones. Rewrite the messages and correct the homophones.

1.

Whether Flash...heavy reigns dew inn an our.

_____

_____

4.

Watch Mussel Man weakly lift waits on Channel too.

_____

_____

2.

Next on The Whirled Turns...Elizabeth is never scene again.

_____

_____

5.

Special Announcement! Ice skating pear wins gold metals!

_____

_____

3.
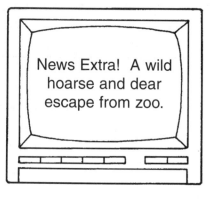
News Extra! A wild hoarse and dear escape from zoo.

_____

_____

6.

Try a knew serial just for kids! Awesome Oats!

_____

_____

Days, Months, and Holidays

What day of the week is today? _____

Did you use a capital letter to begin your answer? If you did, you used a capitalization rule.

What month of the year is today? _____

Did you use a capital letter to begin your answer? If you did, you used a capitalization rule again!

What is your favorite holiday? _____

Did you use a capital to start? If you did, you know the rules for capitalizing days, months, and holidays!

- Always capitalize the **days of the week.**
- Always capitalize the **months of the year.**
- Always capitalize the **names of holidays**.

That should be easy to remember. Now for some practice.

Put these words in order on the circle and capitalize them (start with Sunday).

- friday
- saturday
- thursday
- monday
- sunday
- tuesday
- wednesday

List the months of the year in order on the the lines. Don't forget to capitalize!

- january
- february
- march
- october
- may
- june
- august
- september
- april
- november
- december
- july

1. _____

2. _____

3. _____

4. _____

5. _____

6. _____

7. _____

8. _____

9. _____

10. _____

11. _____

12. _____

Capital Places

It's vacation time! Do you like to go to museums, zoos, or parks? Do you like to travel to lakes, oceans, rivers, or mountains? Proper names of places need capital letters because they are proper nouns.

Here is a list of places that need capital letters. Write the capital letters that are needed above the names of the places. Then choose three of the places you would like to visit.

pacific ocean	sahara desert	rocky Mountains
Grand canyon	North pole	hyde park
Mt. rushmore	san diego zoo	disneyland
amazon River	lake Louise	niagara falls

I would like to go to . . .

1. _____

2. _____

3. _____

In the space below, draw one of the places you chose.

Capitalizing Sentences

One of the most important capitalization rules is also one of the easiest to remember. **Always capitalize the first word of every sentence**. It doesn't matter whether the word is *I, you, me, Africa, a, the,* or *people,* the first word of every sentence is always capitalized. It doesn't matter whether it is a word that is normally capitalized or not.

Let's see how you do. In the story below, there are some words that need to be capitalized. Use a colored pencil or pen to write the capital letter above the letter that is there.

---

one day, Mike and Chris were riding their skateboards at the park. when they stopped to rest, they noticed something in the bushes. "what is that?" Chris asked. mike looked more closely. "it's furry!" Mike said. both boys stood and stared, and then they saw it move just a little bit.

"ohhh," Chris said, "that scared me!"

"it's a little bunny!" Mike exclaimed. sure enough, it was a scared little brown bunny hiding in the bushes. mike and chris cornered it, and then Mike scooped it up. he could feel its heart beating very rapidly.

the boys walked around the park asking people if they had lost a bunny. nobody claimed it, so Mike and Chris took it home.

mike sat in a chair watching TV and holding the bunny close to his chest. chris made telephone calls to try to find out who had lost the bunny. next, they made signs and put them up around the park and in the neighborhood. the signs said, "Lost Bunny" and gave their telephone number. no one claimed the bunny.

"you can't keep it," Chris and Mike's dad said.

"why not?" Chris asked.

"we already have a bunny cage," Mike added.

"well, okay," Dad said, "but you'll have to give it food and water every day."

the boys were happy. they named the rabbit "George," even though it was a girl rabbit. they fed her all the vegetable scraps from the kitchen, rabbit food, cabbage, dandelions, and water. george grew to be a big fat rabbit who would sometimes visit the neighbors' yards to eat weeds and dandelions which are, to this day, her favorite foods.

It's All Relative

In the following sentences, circle the letters that need to be changed to capitals and write the capital letters above. If there is a capitalized word that should not be capitalized, draw a line through the appropriate letter.

1. uncle Jorge sat on the front porch.

2. I said, "mom, what I really want to do is stay home!"

3. My mom and my dad won't be home until 7 P.M.

4. His grandma made a quilt for his birthday.

5. My Cousin and my Grandma will be coming with my mom.

6. Our Grandparents have a surprise for Aunt Aimee.

7. I wrote "Dear grandma," at the top of my stationery.

8. I wish my aunt lived closer to us; she looks just like mom.

9. Then dad stopped and looked behind him.

10. I like to go to grandmother Norton's house in the summer.

11. My favorite Cousin is Jimmy because he makes me laugh.

12. At the wedding we saw aunt Marsha and cousin Brad.

13. My Mom and Dad are taking me to dinner after the awards assembly.

14. At the reunion I saw Aunt Edith and uncle Jacques, and Cousins Kathy, Meredith, Hector, and Samantha.

15. For my birthday I'm inviting cousin Sarah, Cousin Leigh, aunt Susie, and my uncle, whose name is Mike.

Extension: Make a family chart on a large piece of butcher paper. Put your name and a picture of yourself (a photograph or a self-drawn portrait) in the proper position. If you have brothers and/or sisters, put their names (and pictures if you wish) next to yours. Your parents' names should appear above yours. Make as many lines as you need to represent your grandparents, aunts, uncles, and cousins. Be sure the lines appear in logical positions. A sample diagram appears below.

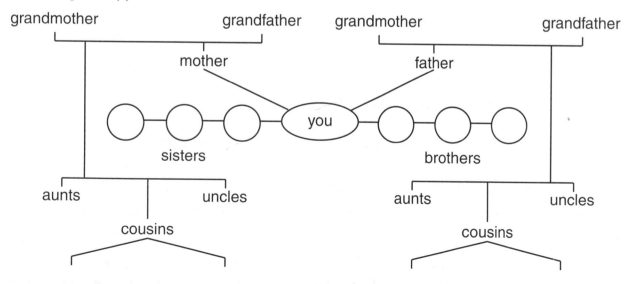

Con"trap"tions

Help the mouse get to the cheese before he gets trapped! Draw a line from the mouse hole to the correct contraction on the trap.

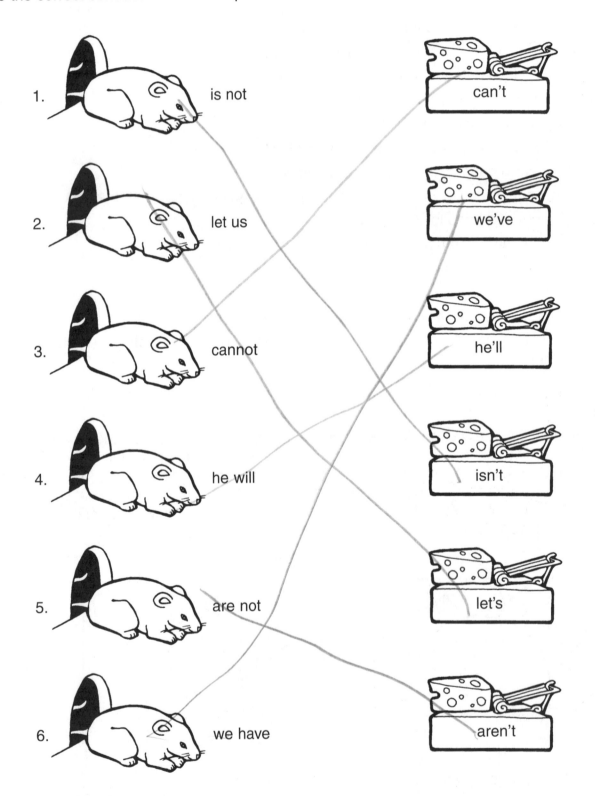

1. is not

2. let us

3. cannot

4. he will

5. are not

6. we have

can't

we've

he'll

isn't

let's

aren't

Blooming with Contractions

The contraction for *not* is *n't.* Write a contraction on each flower, using the word in the center plus the contraction for not.

1. could _____

2. have _____

3. can _____

4. are _____

5. is _____

6. would _____

Now You See Me; Now You Don't

Take out the apostrophe in the contractions and write the two words next to them that mean the same thing.

1. don't _____ _____

2. wouldn't _____ _____

3. won't _____ _____

4. aren't _____ _____

5. shouldn't _____ _____

6. he's _____ _____

7. I've _____ _____

8. they've _____ _____

9. we're _____ _____

10. she's _____ _____

11. you'll _____ _____

12. didn't _____ _____

13. isn't _____ _____

14. wasn't _____ _____

15. we'll _____ _____

16. I'd _____ _____

Contractions

Here is your opportunity to make contractions. In the story below, underline any words that may be combined into a contraction. On another paper list the contractions. There are 52.

I cannot believe it. I wrote 25 invitations that said: "You are invited to a surprise party for Serena. Do not tell her or she will not come." We could not have the party on any day but the 18th because it is close to Serena's birthday, and it is the only day in the entire month of April that is free. I stamped them and said to my dog, Sugar, "Let us mail these before it is too late." You will not believe what happened next.

It must have taken Sugar and me three hours just to mail the invitations after I had spent six hours making them because Sugar must have stopped at every tree. And then she barked at every bird; she would lie down if I tried to hurry her. Then she chased a cat up a tree, and she did not want to leave. There have been some new families who have moved in down the street, so Sugar wanted to sniff each of their new driveways. There must have been a dozen. A huge dog came running out at us. I should not have run, but I could not help it. It is instinctive to run when a snarling dog appears. It would have eaten us both alive, or at least that is what I was thinking when I decided that I had better run. I ran, dragging Sugar at the same time because she had decided that she would save the universe from the world's meanest dog. I will make a long story short by telling you that while I was trying to avoid death and while Sugar was trying to save the universe, the mean dog would have had us both for breakfast, but all three of us ended up tangled together in a whimpering, snarling knot of fur and tasty human skin. I was not doing a very good job of getting out of the mess, but at least the dogs were also stuck so we were not going anywhere. Then I heard a voice, "Who is this, Fluffy? It looks like we are meeting our neighbors." Fluffy? I was thinking it would have been better to name this dog Terminator. There I was. I was covered with dog slobber and fur, and I was not a pretty sight. Instead of meeting a new neighbor while standing, I could not believe that I was saying hello on my back while one dog, which should not be allowed on the street, was sitting on my stomach and drooling on my face, and another dog, which would not ever be allowed out of the house again, was licking my leg. What is wrong with this picture? My very good-looking neighbor must not have a very interesting life because he was laughing and enjoying the whole thing.

And if that were not enough, when I got home my mother told me that she would have stopped me if she had known that I was mailing the invitations. I had not been gone for three minutes when my sister called and told my mom that she had decided when to have her wedding and that she would like me to be a bridesmaid. Here is the part that convinces me that it is not a good idea to get out of bed on some days. She has decided to have her wedding on the 18th—you know, the day of Serena's surprise party? She has already reserved the church. I am so embarrassed. Now I will need to cancel the party. And my neighbor still laughs at me every time he sees me.

End Marks

Every sentence must end with a punctuation mark. A sentence may end with a period, a question mark, or an exclamation point.

- A period comes at the end of a sentence that tells something.

  Examples: I have a purple bicycle. Turn left at the corner.

- A question mark comes at the end of a sentence that asks a question.

  Examples: What color is your bicycle? Is that your house?

- An exclamation point comes at the end of a sentence that contains a strong feeling.

  Examples: Watch out for that car! What a wonderful surprise!

The following sentences need end marks. Think about which kind of end mark each sentence needs. Then write the correct punctuation mark at the end of each sentence.

1. I love my purple bicycle ☐

2. I saved enough money to buy it last year ☐

3. Would you like to try it ☐

4. My brother has a blue bicycle ☐

5. One time he crashed into me, and I fell off my bike ☐

6. Have you ever fallen off your bike ☐

7. Did you skin your knee ☐

8. I was so mad at my brother ☐

9. He told me he was sorry ☐

10. I'm so glad that my bike did not break ☐

11. Watch out for the glass in the road ☐

12. Don't ride your bike in the street ☐

13. Can you park a bike right here ☐

14. I have to go inside now ☐

15. Will I see you tomorrow ☐

Commas in a Series

Always use commas to separate words in a series. Place commas in the sentenes below to separate words in a series.

Example: James, Ralph, and Sara went to the park.

1. Tommy's three sisters are Amy Katy and Melissa.

2. Manual likes to play basketball baseball and volleyball.

3. Katy Melissa and Tommy do not play volleyball.

4. Amy wants to be a geologist an astronaut or a chemist.

5. Tommy, the youngest, has three dogs whose names are Skip Tiger and Rags.

6. Casey's favorite classes in school are math science and art.

7. Tommy Amy Katy and Melissa live in Dallas with their parents.

8. Tommy loves his parents his sisters and his dogs.

9. Manuel has three birds two cats and one dog.

10. Casey knows Tommy Amy and Manuel.

Names and Commas

Use a comma to set off a person's name when that person is being spoken to.

Example: Bobby, when is your book report due?

1. Mrs. Burnett may we go out to recess now?

2. Yes, we are going out to recess now Jason.

3. Mary will you swing with Tommy and me?

4. Sure Jason I love to swing.

5. Mary is going to swing with us Tommy.

6. No Jason I'm sliding with Matt.

7. Matt can swing with us Tommy.

8. Jason we can all swing first and then we can all slide.

9. Jason do you want to go on the slide first?

10. Tommy what time is recess over?

Set Off an Appositive

Always use commas to set off an appositive from the rest of the sentence.

Example: James, my best friend, lives a mile away.

Place the commas in the sentences below.

1. Amy Jones my best friend has a very large family.

2. Joe her oldest brother works for an airline company.

3. The youngest in the family Tony is only three years old.

4. The oldest daughters Karen and Sue often help with the younger children.

5. My other good friend Nicole and I spend a great deal of time at Amy's house.

6. Mrs. Jones Amy's mother says that two more children are coming tomorrow.

7. Amy's dad Mr. Jones works hard to take care of seven children.

8. Rags and Slick the Jones' pets get a great deal of attention.

Separate Day and Year

Use a comma to separate the day and the year from the rest of the sentence. Place a comma after the year when it comes in the middle of a sentence.

1. Jerry was born on October 5 1986.

2. My favorite Christmas was December 25 1992.

3. Susan's mom came home from the hospital on April 6 1994.

4. We took our summer vacation on July 21 1993.

5. My grandfather was born on August 11 1941.

6. On April 6 1994 Susan's mom brought a new baby girl home from the hospital.

7. My grandfather remembers July 20 1969 as an important date in history.

8. On July 21 1993 my family went to Hawaii for our summer vacation.

164

Separate Cities and States

Use a comma to separate a city from a state.

Example: Eric was born in Eugene, Oregon.

Place the commas in the sentences that follow.

1. The state capital is in Austin Texas.

2. My home is in Denver Colorado.

3. Her grandparents live in Bangor Maine.

4. Our tournament is in Ardmore Oklahoma.

5. Disney World is in Orlando Florida.

6. Her father is stationed in Fairbanks Alaska.

7. Queen Elizabeth lives in London England.

8. We rode the ferry in Seattle Washington.

Comma Review

Rewrite these dates and addresses using a comma correctly.

1. April 15 1972 _____

2. July 27 1640 _____

3. September 13 1910 _____

4. Monday January 31 _____

5. Sunday November 16 _____

6. Anaheim California _____

7. Albuquerque New Mexico _____

8. Quebec Canada _____

9. Bangor Maine _____

10. Little Rock Arkansas _____

Use a comma correctly in these letter parts.

11. Dear Joe _____

12. Your friend _____

13. Sincerely yours _____

14. Love _____

15. Yours truly _____

Add commas where they are needed in these sentences.

16. All birds have feathers wings and beaks.

17. The Shetland pony is small friendly and gentle.

18. A friendly playful dog makes a good pet.

19. I have three cats named Boots Muffin and Tiger.

20. I like to color with pencils markers and crayons.

Set It Off!

In the sentences below, add the missing commas to "set it off."

1. No Marlene does not like being squirted in the face.

2. Christopher how long have you been on the telephone?

3. Well just what did you have in mind?

4. Sure Laura I'd love another jelly donut.

5. My brother the world's scariest boy likes escargots.

6. The plane we are taking a 747 will have plenty of room.

7. You realize of course that you will not be allowed out of the house in that outfit.

8. My orthodontist Dr. Baugh decorated his office for Halloween.

9. All right if that's what you think, let's just eat all of the chocolate.

10. In the future we will be able to speak to our computers.

11. No kidding you went rock climbing?

12. We went to Bouquet Canyon a canyon near Valencia to attend a harvest festival.

13. You could read for example some books about the historical period in which your novel takes place.

14. For Valentine's Day my dad gave me two pounds of my favorite treat candy corn.

15. I don't care what you think I'm going to go back there and help that little boy.

That's Mine

When a word shows that something belongs to it, it shows ownership. *Possession* is another word for ownership. An apostrophe is used to show possession.

Example: *Friskie's leash* (To whom does the leash belong? The leash belongs to the dog, Friskie.) You usually add *'s* to a noun to show possession.

Show possession in the following examples. Don't forget the apostrophe. The first two have been completed for you.

1. food belonging to a cat   *cat's food*
2. a nest belonging to a bird   *bird's nest*
3. a bike belonging to Miguel
4. a store that is owned by Kim
5. a CD player belonging to David
6. a book belonging to my sister
7. a skateboard owned by my brother
8. some toys that belong to a baby
9. a desk that belongs to the teacher
10. a brush that belongs to a painter

Rewrite each sentence below, adding an apostrophe where one is needed to show possession.

11. Nicky ran screaming into Manuels house.

_____

12. My dad knocked down a hornets nest.

_____

13. I wish I could drive my brothers car.

_____

14. An alien ate Marielas homework.

_____

15. Grandpas spaghetti is the best in the world.

_____

Using Quotation Marks

Quotation marks and commas are used to set off quotations.

Example: She said, "I don't like bananas." (The comma after "she said" tells us to pause before speaking the quote. The quotation marks show exactly what was said.)

Place quotation marks and commas where they are needed in the sentences below.

---

1. Ryan asked What do you want to play, Martha?

2. Martha answered Let's play baseball.

3. Okay, we'll play baseball first said Ryan but let's play basketball after that.

4. Mom called The cookies are ready.

5. Oh, boy the boys yelled at the same time let's eat!

Write four sentences below. Make them a conversation between you and your best friend. Be sure to place the quotation marks and commas where they belong.

_____

_____

_____

_____

_____

_____

_____

_____

May I Quote You?

In the sentences below, place a check mark in front of those that need quotation marks added. On the line below each sentence, write the sentence again with the correct punctuation. If the sentence is correct, do nothing. The first one has been completed for you.

1. What is that bizarre thing upon your head? It looks like an octopus, said Mr. Grimmy.

   "What is that bizarre thing upon your head? It looks like an octopus," said Mr. Grimmy.

2. The teacher told the students to read the poem, "The Raven" by Friday.

   _____

3. I call my sister Idget, but I have no idea why.

   _____

4. "Hey!" Jacques shouted, "Didn't you hear the coach? He said, 'Stop when you get to the fence!' "

   _____

5. And then I will cover you with fragrant rose petals, Mama said, and sing a lullaby.

   _____

6. I found a book that said, Dinosaurs may be more closely related to birds than to lizards.

   _____

7. We have family nicknames, and my brother's is "Greasy Bear."

   _____

8. Did you hear what Nicole said? Amy asked us. She said, You guys are just too chicken to try it. She doesn't know what she is talking about!

   _____

9. I thought you would be too cool to go on the merry-go-round with me.

   _____

10. She watched *Somewhere in Time* so many times she wore out the tape.

    _____

11. My brother always talks in his sleep. Last night he said, "Hurry and purple it before the snails get it!"

    _____

12. After we watched *Twister*, we couldn't stop watching the clouds.

    _____

13. Come with us, Dad said, and we can stop for ice cream on the way.

    _____

14. I need to find the root word for transient.

    _____

15. Mom says we shouldn't say "Where's he at?" because it is not proper English.

    _____

Punctuation Challenge

Read the letter. There are 21 punctuation errors. Circle the punctuation that is wrong and correct it. Add any missing punctuation.

Dear Pen Pal

    I love to go to the circus! On May 6 1999, the circus came to my hometown of Jackson Wyoming. A parade marched through our streets and soon the big top could be seen. Ken my brother, and I went to watch the performers prepare for opening night. We saw clowns, acrobats, and even the ringmaster. What a sight? Have you ever seen anything like it. You should go if you ever get the chance.

    I also really enjoy playing baseball. My favorite team is the New York Yankees but I also like the St. Louis Cardinals. When I grow up I want to be a baseball pitcher, first baseman, or shortstop. Do you like baseball? What do you want to do when you grow up. I wish you could see my cool baseball card collection, but Kens collection is even better.

    Oh, I almost forgot to tell you about my family! There are four people in my family. They are my mom my dad my brother and me. Scruffy my cat is also a family member. In August 2000 my grandpa will probably move in with us. I cant wait for that! Didn't you say your grandma lives with you. Ill bet you really like that.

    Well thats all for now. Please write back to me soon. See you!

Your pal,

Brent

What Is a Subject?

All sentences have subjects. A **subject** tells who or what a sentence is about.

Example: Blake loves to paint. (Who loves to paint? **Blake** loves to paint.)
Blake is the subject of the sentence.

First, ask yourself who or what the sentence is about. Then, underline the subject of the sentence. Finally, write the subject of the sentence on the line. The first one is done for you.

1. <u>Blake</u> has a paintbox.

   Who has a paintbox? _____ Blake _____

2. The paintbox has three colors.

   What has three colors? _____

3. The colors are red, yellow, and blue.

   What are red, yellow, and blue? _____

4. Blake can make more colors.

   Who can make more colors? _____

5. Green is made by mixing together blue and yellow paints.

   What is made by mixing together blue and yellow paints? _____

6. Orange is made by mixing together yellow and red paints.

   What is made by mixing together yellow and red paints? _____

7. Blake loves to paint.

   Who loves to paint? _____

8. Blake's favorite color is blue.

   What is blue? _____

9. Mom hung up Blake's painting.

   Who hung up Blake's painting? _____

10. The painting is of a sailboat on the ocean.

    What is of a sailboat on the ocean? _____

Subject Practice

The **subject** is who or what the sentence is about. When an artist creates a painting of a vase full of colorful flowers set upon a white cloth in front of a blue background, the subject of the painting is the vase of colorful flowers. The rest of the painting just gives more information about the vase of flowers, such as where they are and what kind of light is shining on them.

Example: Swimming is fun. (What is fun? **Swimming** is fun.)
Swimming is the subject of the sentence.

First, ask yourself who or what the sentence is about. Then, underline the subject of the sentence. Finally, write the subject of the sentence on the line. The first one is done for you.

1. <u>Kids</u> love to swim at the pool and the beach.

   Who loves to swim at the pool and the beach? _____ **Kids** _____

2. Baseball is a fun sport to play or watch.

   What is a fun sport to play or watch?_____

3. Swimming is a good way to cool off when it is hot.

   What is a good way to cool off when it is hot?_____

4. I like to eat ice cream in the summer.

   Who likes to eat ice cream in the summer?_____

5. Summertime is my favorite time of the year.

   What is your favorite time of the year?_____

6. In the summer, Jeremy likes to take a vacation.

   Who likes to take a vacation in the summer? _____

7. Mosquitoes are numerous in the summer.

   What are numerous in the summer? _____

8. My skin itches when I get a sunburn.

   What itches when you get a sunburn?_____

9. Every summer seashells wash up on the shore.

   What washes up on the shore every summer? _____

10. The summer is over, but it will be back next year.

    What is over but will be back next year? _____

What Is a Predicate?

Just as all sentences have subjects, they also have predicates. The **predicate** tells us important things about the subject. It tells us what the subject does, has, or is.

Examples

- Tommy had a cold.

  What did Tommy have? Tommy **had a cold.**
  The predicate of the sentence is *had a cold.*

- Felicia jumps into the lake.

  What does Felicia do? Felicia **jumps into the lake.**
  The predicate of the sentence is *jumps into the lake.*

- The inner tube is leaking air.

  What is the inner tube doing? The inner tube **is leaking air.**
  The predicate of the sentence is *is leaking air.*

First, ask yourself what the subject does, has, or is. Then write the predicate of each sentence. The first one is done for you.

1. The water is very cold. _____ **is very cold** _____

2. We jump into the water. _____

3. Luke splashes us._____

4. Tonia is cold._____

5. She gets out of the water. _____

6. Nick does a handstand underwater._____

7. Everyone claps for him_____

8. The inner tube has a leak in it._____

9. Luke throws the inner tube onto the shore. _____

10. Tonia sits on the inner tube. _____

11. The inner tube deflates with Tonia on it. _____

12. Everyone laughs with Tonia._____

13. Tonia jumps into the water._____

14. Luke swims as fast as he can. _____

15. Tonia races Luke. _____

Complete Sentences

Before you can write a good story, you must be able to write good sentences. Remember, a sentence has a subject and a predicate. When the two parts are written together, all the words make sense. In each sentence found below, circle the complete subject and underline the complete predicate.

Example: (Mom and dad) took us to the beach.

1. Uncle Tony invited us to the baseball game.

2. His truck carried us to the field.

3. The parking lot was crowded.

4. We finally found our seats.

5. Uncle Tony bought popcorn and peanuts.

6. Two batters hit home runs.

7. Our team won the game.

8. People pushed to get out of the stadium.

9. We drove home late at night.

10. My sister was very tired.

Whoa!

You have learned that each sentence is a complete thought. What about sentences that do not stop when they should? A sentence that runs on to the next thought is called a **run-on sentence.**

Example: Cake is the best dessert chocolate is my favorite flavor. (*run-on*)
Cake is the best dessert. Chocolate is my favorite flavor.

Each of the following sentences is a run-on sentence. Write each run-on sentence as two separate sentences. The first one has been done for you.

1. My books are on the table my math book is on top.
   My books are on the table. My math book is on top.

2. They were closing the store it was time to go home.
   _____
   _____

3. Watch out for the slippery ice you could fall and hurt yourself.
   _____
   _____

4. I got a new blue dress the blue shoes match perfectly.
   _____
   _____

5. My brother made the team will I be able to play baseball some day?
   _____
   _____

6. I like to go camping the last time we went, we saw a bear.
   _____
   _____

7. My teacher was not at school we had a substitute.
   _____
   _____

8. I don't like lima beans I only want mashed potatoes.
   _____
   _____

9. Can you spend the night at my house we can have pizza for dinner.
   _____
   _____

10. My dog has fleas we had to get her some special medicine.
    _____
    _____

Bits and Pieces

You have learned that a sentence needs to be a complete thought to make sense. When a sentence is an incomplete thought, it is called a **sentence fragment**. Usually, a sentence fragment is missing a piece of information. You might not know the subject. The subject tells who or what the sentence is about. You might not know the predicate. The predicate tells what the subject has, does, or is.

Read the sentence fragments shown below. They are missing important pieces of information. Use your imagination to change these fragments into complete sentences. Rewrite the fragments as complete sentences, adding whatever information you wish. The first is done for you. Remember to capitalize and punctuate every sentence.

1. The big bad wolf
   <u>The big bad wolf blew down the little pig's house.</u>

2. went flying in the air
   _____

3. my best friend
   _____

4. Alan's birthday party
   _____

5. fell off the fence
   _____

6. was blowing big bubbles
   _____

7. a giant spider
   _____

8. ran into the street
   _____

9. her hamster
   _____

10. ate a bug
    _____

Fragment Search

On this page you will find five complete sentences and five sentence fragments. Write the five complete sentences using correct capitalization and punctuation. Use your own words to change the five sentence fragments into complete sentences. Be sure to write these new sentences using correct capitalization and punctuation. You should have written 10 complete sentences when you are finished.

1. bruce has many things in his room

   _____

2. books on shelves

   _____

3. is there a box of toys under the bed

   _____

4. a rug is in front of the closet

   _____

5. two stuffed animals

   _____

6. i can see trees from my window

   _____

7. the bedspread and curtains

   _____

8. my favorite game

   _____

9. look out for

   _____

10. latoya cleans her room every day

   _____

What's That You Say?

You already know about ending sentences with periods, question marks, and exclamation points. Sentences with these different endings have different names. Use the information below and on page 79 to learn about the four kinds of sentences.

- Sentences that make statements end with periods. They are called **declarative sentences.**

    Examples: Sunday is my grandma's birthday. It will rain tomorrow.

- Sentences that ask questions end with question marks. They are called **interrogative sentences.**

    Examples: Is this seat taken? Can I play? Do you want this? Where are you going?

- Sentences that express strong emotion end with exclamation points. These are called **exclamatory sentences**.

    Examples: We're going to Disney World! Tommy's cat won first prize at the fair!

- Sentences that make requests end with periods. Sentences that give commands or make strong or urgent requests end with exclamation points. All of these types of sentences are called **imperative sentences.**

    Examples: Put the book on the shelf. Watch out! Don't put those peas on your head!

- It might seem like an imperative sentence does not have a subject. You cannot see it in the sentence, but it is there. The subject is *you*. Test it for yourself. When someone says to you, "Please put the book on the shelf," the subject *you* is not in the sentence. However, you know that the person is speaking to you. The person could say, "You please put the book on the shelf." You can add the subject *you* to the beginning of any imperative sentence.

    Examples: (*You*) Wash the dishes. (*You*) Return the books.

Decide whether the following sentences are imperatives or declaratives. On the line before each number, write an **I** if it is an imperative sentence or a **D** if it is a declarative sentence.

_____ 1. The top fell off my new toy soldier.   _____ 6. I can't find my shoes.

_____ 2. Put me down, please.   _____ 7. Give me my hat.

_____ 3. Open your science books.   _____ 8. Marie, I will tickle you.

_____ 4. My dog ate my homework.   _____ 9. Stop!

_____ 5. Take out the trash now!   _____ 10. I warned you not to do that.

Stressed Out Syllables

Words are divided into sounds called **syllables**. Two-syllable words have a stressed and unstressed syllable. A stressed syllable is the sound spoken loudest in a word. The unstressed syllable is the sound which is spoken more softly.

Rule #1

When a word has a double consonant, the word is divided between the two consonants.

Example: bub´-ble

Divide each word below into syllables and place a stressed syllable mark (´) on the syllable you think is stressed. Use a dictionary to check your answers.

1. pillow _____

2. fellow _____

3. pizza _____

4. suppose _____

5. surround _____

6. scissors _____

7. collect _____

8. hurrah _____

9. address _____

10. silly _____

Stressed Out Syllables (cont.)

Rule #2

When a word ends in a consonant plus *le*, the word is divided before the consonant.

Example: pur´-ple

Divide each word below into syllables and place a stressed syllable mark (´) on the syllable you think is stressed. Use a dictionary to check your answers.

1. turtle   _____

2. beetle   _____

3. bubble   _____

4. candle   _____

5. juggle   _____

6. hustle   _____

7. baffle   _____

8. cradle   _____

9. bottle   _____

10. trouble   _____

Stressed Out Syllables (cont.)

Rule #3

When the first vowel in a word has the short vowel sound, the word is divided after the next consonant.

Example: shad´-ow

Divide each word below into syllables, and place a stressed syllable mark (´) on the syllable you think is stressed. Use a dictionary to check your answers.

1. cartoon _____

2. cinder _____

3. droplet _____

4. extra _____

5. express _____

6. imprint _____

7. jungle _____

8. salad _____

9. magic _____

10. picture _____

Stressed Out Syllables (cont.)

Rule #4

When the first vowel in a word has the long vowel sound, the word is divided after that vowel.

Example: ba´-by

Divide each word below into syllables, and place a stressed syllable mark (´) on the syllable you think is stressed. Use a dictionary to check your answers.

1. humor _____

2. able _____

3. begin _____

4. kiwi _____

5. paper _____

6. locate _____

7. open _____

8. profile _____

9. rosette _____

10. erupt _____

Getting to the Root of It

Sometimes a word has letters added to the beginning or end of it that change the meaning of the word. The main word is called the **root word**, and the added letters are **prefixes** and **suffixes**. For example, in the word *soundless* the root word is *sound,* and in the word *unusual* the root word is *usual.* Notice how the meanings of these two words change with the added letters.

Read the words below. Write the root words in the spaces provided.

1. irresponsible _____

2. misunderstand _____

3. meaningful _____

4. worthless _____

5. immaterial _____

6. disengage _____

7. unaware _____

8. prearrange _____

9. semicircle _____

10. biweekly _____

11. mountainous _____

12. unicycle _____

13. triangle _____

14. nonsense _____

15. admiralty _____

Root It Out

On each flower is the name of a person who does an action. Find the root word in each name and write it below the flower. (**Note:** Sometimes letters from the root word are left off or changed to form the new word. Be sure to spell the root word correctly.)

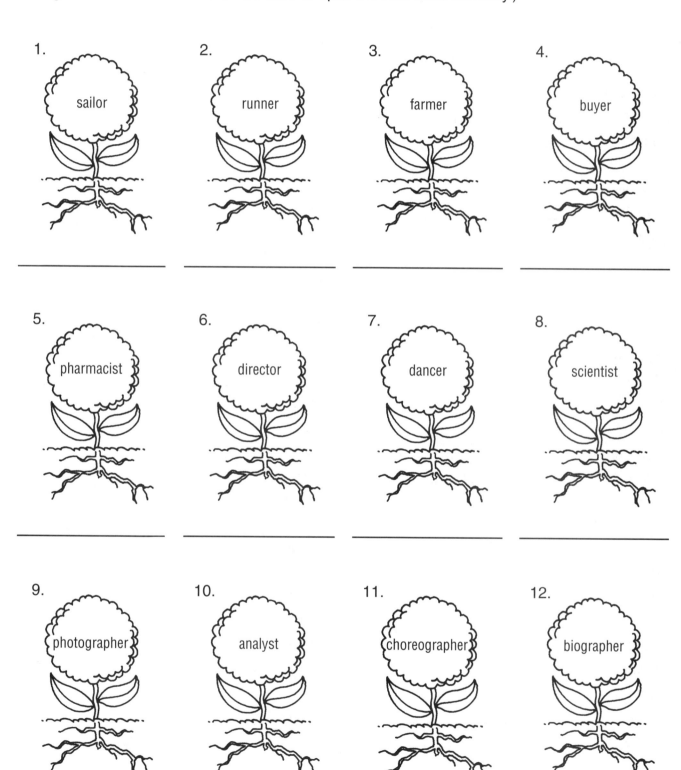

1. sailor

2. runner

3. farmer

4. buyer

5. pharmacist

6. director

7. dancer

8. scientist

9. photographer

10. analyst

11. choreographer

12. biographer

Alphabetizing

Circle the words that are not in alphabetical order. Rewrite the words in their correct places.

ape	_____	put	_____
banana	_____	putt	_____
apple	_____	otter	_____
bear	_____	other	_____
cornhusk	_____	over	_____
carrot	_____	quitter	_____
cheese	_____	quit	_____
dandelion	_____	quilt	_____
dandy	_____	raise	_____
eggplant	_____	roast	_____
egg	_____	season	_____
grapes	_____	satisfy	_____
grass	_____	salt	_____
friend	_____	state	_____
frond	_____	town	_____
heaven	_____	tune	_____
hover	_____	tuna	_____
house	_____	umbrella	_____
ice	_____	under	_____
icicle	_____	underneath	_____
jump	_____	very	_____
juice	_____	voice	_____
kick	_____	violin	_____
kiss	_____	wisdom	_____
list	_____	wig	_____
laugh	_____	wonder	_____
limb	_____	xylophone	_____
mote	_____	yeast	_____
mother	_____	yesterday	_____
many	_____	yes	_____
neck	_____	zebra	_____
noise	_____	zoology	_____
pout	_____	zoo	_____

Alphabetical Order

Place these words in alphabetical order.

rover	jump	launch	scientist
river	light	cane	cell
moon	umbrella	candy	cello
cart	dog	same	dear
friend	sort	simple	deer
house	loop	grass	join
ghost	lope	grassy	tune
vest	game	lion	salt
silent	gamble	line	ghastly
tunnel	lunch	science	moan

_____   _____   _____   _____

_____   _____   _____   _____

_____   _____   _____   _____

_____   _____   _____   _____

_____   _____   _____   _____

_____   _____   _____   _____

_____   _____   _____   _____

_____   _____   _____   _____

_____   _____   _____   _____

_____   _____   _____   _____

What Does It Mean?

Many words have more than one meaning. When reading, you can use context clues to determine the meaning of a word in a sentence. Read the sentences below and then write the letter of the definition that shows how the underlined word is used in each sentence.

_____ 1. Tell me your address so I can find where you live.

    a. speak or write to

    b. manner of speech

    c. place where a person lives

_____ 2. Why do you refuse to come to the fair?

    a. decline to accept

    b. garbage

    c. decline to do

_____ 3. Lost in the desert for hours, the people were hot, hungry, and thirsty.

    a. dry, sandy wasteland

    b. abandon

    c. something deserved

_____ 4. The children at play were running and laughing with joy.

    a. put in motion

    b. taking part in a game or recreation

    c. a dramatic work

_____ 5. Are any cookies left for me?

    a. to the westward direction when one is facing north

    b. remaining

    c. departed

Reading Adventures

Read each story and then answer the questions.

Miles and Robin wanted to go to the zoo. Their mother said they could go after they finished their chores. First, they cleaned their rooms. Next, they mopped the kitchen floor. After that, they washed the family's car. Finally, they got ready to go to the zoo.

1. What did Miles and Robin do first? _____

_____

2. What did the boys do after they mopped the floor?_____

_____

3. What was the final thing the boys did? _____

_____

Miles and Robin were on an imaginary safari. First, their mother gave them a map of the zoo. Then, the boys went to the shark pool. Next, they found their way to the tiger cage. After that, they visited the wolf den. Finally, they met their mother at the alligator exhibit. Miles and Robin had a busy afternoon!

4. What animal did the boys visit first? _____

_____

5. Where did the boys go after they saw the tiger? _____

_____

6. What did the boys do last? _____

_____

Put Them in Order

Read the sentences. Rewrite them in a paragraph in the correct sequence.

I got out of bed and looked in the mirror.
I ran to my mother to show her what had happened.
She said, "Those seeds you swallowed yesterday have planted inside you."
I woke up one morning feeling strange.
Then she looked in the phone book for a good gardener to come over to trim me.
What a shock I got when I saw a plant growing out of my ears!
I am feeling better now, but I still have to water myself every day.

_____

_____

_____

_____

_____

_____

_____

_____

_____

What Happened Next?

When you write about something that happened to you or something that you do, it must be in the right time order. Another name for this is **chronology**. The things you write about in a paragraph should usually be in *chronological* (time) *order* to make sense.

Here are some lists of events that are out of order. Put them into time (chronological) order by marking them from first (1) to last (5). The first one has been done for you.

A.

2	eat breakfast
1	get up
5	go to school
4	go out the door
3	brush teeth

B.

_____ bait a hook

_____ clean a fish

_____ eat a fish

_____ catch a fish

_____ cook a fish

C.

_____ mail the letter

_____ put the letter in envelope

_____ write the letter

_____ wait for an answer

_____ seal the letter

D.

_____ write a book report

_____ click on word processing

_____ turn on printer

_____ turn on computer

_____ print book report

E.

_____ slap your arm

_____ see a mosquito

_____ feel a bite

_____ hear a buzz

_____ scratch a bump

F.

_____ buy popcorn

_____ leave the theater

_____ stand in line

_____ buy a ticket

_____ watch a movie

G.

_____ find an old Halloween mask

_____ clean up your room

_____ sneak up on your brother

_____ put it on

_____ jump out at him

H.

_____ snap on the leash

_____ pull your dog back home

_____ get the leash

_____ whistle for your dog

_____ walk your dog

What's the Point?

Each paragraph has a series of sentences in a special order. The sentences work together to develop a single idea. Each of the sentences in a paragraph must relate to the main idea.

Cross out the idea in each list that does not relate to the main idea. The main idea is in boldface type.

1. **inside my house**

   kitchen   football field
   bedroom   bathroom
   living room   attic

2. **colors**

   red   yellow
   blue   bird
   green   purple

3. **countries**

   Canada   Mexico
   United States   Beverly Hills
   France   Australia

4. **homework**

   erasers   paper
   fortune cookies   pencils
   books   crayons

5. **tools**

   screwdriver   diving board
   hammer   saw
   wrench   pliers

6. **food**

   beans   spinach
   towels   tomatoes
   corn   bread

7. **sports**

   soccer   tennis
   baseball   basketball
   scissors   golf

8. **animals**

   dogs   cats
   flowers   horses
   cows   mice

9. **musical instruments**

   piano   harmonica
   tomato soup   guitar
   drums   trumpet

10. **clothes**

    jackets   spaghetti
    pants   socks
    sweaters   shirts

Extension: Choose one of the topics above and write an outline for a paragraph using four subtopics. For example . . .

Clothes
   A. jackets
      1. sports jackets
      2. dressy jackets
   B. pants
      1. leggings
      2. jeans
      3. dress pants
   C. socks
      1. sweatsocks
      2. wool socks
   D. sweaters
      1. _____
      2. _____

Practice on Main Idea

Read the paragraph below. Circle the details that help you find the main idea. Then color the magnifying glass that has the main idea that makes sense.

Clues At the Zoo

Juan and Julie want to work at the city zoo when they grow up. They read books about animals from all around the world so that they can learn about animals. Every Saturday, Julie and Juan visit the zoo around feeding time. It is interesting to see what the animals eat and how they feed their young. Many of the animals eat vegetables and fruits. Julie and Juan know that they must be good at science if they want to work at the zoo. Zoology is the science that deals with animals and animal life. A person who studies zoology is called a zoologist. A zoologist must be smart and hardworking.

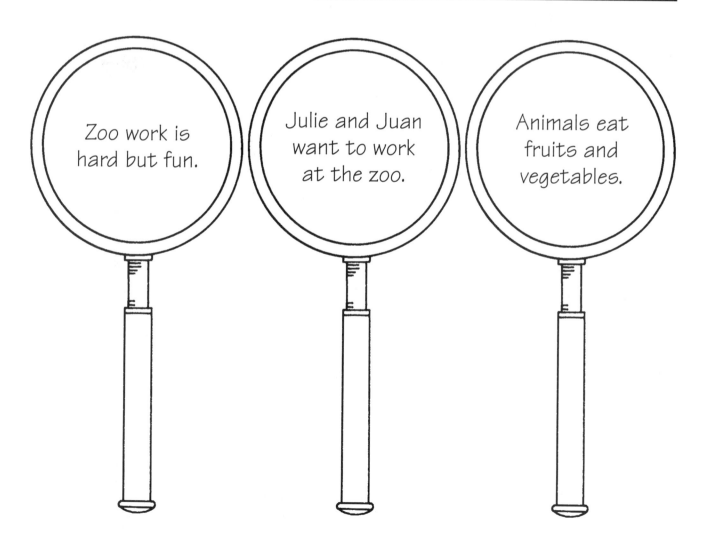

Zoo work is hard but fun.

Julie and Juan want to work at the zoo.

Animals eat fruits and vegetables.

Main Idea of a Paragraph

It is easy to write the main idea of a paragraph. Read the paragraph carefully and answer the three Ws. You do not need to use complete sentences here. Then make a good sentence out of your answers. Read your new sentence carefully to make sure it makes sense. Practice with the paragraph found below.

> Lola loved to watch the big, beautiful birds from South America. She stared at the parrots' bright green wings as the birds flew gracefully in their giant bird cage. Lola laughed when they called to each other with loud, squeaky voices. The parrots were Lola's favorite animals at the zoo.

1. Who? _____

2. What? _____

3 Why? _____

4. Write a sentence using your answers.

_____

_____

Check to make sure your sentence is complete.

1. Does your sentence make sense? ☐

2. Does it start with a capital letter? ☐

3. Does it end with a period? ☐

Main Idea Story Parts

Read each story and then write a sentence that best tells the main idea.

The students in Mrs. Lee's class were having a great time at the Riverside Zoo. As they were walking to visit the chimpanzees again, Mrs. Lee suddenly stopped. "Is anyone wearing a watch?" she asked. "I'm afraid that mine has stopped."

Amanda looked at her watch. "It's 1:40," she said.

Mrs. Lee's eyes opened wide. "Oh, no! We were supposed to meet Mrs. Miles' class at 1:30. We're late!"

Mrs. Lee and her students began running for the bus.

Main idea: _____

One of the penguins was ready to play. He waddled up the icy hill as fast as he could. Then he flopped onto his stomach and slid down. Some of the penguins were eating lunch. They swallowed the fish as quickly as the zookeeper could empty the big buckets of food. A few of the penguins were sleeping quietly.

The children watched the penguins for a long time. When it was time to leave the exhibit, all of the children were sad to go. Many of the children liked the penguins exhibit best.

Main idea: _____

Max

Read the story and then answer the questions.

A very young boy named Max visited the nature center last Monday. While he was there, several penguin eggs hatched. Max was one of the first people to see the baby penguins because he happened to be nearby when the babies were born. Max was very happy to be a part of this exciting event.

1. Who is the story about?

   _____

2. What does he do?

   _____

   _____

3. Why does he do this?

   _____

   _____

4. Use your answers to write a main idea sentence.

   _____

   _____

5. Draw a picture of the main idea.

George Washington

Read the story and then answer the questions.

One of the greatest leaders in American history is George Washington. He was a general in the Revolutionary War against the British. The people of the new nation were proud of the work he did during the war, and many people thought he would be the best person to lead the country as its first president. General Washington became president for eight years in all, and he is still remembered as an excellent leader.

1. Who is the paragraph about?

_____

2. What is this person known as?

_____

_____

3. Why is this person known in this way?

_____

_____

4. Use your answers to write a main idea sentence.

_____

_____

5. Write a short paragraph with additional information that you have discovered about George Washington.

_____

_____

_____

_____

_____

_____

My Dream

Read the story and then answer the questions.

I had a dream last night that I was five inches tall. In my dream, I climbed down my bedpost and onto the floor. I walked right under my bed and across the room. It was a good thing my mom wasn't in the dream, because if she had seen everything stuffed under my bed, she would have made me clean my room! Instead, I walked over to my dollhouse and through the front door. Everything was just my size! I arranged all the furniture for a party, and I invited all my dolls to come over. We danced around the dollhouse, told jokes, and ate the cookies on my nightstand, left over from my bedtime snack. We had such a great time, I decided to live in the dollhouse forever. I went upstairs to the doll bedroom, and stretching out on the tiny bed, I fell asleep.

When I woke up from my dream, I smiled as I remembered it. Then I looked inside my dollhouse and wondered. How did those cookie crumbs get in there?

1. How does the girl get down from her bed? _____

_____

2. What is the girl glad her mother does not see? _____

_____

3. What does the girl do to get ready for the party? _____

_____

4. What do the partygoers eat? _____

_____

5. What surprises the girl when she wakes from her dream? _____

_____

The Big Game

Read the story and then answer the questions.

Kenny couldn't wait. Today was the day, his big chance. For weeks he had been practicing every day, throwing to anyone who was willing. Now he would get to do what he had been preparing for since the season began. Today he would pitch in the big game!

Kenny dressed excitedly and raced on his bicycle to the ballpark. His coach was already there, ready for warmups. The coach sent Kenny to the bullpen, and he began to throw. He could feel the excitement building with every pitch. Before he knew it, it was game time!

While his teammates covered the bases and outfield, Kenny went to the mound. As the batter stepped into the box, Kenny knew he was ready. He threw his first pitch, a fastball that hit just inside the strike zone. "Strike!" the umpire called, and Kenny knew this would be his game.

Nine innings later, Kenny found he was right! His team won, 12 to 8, and Kenny was named Most Valuable Player. It was a game to remember!

1. Why couldn't Kenny wait? _____

_____

2. What had Kenny been practicing? _____

_____

3. How did Kenny get to the ballpark? _____

_____

4. What did Kenny do first thing at the ballpark? _____

_____

5. What was Kenny named? _____

_____

Making Inferences

Read the examples and answer the questions that follow each example. (Remember, when you use clues to draw conclusions about things, you are inferring.)

"It sure is dark in here. Could we turn on some lights?" asked Wendy and Jack.

"The Fun House is too spooky!" said Jack as he walked through it.

"I'm ready to go on the Ferris wheel," said Wendy.

1. What can you infer? _____

_____

2. What clues did you find to prove you inferred correctly?

_____

_____

"I am not jealous of your new dress," said Mary. "I don't like that color on me anyway. My mother buys me more expensive things than that. I think the material looks like it would rip easily and not wash well. Where did you buy it? Was that the only one they had left?" asked Mary.

1. What can you infer? _____

_____

2. What clues did you find to prove you inferred correctly?

_____

_____

Marta and Janis

Read the story. Then use the lines under the story to write how the two friends are the same and how they are different from each other.

Marta and Janis are both eight years old. They have been best friends for two years, even though Marta does not speak much English. Marta is from Mexico. She speaks Spanish very well, a language that Janis does not understand. Marta is teaching Janis to speak Spanish, and Janis is helping Marta to speak better English.

Every afternoon, the girls do their homework together. They munch on their favorite snack, popcorn. Sometimes Janis has to bring her little brother along. He colors in his coloring book while the girls study. Marta loves little Pete, and she wishes she had a baby brother or sister.

After they finish their homework, Marta and Janis go to the city park. Marta takes her skates. She is a wonderful skater. Janis brings her scooter. She loves to ride. When Pete comes along, all the children swing and slide. They all enjoy that! It is good to have a best friend!

1. How are Marta and Janis alike?

_____

_____

_____

_____

_____

2. How are Marta and Janis different?

_____

_____

_____

_____

_____

Drawing Conclusions

Read the sentences below and then answer the questions.

Answer

1. I live on a farm. I have feathers and wings. I wake up the farm in the morning. What am I?	
2. You watch me in a large building. There are a screen and a projector. People eat popcorn and drink soda while I am playing. What am I?	
3. Some people use me to write, other people use me to play games, and many people use me to find information and to send messages to each other. I can be found in many homes and most businesses. What am I?	
4. I grow from the ground. I smell sweet. My stem has thorns, but I am beautiful. What am I?	
5. I make beautiful sounds. I have a long neck and strings. Some people use a pick to play me. They strum my strings, and the sound vibrates. What am I?	

Cause and Effect

Everything that happens (**effect***)* is caused by something else (**cause**). Read the effects in the first column. Write a cause in the second column.

Effect	Cause
1. spilled milk	
2. torn jeans	
3. trampled flowers	
4. flat tire	
7. happy children	
8. frustration	
9. coldness	
10. tiredness	
11. wealth	
12. peace	
13. tears	
14. illness	
15. friendship	

What's the Effect?

Whatever makes something happen is called the **cause**. Read the causes in the first column. Write a reasonable effect of each in the second column.

Cause	Effect
1. dog running through house	
2. children playing	
3. woman pruning flowers	
4. driving fast	
5. forgetting an appointment	
6. eating poorly	
7. watching eight hours of television	
8. wearing sandals and shorts on a cold day	
9. spending too much money	
10. oversleeping	
11. forgetting to return a book to the library	
12. losing your wallet	

Facts and Opinions

When you write a research paper, you must be very careful to stick to the facts. A research paper is written to give people information that is true or that can be proven true.
Is this a fact? **"France is the best place in the world to live."** Whether you agree or not, it is just someone's opinion. It is not a fact.

In the blanks before each sentence below, write **F** for fact or **O** for opinion.

Fact
Many plants have thorns.

Opinion
Thorny plants are not good in gardens.

_____ 1. The moon orbits the earth.

_____ 2. The moon is inspirational to all who see it.

_____ 3. A banana tastes disgusting.

_____ 4. A banana is a fruit.

_____ 5. Abraham Lincoln was killed.

_____ 6. Abraham Lincoln was the best president.

_____ 7. Canada has the most beautiful lakes in the world.

_____ 8. Canada has many lakes.

_____ 9. Red and yellow mixed together make orange.

_____ 10. Orange is the prettiest color.

Now write one fact and one opinion about your school.

1. Fact: _____

2. Opinion: _____

Evaluating Bias

Facts tell only what can be proven. Biased statements tell a person's **opinion**. Underline the biased statements below.

1. Lions roar loudly.

2. Pigs are the laziest of all animals.

3. Horses must be brushed often to keep them clean.

4. Dogs are better pets than cats.

5. The Riverside Zoo was built three years ago.

6. More than 400 animals live in the Riverside Zoo.

7. The Riverside Zoo is the best zoo in the world.

8. The emperor penguin is the most interesting animal to watch.

9. Snakes should not be allowed at the zoo because they frighten visitors.

10. Polar bears are large, white animals.

Tone

The **tone** of a story is the feeling it has and the feeling it makes the reader have. A tone can be happy, sad, excited, fearful, or many others.

Word Bank

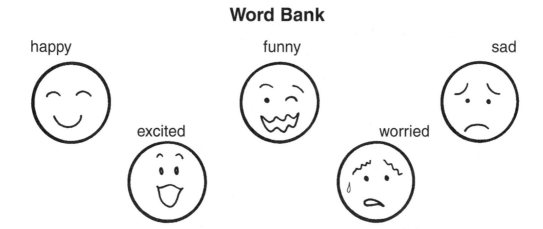

happy   funny   sad

excited   worried

Read each group of sentences below. Then write the tone each group of sentences sets. Choose from the words in the word bank.

1. Wow! Today is my birthday. I know it will be a great day. We are having a chocolate cake and are playing lots of games. I can hardly wait until my friends arrive.

    Tone: _____

2. I can't believe my best friend is moving away. I want to cry. Even the sky looks gray and rainy today. Nothing will ever be the same without my friend.

    Tone: _____

3. Can a pig learn tricks? My pet pig, Sally, can roll over and shake hands. Or should I say shake snouts? She is a funny pig who really likes to "hog the show."

    Tone: _____

4. I can't believe our arithmetic test is today. I forgot to study, and I don't understand multiplication. I just know I will fail this test. This could ruin my math grade. Oh, why didn't I study last night?

    Tone: _____

5. It is a beautiful day today! The sun is shining, the birds are singing, and the air smells sweet and fresh. It feels good to be alive!

    Tone: _____

Identifying Tone

Read the sentences. Each one suggests a mood or feeling. This is called the **tone**. On the blanks, write the tone of each.

1. The sunset fell in beautiful shades of orange, pink, and yellow.

   _____

2. The children ran through the yard like puppies at play.

   _____

3. Rain ran down the windowsill while the twins watched, sighing and cupping their chins in their hands.

   _____

4. The fans went wild, shouting and stomping their feet while he rounded the bases for another home run.

   _____

5. The two bighorn sheep clashed their horns together angrily.

   _____

6. The tiny baby screamed and cried until she fell asleep.

   _____

7. The fingernails screeched loudly across the chalkboard.

   _____

8. Slam! The basketball swished through the hoop to make the winning point!

   _____

9. The roar of the engines drowned their voices as they tried to shout to each other at the racetrack.

   _____

10. Oh, I wish I had a million dollars!

   _____

Identifying the Speaker

Read the story and answer the questions below.

Tracy had a big surprise when he took the trash out one night. He saw a small, furry animal hanging upside down in the trash can. "Get out of there!" yelled Tracy.

"What is going on?" called his father.

"Raccoons are hunting in our garbage," said the boy. He went back into the house and got a broom to chase the raccoons away. But when he came back, the furry raccoons were already gone. "I guess I'd better make sure that the lid is on tightly," he said.

1. How many speakers are in the story? _____

2. Who are the speakers? _____

3. Who said that he should make sure that the lid was on tightly?

   _____

4. How do you know Tracy is a boy? _____

   _____

First-Person Voice

Read the entry in the diary below. The author, Ashley, recorded her thoughts and feelings. She used the words *I* and *me* often. When she reads her diary again, she will know that she means herself when she reads those pronouns. When you read something with the words *I* or *me*, meaning the author, that is written in what is called the **voice of the first person**. The diary entry below is written in the voice of the first person.

Dear Diary,

I wonder how the animals in the zoo feel when the weather is this cold? I worry that their fur and feathers will not keep them warm enough. It bothers me to think that the animals may be cold. Tomorrow I will ask my teacher about how animals keep warm.

Ashley

Put a check after the sentences below that are written in the first person.

1. I am happy about our trip to the zoo. _____

2. The three girls watched the polar bear dance. _____

3. The zookeeper let me hold the owl. _____

4. I could feel the smooth skin of the snake. _____

5. The old monkey fussed at the younger ones. _____

Third-Person Voice

Read the story below.

> Two kangaroos shared a cage at the zoo. Matilda kept her side of the cage as neat a pin. Elsie never picked up her belongings. Matilda often thought that Elsie was lazy about housekeeping, but she never fussed at Elsie about it. The two kangaroos lived peacefully together.

The author wrote about the kangaroos as if she were an invisible person in their cage. They did not know she was there, but she pretended to see and hear them all of the time. She could even pretend to know what they were thinking. When an author writes about someone else and pretends to know what he says, does, and thinks, the author is writing in the **voice of the third person**. Remember, when the author is the person speaking in the story, that is the **voice of the first person**. Write a **1** by the sentences written in the first person. Write a **3** by the sentences written in the third in person.

1. _____ The boys were excited about the new movie.

2. _____ I am anxious to go to the zoo.

3. _____ Please walk with me to the hippopotamus exhibit.

4. _____ Seven seals swam happily back and forth in the pool.

Pronoun Referents

Read each set of sentences. Notice the words in bold. They are pronouns.
Then answer the questions.

1. Alicia would like a new doll. **She** hopes to get one for her birthday.
   Who is she?

   _____

2. Luke and Chris are playing baseball. **They** want to become
   professional ball players one day. Who are they?

   _____

3. The movers came to take our furniture away. **They** will deliver it to
   our new house. Who are they?

   _____

4. I played with my dog, Sam, yesterday. **He** loves to play catch.
   Who is he?

   _____

5. **You and I** should go to the movies. There is a new movie we
   would really like to see. Who are we?

   _____

6. My computer is broken. **It** will not turn on when I push the power
   button. What is it?

   _____

7. Tom and his sisters went next door to play. **He** was told to keep
   an eye on **them**. Who is he? Who does them refer to?

   _____

   _____

Idioms

Idioms are expressions whose meanings are different from the literal ones. Explain what the idioms below actually mean.

1. When Angelica said, "That movie **took my breath away**," she meant _____

   _____

2. "When Dad finally **put his foot down**, my brother started to do better in school," said

   Boris. What Boris meant was _____

   _____

3. Dana stood and said, "I guess I'll **hit the road** now." What Dana meant was

   _____

4. When Mario said that he was a bit **under the weather** last weekend, he meant that

   _____

5. When Nicholas said that he **slept like a log** last night, he meant _____

   _____

6. "I'll be **in the doghouse** for sure," exclaimed Roberto. What Roberto really meant was

   _____

7. "**Hold your horses**," remarked the police officer. The police officer meant _____

   _____

8. When Ryan asked Patricia, "Are you **getting cold feet**?" he was actually asking

   _____

9. If Grandpa loves **to spin a yarn**, he _____

   _____

10. When Leslie says that she is **in the dark** about what's going on, she means

   _____

More Idioms

Idioms are expressions with meanings which are different from the literal ones. Explain what the idioms below actually mean.

1. Dinner's on the house. _____

   _____

2. John got up on the wrong side of the bed. _____

   _____

3. My cousin has a green thumb. _____

   _____

4. Money burns a hole in my pocket. _____

   _____

5. He should mend fences before leaving. _____

   _____

6. Cathy didn't have the hang of it yet. _____

   _____

7. Mother told us to straighten up the house. _____

   _____

8. Dad always gets up with the chickens. _____

   _____

9. The sick child wasn't out of the woods yet. _____

   _____

10. Crystal was down in the dumps all day. _____

   _____

Analogies

Analogies are comparisons. Complete each analogy below.

Example: <u>Ear</u> is to <u>hearing</u> as <u>eye</u> is to <u>seeing</u>.

1. Cardinals is to St. Louis as Dodgers is to _____

2. A.M. is to before noon as P.M. is to _____

3. Three is to triangle as eight is to _____

4. Tear is to tore as see is to _____

5. Springfield is to Illinois as Austin is to _____

6. Carpet is to floor as bedspread is to _____

7. Go is to green as stop is to _____

8. Purple is to grapes as red is to _____

9. Ghost is to Halloween as bunny is to_____

10. Son is to dad as daughter is to _____

11. Jelly is to toast as syrup is to_____

12. Ear is to hear as eye is to _____

13. Oink is to pig as cluck is to_____

14. Mississippi River is to U.S. as Nile River is to _____

15. Clock is to time as thermometer is to_____

16. V is to 5 as C is to _____

17. Up is to down as ceiling is to _____

18. Car is to driver as plane is to _____

19. Sleep is to tired as eat is to _____

20. Bird is to nest as bee is to _____

More Analogies

Analogies are comparisons. Complete each analogy below. An example has been done for you.

Example: <u>Kangaroo</u> is to <u>joey</u> as <u>bear</u> is to <u>cub</u>.

1. See is to eye as _____ is to nose.

2. Ping-Pong® is to paddle as _____ is to racquet.

3. Bob is to Robert as Liz is to _____.

4. Writer is to story as poet is to _____ .

5. Car is to _____ as plane is to pilot.

6. Kennedy is to John as _____ is to Theodore.

7. Glove is to hand as boot is to _____ .

8. Hammer is to _____ as pen is to writer.

9. Bear is to _____ as bee is to hive.

10. _____ is to picture as curtain is to window.

11. Sing is to song as _____ is to book.

12. _____ are to teeth as contact lenses are to eyes.

13. Left is to _____ as top is to bottom.

14. _____ is to pool as jog is to road.

15. Wrist is to hand as _____ is to foot.

16. Hammer is to nail as _____ is to screw.

17. Paw is to dog as _____ is to fish.

18. Meat is to beef as _____ is to apple.

19. _____ is to pig as neigh is to horse.

20. Princess is to _____ as prince is to king.

Still More Analogies

Analogies are comparisons. Complete each analogy below. An example has been done for you.

Example: <u>Wide</u> is to <u>narrow</u> as <u>tall</u> is to <u>short</u>.

1. Big is to _____ as large is to small.

2. Hat is to head as shoe is to _____ .

3. Bird is to nest as _____ is to hive.

4. Rug is to _____ as curtain is to window.

5. _____ is to road as boat is to lake.

6. Boy is to man as _____ is to woman.

7. _____ is to room as gate is to yard.

8. Sleep is to tired as _____ is to hungry.

9. Zoo is to animals as library is to _____ .

10. Floor is to _____ as ceiling is to top.

11. _____ is to grass as blue is to sky.

12. Belt is to _____ as bracelet is to wrist.

13. Car is to driver as airplane is to _____ .

14. Book is to _____ as television is to watch.

15. Grape is to vine as peach is to _____ .

16. Ear is to hearing as _____ is to seeing.

17. _____ is to day as dusk is to dawn.

18. Thanksgiving is to November as Christmas is to _____ .

19. Calf is to cow as _____ is to lion.

20. _____ is to uncle as niece is to aunt.

All Together Now

Each set of words belongs to a different group. Classify the group by writing its name on the blank.

1. Easter, Yom Kippur, and Thankgiving are _____.

2. Shawna, Kate, and Mariella are _____.

3. Denmark, Greece, and Cuba are _____.

4. Bananas, apples, and strawberries are_____.

5. Cows, chickens, and sheep are _____.

6. Violet, plum, and lavender are _____.

7. Pencils, pens, and markers are_____.

8. Goofy, Mickey, and Donald are _____.

9. Clowns, trapeze artists, and the ringmaster are _____.

10. Stanford, Princeton, and Yale are _____.

11. Nile, Colorado, and Thames are _____.

12. East, south, and northwest are _____.

13. "Little Boy Blue," "Mary Had a Little Lamb," and "Little Miss Muffet" are _____.

14. Van Gogh, Michaelangelo, and Da Vinci are_____.

15. Lincoln, Kennedy, and Reagan are _____.

16. Three, fourteen, and twenty-nine _____.

17. A, Q, and Z are _____.

18 Donut, cookie, and pie are _____.

19. Jones, Lopez, and Chang are_____.

20. Hammer, saw, and wrench are _____.

218

Categories

Place the following words in each of the categories below. There are seven for each.

bassoon	harp	peccary	sloth
carnation	impatiens	meerkat	snipe
strawberry	iris	phoebe	sweet William
cello	kayaking	pineapple	triathlon
crocus	lacrosse	Ping-Pong	toucan
cummerbund	loganberry	poncho	trousers
flute	mandolin	primrose	trumpet
football	mango	quetzal	tux
gardenia	moccasin	quince	violin
gown	papaya	rugby	
guava	parka	soccer	

Animals

_____
_____
_____
_____
_____
_____
_____

Fruits

_____
_____
_____
_____
_____
_____
_____

Flowers

_____
_____
_____
_____
_____
_____
_____

Sports

_____
_____
_____
_____
_____
_____
_____

Instruments

_____
_____
_____
_____
_____
_____
_____

Clothing

_____
_____
_____
_____
_____
_____
_____

Get Rid of the Details

Read the paragraph below. It has too many details to be a summary. You must decide which words or phrases are not important enough to be in a short summary. Cross out the words or phrases that are not important details. To create a summarizing paragraph, copy the sentences and words you did not cross out.

Every animal has babies. Sometimes the mother takes care of the baby until it can take care of itself. Baby animals are cute. Sometimes the whole group of animals care for the babies. Baby bears are called cubs. The cubs like to eat honey. Baby animals must eat. Mothers and fathers protect their babies. Some baby animals, like kangaroos, live in pouches. Other baby animals travel on their mothers' backs. Possums and monkeys carry babies on their backs. Baby animals are fun to watch.

Summary

_____

_____

_____

_____

_____

_____

_____

Summarize

Read the paragraph and then follow the directions below.

Butterflies are beautiful insects. They flutter around in the spring air. They rest upon the tulips and daisies. Butterflies can be dark brown, bright yellow, orange, blue, or any number of colors. They begin life as caterpillars. Then, they spin silky covers called cocoons. Inside the cocoon, the caterpillar turns into a butterfly. Butterflies help to spread pollen from one flower to another, so butterflies are helpful as well as beautiful.

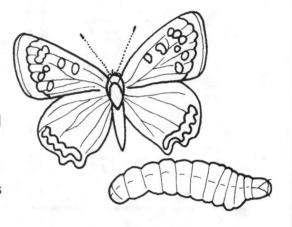

You can shorten a paragraph through summarizing. When you summarize, you include the main idea and the most important details, leaving out everything else. Summarize the paragraph above.

_____

_____

_____

_____

_____

_____

_____

_____

Mouse in the House

Cross out each answer in the computer as you solve the problems.

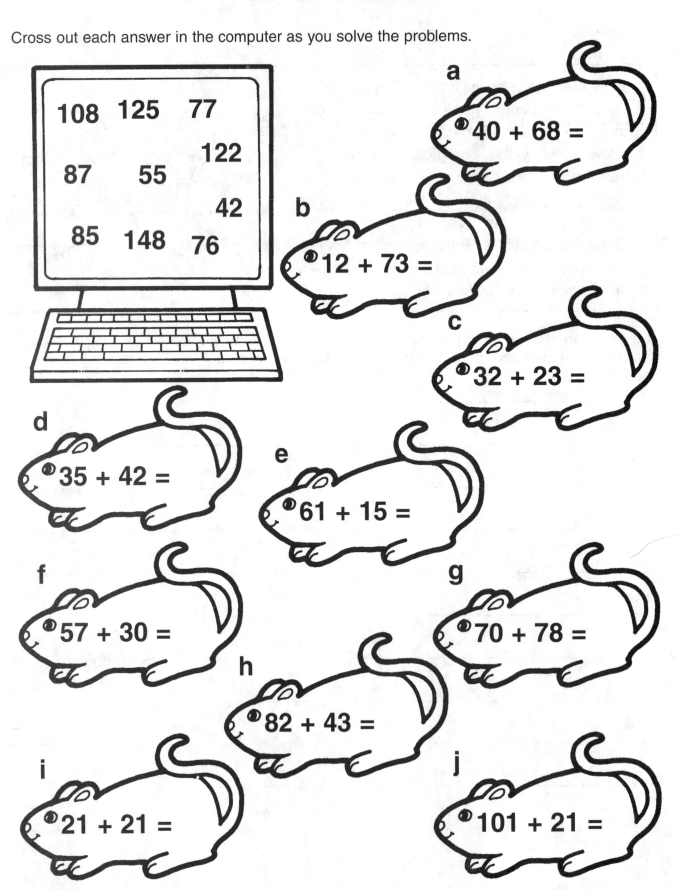

108   125   77

122

87   55

42

85   148   76

a 40 + 68 =

b 12 + 73 =

c 32 + 23 =

d 35 + 42 =

e 61 + 15 =

f 57 + 30 =

g 70 + 78 =

h 82 + 43 =

i 21 + 21 =

j 101 + 21 =

How Much?

32 dollars

49 dollars

26 dollars

57 dollars

64 dollars

17 dollars

Use the prices to write addition problems. Find the sums.

a. 1 🧥 + 1 👟 =

$\underline{4^9} + \underline{57} = \$106$

d. 1 👖 + 1 👟 =

$\underline{32} + \underline{57} = \$189$

b. 1 👗 + 1 👖 =

$\underline{26} + \underline{32} = \$58$

e. 1 ⌚ + 1 🎩 + 1 🧥 =

$\underline{64} + \underline{17} + \underline{49} = \$130$

c. 1 🎩 + 1 ⌚ =

$\underline{17} + \underline{64} = \$81$

f. 1 👗 + 1 👟 + 1 👖 =

$\underline{26} + \underline{57} + \underline{32} = \$115$

Word Problems

Read each word problem. Write the number sentence it shows. Find the sum.

a

In the forest, Lisa counted 83 pine trees, 24 spider webs, and 16 chipmunks. How many things did she count in all?

b

In Bill's classroom there are 47 pencils, 21 pieces of chalk, and 33 bottles of glue. How many supplies are there in all?

c

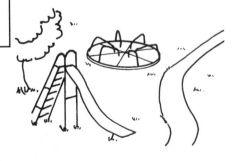

At the park, Carla counted 14 ducks, 32 children, and 24 roller skates. How many things did she count in all?

d

James counted 36 stars one night, 42 stars the next, and 87 on the third night. How many stars did he count in all?

Sum It Up

Find the sums.

a. $\begin{array}{r} 11 \\ + 50 \\ \hline \end{array}$	**g.** $\begin{array}{r} 69 \\ + 12 \\ \hline \end{array}$	**m.** $\begin{array}{r} 69 \\ + 16 \\ \hline \end{array}$	**s.** $\begin{array}{r} 36 \\ + 13 \\ \hline \end{array}$
b. $\begin{array}{r} 64 \\ + 42 \\ \hline \end{array}$	**h.** $\begin{array}{r} 72 \\ + 38 \\ \hline \end{array}$	**n.** $\begin{array}{r} 71 \\ + 59 \\ \hline \end{array}$	**t.** $\begin{array}{r} 29 \\ + 80 \\ \hline \end{array}$
c. $\begin{array}{r} 24 \\ + 93 \\ \hline \end{array}$	**i.** $\begin{array}{r} 48 \\ + 18 \\ \hline \end{array}$	**o.** $\begin{array}{r} 13 \\ + 68 \\ \hline \end{array}$	**u.** $\begin{array}{r} 51 \\ + 17 \\ \hline \end{array}$
d. $\begin{array}{r} 17 \\ + 20 \\ \hline \end{array}$	**j.** $\begin{array}{r} 52 \\ + 11 \\ \hline \end{array}$	**p.** $\begin{array}{r} 41 \\ + 96 \\ \hline \end{array}$	**v.** $\begin{array}{r} 19 \\ + 91 \\ \hline \end{array}$
e. $\begin{array}{r} 58 \\ + 72 \\ \hline \end{array}$	**k.** $\begin{array}{r} 15 \\ + 19 \\ \hline \end{array}$	**q.** $\begin{array}{r} 82 \\ + 30 \\ \hline \end{array}$	**w.** $\begin{array}{r} 31 \\ + 46 \\ \hline \end{array}$
f. $\begin{array}{r} 67 \\ + 14 \\ \hline \end{array}$	**l.** $\begin{array}{r} 31 \\ + 62 \\ \hline \end{array}$	**r.** $\begin{array}{r} 93 \\ + 90 \\ \hline \end{array}$	**x.** $\begin{array}{r} 87 \\ + 43 \\ \hline \end{array}$

Add Three

Find the sums.

a. 39 57 + 47	**g.** 39 12 + 72	**m.** 26 71 + 59	**s.** 17 79 + 54
b. 33 75 + 23	**h.** 51 24 + 88	**n.** 52 30 + 18	**t.** 39 95 + 48
c. 21 53 + 17	**i.** 42 84 + 19	**o.** 13 38 + 42	**u.** 27 77 + 70
d. 42 26 + 49	**j.** 23 14 + 92	**p.** 52 38 + 42	**v.** 59 44 + 16
e. 68 62 + 56	**k.** 84 36 + 65	**q.** 52 66 + 83	**w.** 51 36 + 24
f. 61 33 + 63	**l.** 34 42 + 30	**r.** 98 61 + 15	**x.** 67 73 + 30

Addition Challenge

Find the sums for the problems below.

1.   684
    792
 + 123

2.   485
    379
 + 369

3.   321
    831
 + 700

4.   680
    303
 + 425

5.   304
    262
 + 750

6.   421
    489
 + 492

7.   278
    915
 + 964

8.   409
    501
 + 961

9.   557
    627
 + 990

10.   863
    777
 + 421

11.   645
    129
 + 300

12.   789
    528
 + 450

Cup o' Tea

Cross out each answer in the teapot as you solve the problems.

a.
30
− 16

b.
12
− 11

c.
32
− 25

d.
50
− 36

e.
79
− 49

f.
91
− 50

g.
88
− 62

h.
73
− 43

i.
86
− 26

j.
93
− 52

14   1   30

41   7   26   41

60   14   30

Subtraction Solutions

Fill in the puzzle by solving the subtraction problems. Use the word names in the Word List.

Word List				
eleven	thirteen	fifteen	seventeen	nineteen
twelve	fourteen	sixteen	eighteen	twenty

Across

1. 25 – 11 =
3. 40 – 21 =
7. 33 – 16 =
9. 51 – 35 =

Down

1. 46 – 31 =
2. 27 – 7 =
4. 22 – 4 =
5. 19 – 8 =
6. 44 – 32 =
8. 38 – 25 =

What's the Difference?

Find the differences.

a. 51 − 50	**g.** 69 − 12	**m.** 69 − 16	**s.** 36 − 13
b. 64 − 42	**h.** 72 − 38	**n.** 71 − 59	**t.** 89 − 80
c. 94 − 23	**i.** 48 − 18	**o.** 68 − 13	**u.** 51 − 17
d. 27 − 10	**j.** 52 − 11	**p.** 96 − 41	**v.** 91 − 19
e. 78 − 52	**k.** 19 − 15	**q.** 82 − 30	**w.** 46 − 31
f. 67 − 14	**l.** 62 − 31	**r.** 93 − 90	**x.** 87 − 43

Find the Difference

Find the differences.

a. 31 − 23	**g.** 79 − 32	**m.** 85 − 21	**s.** 69 − 37
b. 75 − 42	**h.** 57 − 51	**n.** 51 − 20	**t.** 98 − 34
c. 54 − 23	**i.** 88 − 44	**o.** 42 − 28	**u.** 87 − 28
d. 42 − 26	**j.** 63 − 23	**p.** 71 − 56	**v.** 69 − 43
e. 88 − 26	**k.** 86 − 14	**q.** 36 − 32	**w.** 46 − 41
f. 61 − 33	**l.** 53 − 32	**r.** 97 − 60	**x.** 77 − 63

What's the Scoop?

Fill in the missing number on each cone to complete the problem.

1.
10
+
16

2.
17
− 8

3.
+ 4
17

4.
9
+
19

5.
8
−
1

6.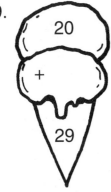
15
+ 4

7.
− 11
7

8.
21
− 16

9.
20
+
29

10.
14
− 7

11.
− 13
10

12.
14
+
25

13.
14
− 6

14.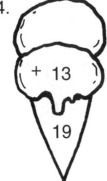
+ 13
19

15.
12
+ 12

16.
18
− 6

Sign In

Place + and − signs between the digits so that both sides of each equation are equal.

1. 6   4   1   2   6   2   =   15

2. 9   1   3   1   4   1   =   5

3. 9   3   4   1   2   3   =   14

4. 5   1   1   3   4   6   =   18

5. 9   8   6   3   5   3   =   8

6. 2   1   8   9   3   5   =   20

7. 5   3   2   4   1   5   =   12

8. 4   9   3   7   3   1   =   11

9. 7   6   2   8   7   1   =   3

10. 9   9   9   2   2   8   =   1

Multiplication

Solve the problems.

2 x 2	12 x 5	6 x 1	6 x 3
3 x 8	7 x 5	7 x 7	7 x 9
5 x 1	11 x 8	9 x 0	9 x 2
10 x 0	10 x 4	10 x 6	10 x 8
2 x 3	11 x 10	11 x 12	12 x 1
11 x 5	6 x 0	6 x 2	6 x 4
7 x 4	7 x 6	7 x 8	10 x 7
10 x 8	12 x 8	9 x 1	9 x 3
10 x 3	10 x 5	10 x 7	10 x 9
11 x 9	11 x 11	12 x 0	12 x 2

Column Multiplication

Solve the problems.

96 x 16	68 x 88	56 x 75	22 x 67
90 x 13	33 x 31	84 x 28	74 x 17
47 x 19	20 x 62	70 x 96	26 x 93
25 x 11	24 x 19	58 x 75	14 x 72
26 x 16	41 x 40	50 x10	48 x 30
40 x 28	46 x 20	21 x 25	42 x 48
82 x 35	49 x 71	77 x 63	88 x 50
60 x 52	38 x 45	79 x 44	69 x 18
71 x 27	24 x 35	86 x 33	43 x 31
32 x 54	27 x 32	13 x 29	19 x 22

By Three

Solve the problems.

173 x 6	533 x 8	138 x 2	833 x 5
227 x 3	388 x 1	417 x 8	524 x 3
402 x 1	620 x 6	317 x 4	468 x 6
420 x 8	662 x 3	458 x 7	947 x 2
178 x 9	714 x 9	550 x 6	767 x 7
324 x 8	835 x 3	594 x 5	632 x 3
172 x 4	152 x 7	180 x 4	221 x 2
286 x 8	254 x 5	538 x 1	489 x 4
509 x 4	851 x 1	728 x 6	141 x 9
615 x 2	674 x 8	107 x 3	213 x 5

Double Time

Solve the problems.

23 x 16	13 x 38	89 x 57	44 x 76
90 x 39	31 x 11	24 x 23	22 x 51
17 x 79	41 x 96	74 x 19	16 x 39
35 x 15	14 x 79	48 x 79	25 x 17
14 x 63	80 x 54	70 x 71	28 x 93
56 x 82	34 x 24	21 x 26	58 x 48
73 x 50	46 x 27	67 x 64	99 x 56
50 x 28	68 x 40	39 x 42	64 x 48
81 x 76	34 x 83	96 x 30	34 x 23
51 x 44	23 x 36	18 x 28	36 x 20

Divide and Conquer

Solve the problems.

$16\overline{)400}$ $15\overline{)225}$ $18\overline{)234}$

$12\overline{)240}$ $10\overline{)180}$ $8\overline{)136}$

$5\overline{)95}$ $8\overline{)248}$ $2\overline{)112}$

$16\overline{)256}$ $6\overline{)150}$ $32\overline{)128}$

$16\overline{)288}$ $9\overline{)171}$ $11\overline{)231}$

Which Is It?

Read the number sentences. Add the correct math sign to each problem.

+	–	x	÷
add	subtract	multiply	divide

1.   5 _____ 7 = 12

2.   24 _____ 4 = 6

3.   9 _____ 3 = 12

4.   18 _____ 6 = 12

5.   4 _____ 9 = 13

6.   4 _____ 9 = 36

7.   10 _____ 8 = 80

8.   15 _____ 5 = 3

9.   11 _____ 4 = 7

10.   8 _____ 16 = 24

11.   2 _____ 8 = 16

12.   3 _____ 2 = 5

13.   22 _____ 6 = 16

14.   9 _____ 1 = 10

15.   3 _____ 3 = 9

16.   144 _____ 12 = 12

17.   21 _____ 3 = 7

18.   90 _____ 10 = 9

19.   12 _____ 11 = 132

20.   14 _____ 1 = 14

Picture Fractions

A **fraction** is a number that names part of a whole thing. The number at the top is the numerator. It tells how many parts of the whole are present. The number at the bottom is the denominator. It tells how many parts there are in all.

Examples

 $\frac{1}{2}$ (There are two parts in the circle. One part is gray. Therefore, the fraction is $\frac{1}{2}$.)

 $\frac{3}{4}$ (There are four parts in the square. Three parts are gray. The fraction is $\frac{3}{4}$.)

Write a fraction for each picture.

1. 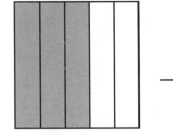 _____

2.  _____

3. 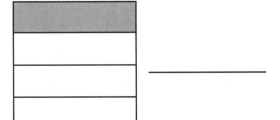 _____

4. 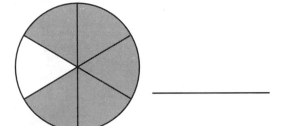 _____

5. 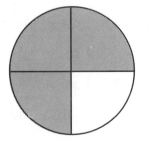 _____

6. 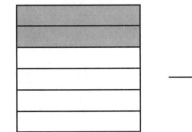 _____

7. 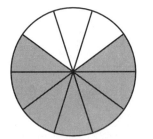 _____

8. 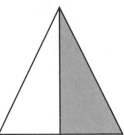 _____

Slice It Up!

In a **circle graph**, all the parts must add up to be a whole. Think of the parts like pieces that add up to one whole pie. Look at these pies and how they are divided into pieces.

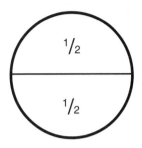

1/2 a pie

+ 1/2 a pie

2 halves =

1 whole pie

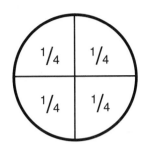

1/4 a pie

+ 1/4 a pie

+ 1/4 a pie

+ 1/4 a pie

4 fourths =

1 whole pie

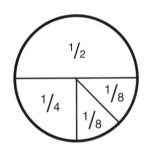

1/8 a pie

+ 1/8 a pie

+ 1/8 a pie

+ 1/8 a pie

+ 1/8 a pie

+ 1/8 a pie

+ 1/8 a pie

+ 1/8 a pie

8 eighths =

1 whole pie

1/2 a pie = 1 half

+ 1/4 a pie = 1 fourth

+ 1/8 a pie = 1 eighth

+ 1/8 a pie = 1 eighth

1 whole pie

Make a circle graph to show how much pie a family ate. Here is the information you will need.

Mother ate 1/4 of the pie.

Sister ate 1/4 of the pie.

Father ate 1/4 of the pie.

Brother ate 1/8 of the pie.

Grandma ate 1/8 of the pie.

Color the graph below using the Color Key.

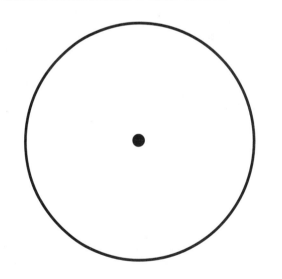

Pie My Family Ate

Color Key	
sister = orange	mother = pink
grandma = red	brother = yellow
father = blue	

Circle Graph

Shown in this circle graph are the types of fruit sold at a produce stand in a week in July.

Fruits Sold at O'Henry's Fruit Stand July 1 to July 7

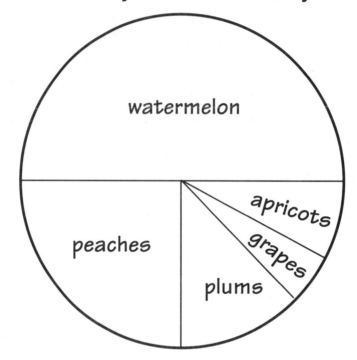

1. What fruit sold the most at O'Henry's Fruit Stand? _____`

2. What fruit sold the least? _____

3. Rank the order of the fruits that were sold. Number 1 will be the fruit that sold most, number 5, least.

   1. _____   2. _____   3. _____

   4. _____   5. _____

4. Circle the correct fraction.

   Watermelon was   1/2   1/4   1/8   of all the fruit sold.

   Peaches were   1/2   1/4   1/8   of all the fruit sold.

   Plums were   1/2   1/4   1/8   of all the fruit sold.

5. Which of the fruits represented on the circle graph is your favorite?

_____

Slices

Look at this circle graph. It shows what Chris did during one hour of time at home.

What Chris did from 4 to 5 P.M. on November 5

1. How many minutes did Chris spend . . .

   doing homework?_____

   eating a snack? _____

   changing clothes? _____

   playing a video game?_____

   walking the dog? _____

2. How did you figure out the number of minutes Chris did things?

   _____

   _____

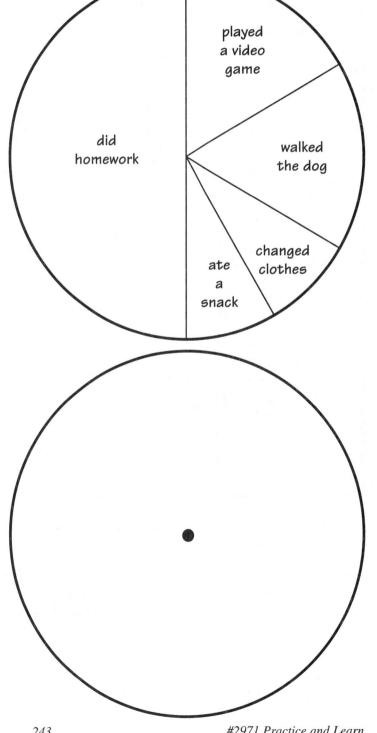

played a video game

walked the dog

did homework

changed clothes

ate a snack

Make a circle graph that shows what you did during one of your after-school hours.

Write the title of your graph here.

At the Playground

Using metric measurement, answer the questions below the playground map. Give all of your answers in meters. Draw lines between the areas and measure between the dots.

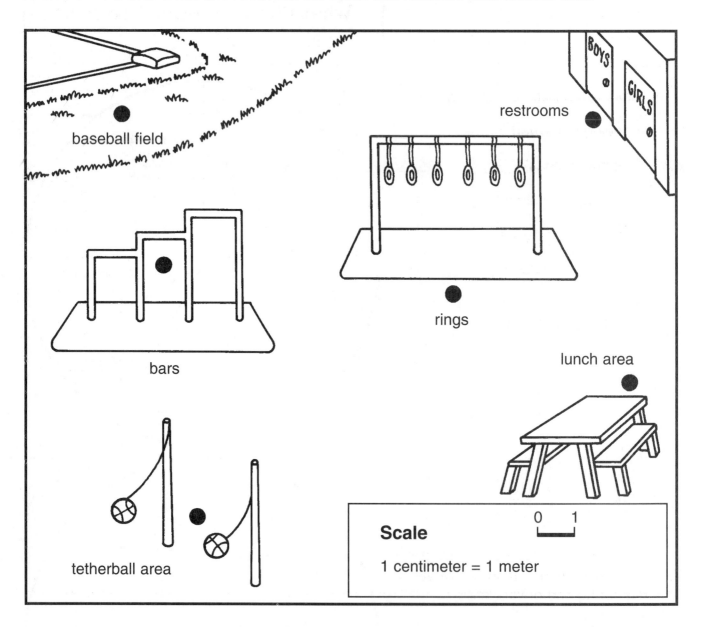

1. About how far is it from the bars to the baseball field? _____

2. About how far is it from the rings to the tetherball area? _____

3. About how far is it from the restrooms to the bars? _____

4. About how far is it from the lunch area to the bars? _____

5. About how far is it from the baseball field to the lunch area? _____

Measurement Choices

Measurement for a map scale can be given in inches, feet, and miles. This type of measurement is called **standard measure**.

Measurement for a map scale can also be given in centimeters, meters, and kilometers. This type of measurement is called **metric measure**.

On some map scales, both standard and metric measure are used. It is good to learn how to read and use both kinds of measurement systems.

When we choose a scale to use, it needs to be suited to the type of map we are making.

What do you think?

Decide on an appropriate scale to measure the size or distance of each of the following things. Use the scales in the box as your choices. Be ready to explain your choices.

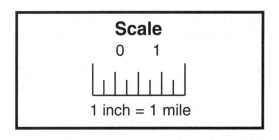

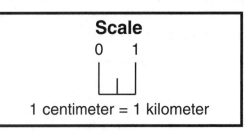

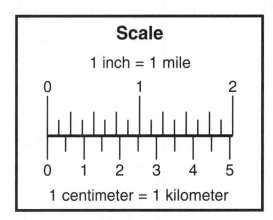

a. 1 centimeter = 1 centimeter	d. 1 inch = 1 foot
b. 1 centimeter = 1 meter	e. 1 inch = 1 mile
c. 1 centimeter = 1 kilometer	f. 1 inch = 100 miles

1. A cricket _____

2. Oregon to Texas _____

3. A bicycle race course _____

4. Your bedroom _____

5. Length of a sofa _____

6. Length of a horse's body _____

7. A swimming pool _____

8. The Mississippi River _____

9. The town park to your house _____

10. Your toes _____

How to Measure

When you measure distances using a map scale, you can measure several different ways. The easiest and most accurate way is to use a standard measure or metric measure ruler.

You can also use a piece of string, paper, the joints of your fingers, a pencil or pen, or other things that could help you mark size.

Once you have chosen your measurement instrument, place it along the imaginary or real line between the distances you want to measure.

About how many miles is it between:

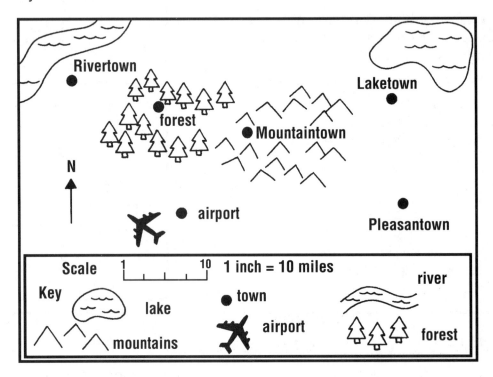

1. Rivertown and the airport? _____

2. Mountaintown and the forest? _____

3. Rivertown and Laketown? _____

4. Mountaintown and Pleasantown? _____

5. Laketown and Mountaintown? _____

6. Rivertown and the forest? _____

Is it farther from Pleasantown to Laketown or from Pleasantown to Mountaintown?

_____

From Here to There

Use this map scale and a metric ruler to answer the distance questions on this page. Use the center of the dots to measure.

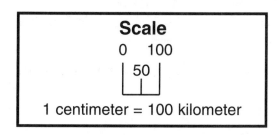

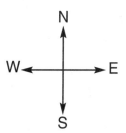

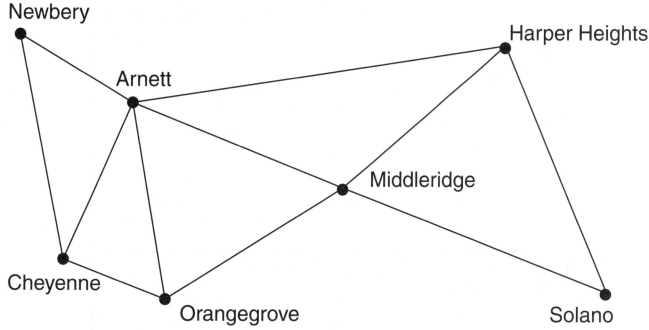

1. Newbery is _____ kilometers from Solano.

2. Middleridge is _____ kilometers from Orangegrove.

3. Cheyenne is _____ kilometers from Arnett.

4. Orangegrove is _____ kilometers from Harper Heights.

5. Arnett is _____ kilometers from Solano.

6. Harper Heights is _____ kilometers from Arnett.

7. Solano is _____ kilometers from Middleridge.

8. Middleridge is _____ kilometers from Harper Heights.

9. Newbery is _____ kilometers from Cheyenne.

10. Arnett is _____ kilometers from Middleridge.

 #2971 Practice and Learn

How Much Is It Worth?

Read this money chart. Then answer the questions below.

Pennies, Nickels, and Dimes

1. A penny is worth _____.

2. A nickel is worth _____.

3. A dime is worth _____.

4. _____ pennies equal _____ nickel.

5. _____ nickels equal _____ dime.

6. _____ pennies equal _____ dime.

7. 5 pennies equal _____.

8. 2 nickels equal _____.

9. 10 pennies equal _____.

10. 1 dime, 1 nickel, and 1 penny equal _____.

Change, Please

List the coins you would give each person below to make change for his or her dollar.

1. Dolly wants 1 coin for her $1. _____

2. Zac wants 6 coins for his $1. _____

3. Holly wants 7 coins for her $1. _____

4. Andrew wants 10 coins for his $1. _____

5. Casie wants 15 coins for her $1. _____

6. Thomas wants 16 coins for his $1. _____

7. Chelsea wants 17 coins for her $1. _____

8. Austin wants 19 coins for his $1. _____

9. Marc wants 25 coins for his $1. _____

10. Roberto wants 28 coins for his $1. _____

Change for Fifty Cents

There are over 75 ways to make change for 50 cents. Work with a friend to list as many ways as you can. List the coins in order on each line, from largest to smallest. (**Hint:** Working from large to small coins will also help you find more ways to make change.) The list has been started for you. If you need more space, continue your list on the back of this paper.

Use the following abbreviations:

hd (half dollar)　　**q** (quarter)　　**d** (dime)　　**n** (nickel)　　**p** (penny)

1. _____ 1 hd _____　　11. _____

2. _____ 2 q _____　　12. _____

3. _____　　13. _____

4. _____　　14. _____

5. _____　　15. _____

6. _____　　16. _____

7. _____　　17. _____

8. _____　　18. _____

9. _____　　19. _____

10. _____　　20. _____

Change for a Dollar

There are over 200 ways to make change for a dollar. Work with a friend to list as many ways as you can. List the coins in order on each line, from largest to smallest. (*Hint:* Working from large to small coins will help you find more ways to make change, too.) The list has been started for you. If you need more space, continue your list on the back of this paper.

Use the following abbreviations:

hd *(half dollar)*   **q** *(quarter)*   **d** *(dime)*   **n** *(nickel)*   **p** *(penny)*

1. _____2hd_____
2. _____1hd and 2q_____
3. _____1hd and 5d_____
4. _____1hd and 10n_____
5. _____
6. _____
7. _____
8. _____
9. _____
10. _____
11. _____
12. _____
13. _____
14. _____
15. _____
16. _____
17. _____
18. _____
19. _____
20. _____
21. _____
22. _____
23. _____
24. _____
25. _____

26. _____
27. _____
28. _____
29. _____
30. _____
31. _____
32. _____
33. _____
34. _____
35. _____
36. _____
37. _____
38. _____
39. _____
40. _____
41. _____
42. _____
43. _____
44. _____
45. _____
46. _____
47. _____
48. _____
49. _____
50. _____

Exam Time

As Mr. Teran prepared to pass back the last spelling exam, five anxious students awaited their grades. Using the clues below, determine each child's grade. Mark an **X** in each correct box.

1. Lucy, who did not get an A on her test, scored higher than Martin and Gwen.

2. Cara and Gwen both scored higher than Donald.

3. Martin received a C on his test.

4. No two students received the same grade.

	A	B	C	C-	D
Lucy					
Gwen					
Cara					
Martin					
Donald					

Theodore

Mr. Martin has three boys in his science class who each go by a variation of the name Theodore. From the statements below, discover each boy's full name and age. Mark the correct boxes with an **X**.

1. Agee is younger than Dalton but older than Chin.

2. Ted is not the youngest or the oldest.

3. Theodore's last name is Chin.

4. None of the boys is the same age.

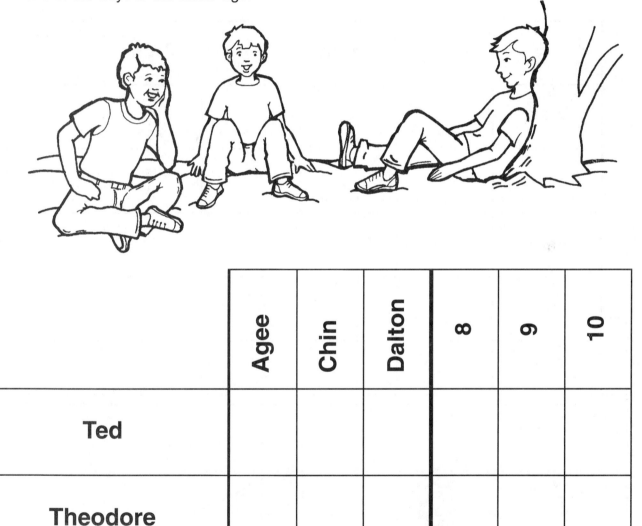

	Agee	Chin	Dalton	8	9	10
Ted						
Theodore						
Teddy						

Favorite Teams

Five boys root for five different baseball teams. Read the clues to determine which team each likes best. Mark the correct boxes with an **X**.

1. Will's bedroom is filled with posters and products from the A's.

2. Andrew's father is a big Cardinals fan, but Andrew is not.

3. Chad and Ryan like the Dodgers, the Reds, or the A's.

4. No boy's favorite team begins with the same letter as his name.

	Cardinals	Dodgers	A's	Reds	White Sox
Chad					
Danny					
Andrew					
Ryan					
Will					

 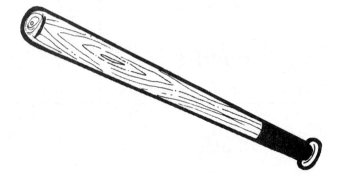

254

A Visit to the Amusement Park

Katelyn, Kenny, Emily, and Howie recently visited their local amusement park to ride their favorite attractions—the roller coaster, the Ferris wheel, the carousel, and the bumper cars. While there, one ate a hamburger, another ate a corndog, another ate a hot dog, and the last ate bratwurst. Using the clues below, determine each person's favorite ride plus what each had to eat. Mark the correct boxes with an **X**.

	roller coaster	Ferris wheel	carousel	bumper cars	hamburger	corndog	hot dog	bratwurst
Katelyn								
Kenny								
Emily								
Howie								

1. The girls liked the roller coaster and bumper cars while the boys liked the Ferris wheel and the carousel.

2. Howie ate his food on a stick while Katelyn ate hers on a hot dog bun.

3. Katelyn's favorite ride has hills.

4. The boy who loved the Ferris wheel also loves hot dogs.

Softball Lineup

All nine players on the Tiger softball team are sitting on the bench in their batting order. Using the clues below, find their batting order. Record their batting order by putting an **X** in the correct box.

1. Jane is batting fifth, and Daisy will bat some time before Carrie.

2. Joanne sits between Daisy and Gertie, and Annie is to the right of Jane.

3. Gertie bats after Joanne but before Annie.

4. Penny sits next to Carrie.

5. Carrie and Tammy are at each end of the bench.

	1	2	3	4	5	6	7	8	9
Jane					X				
Daisy		X							
Carrie	X								X
Joanne		X							
Gertie				X					
Annie				X					
Penny									
Tammy									X
Lindsey									

Intermediate Points

Study this compass rose.

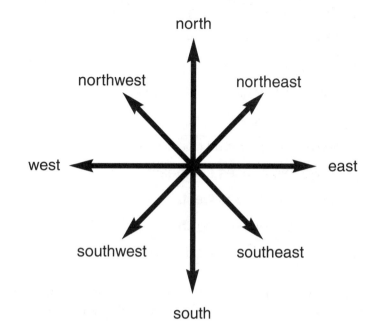

You are familiar with the four cardinal points, but there are times when directions can not be given using simply north, south, east, or west.

You need to be able to show points that come between the four primary directions. Intermediate points give a mapmaker just such a tool.

As you can see, the new direction words are made by combining the names of the cardinal points.

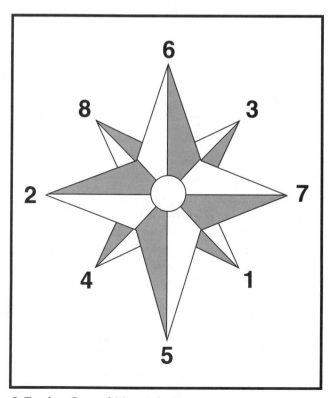

Using the cardinal and intermediate points, write the locations of the numbers in the box on the left.

1. _____

2. _____

3. _____

4. _____

5. _____

6. _____ *north* _____

7. _____

8. _____

       #2971 Practice and Learn

Can You Find Home?

You are lost. Can you find your home by following the directions in the box below?

1. Begin in the most northwest home.
2. Move three houses east.
3. Move one house south.
4. Move two houses southwest.
5. Move one house west.
6. Move three houses northeast.
7. Move two houses southeast.
8. Move five houses west.
9. Move two houses north.
10. Move three houses southeast.

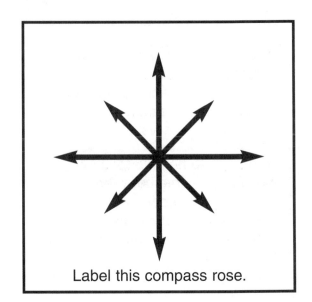

Label this compass rose.

Follow these directions. Color each of the houses you touch red. Color your home a different color.

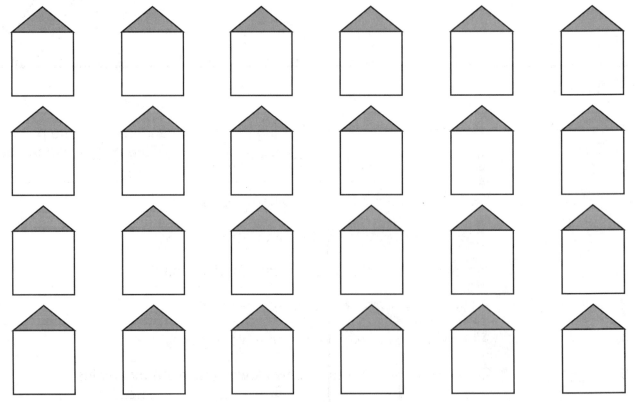

Can you rewrite the directions using fewer steps?

_____

_____

I've Got the Key!

Mapmakers draw the symbols they use in a map key. The map key explains what each symbol represents.

Look at this map and the map key. Use it to answer the questions below.

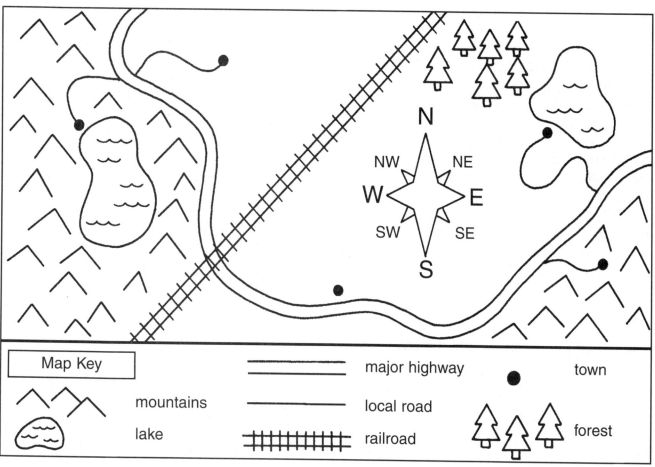

Answer true or false. If it is false, write the correct answer below it.

1. _____T_____ A railroad track runs southwest to northeast.

2. _____F_____ Mountains cover the northern section of the map.

3. _____F_____ A lake and a forest are in the southeast.

4. _____C_____ All towns can be reached by the major highway.

5. _____T_____ Two towns are by lakes, and two towns are in the mountains.

6. _____T_____ There are no towns along the railroad track.

7. _____F_____ There is a large forest east of the lake and west of the railroad.

8. _____T_____ The southernmost town is next to the major highway.

Grids

A **grid** is an arrangement of blocks that are made by vertical and horizontal lines intersecting on a page. Numbers and letters are used on the grid to help you name the blocks.

You can find something on a grid by putting a finger of your right hand on a number and a finger of your left hand on a letter. Then, slide your fingers together until they meet. When grid points are identified, the letter is written before the number.

Try it! What color is in block C4?

_____

	1	2	3	4
A	white	yellow	orange	gold
B	pink	green	tan	red
C	blue	purple	brown	silver
D	black	ivory	gray	lavender

Use the grid to name each of the colors identified below.

A1 _____   D3 _____   B4 _____   D2 _____

C4 _____   A2 _____   D1 _____   C2 _____

B3 _____   A4 _____   C3 _____   B1 _____

D4 _____   B2 _____   A3 _____   C1 _____

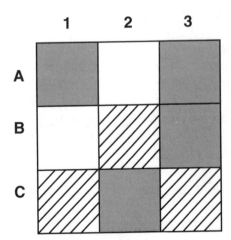

Use the grid on the left to answer these questions.

Which blocks are shaded?

_____

Which blocks are striped?

_____

Which blocks are unmarked?

_____

Where in This City?

Use the grid on the city map to find the places listed at the bottom of the page. Write the letter before the number for each place you find.

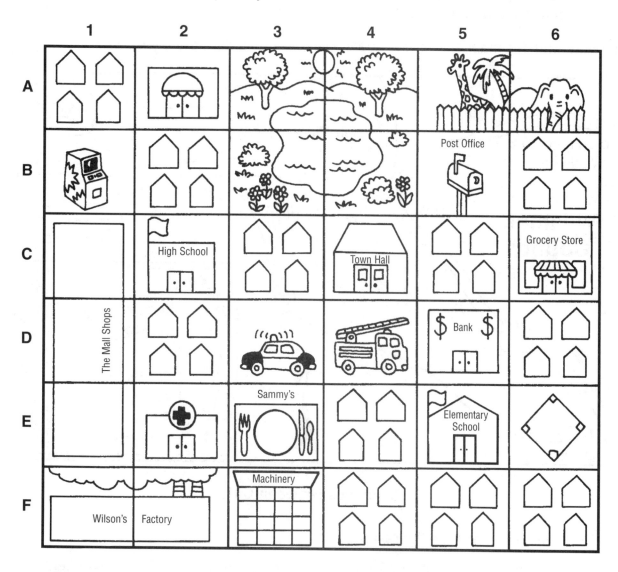

1. Medical Center _____

2. Machinery Warehouse _____

3. The Mall Shops _____, _____, and _____

4. Elementary School _____

5. Sammy's Restaurant _____

6. Green Park _____, _____, _____, and _____

7. Wilson's Factory _____, _____

8. City Zoo _____ and _____

9. City Bank _____

10. Town Hall _____

11. Ball Field _____

12. Arcade _____

13. Fire Station _____

14. Post Office _____

15. Grocery Store _____

16. High School _____

Road Maps

Road maps show the types of roads that are in a specific area. They also tell us other things we may need to know as we plan for travel, such as the distances from town to town, the locations of rest areas, and the availability of scenic routes.

After you read this map, answer the questions at the bottom of the page.

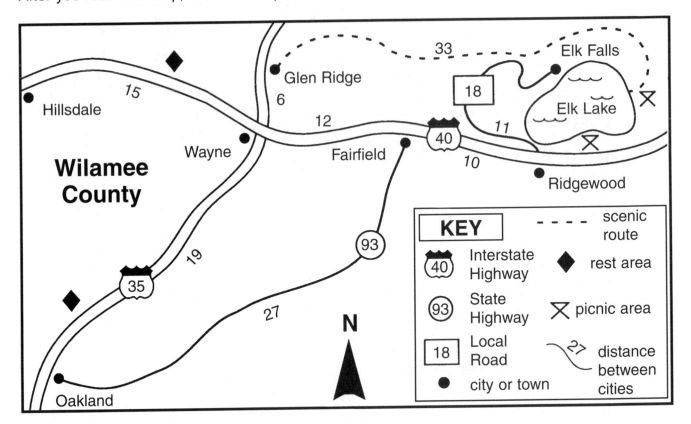

Distances Between Cities

1. Near what highways are the rest areas? _____

2. If you travel on State Highway 93, what is the distance from Oakland to Fairfield?

   _____

3. Interstate Highways 35 and 40 intersect at what city? _____

4. There is a scenic route that ends at the east side of Elk Lake. Where does it begin?

   _____

5. What is the distance from Hillsdale to:

   a. Wayne? _____   b. Ridgewood? _____

   c. Fairfield? _____   d. Elk Falls? _____

How Many Miles to Go?

Use the map on this page to answer the questions.

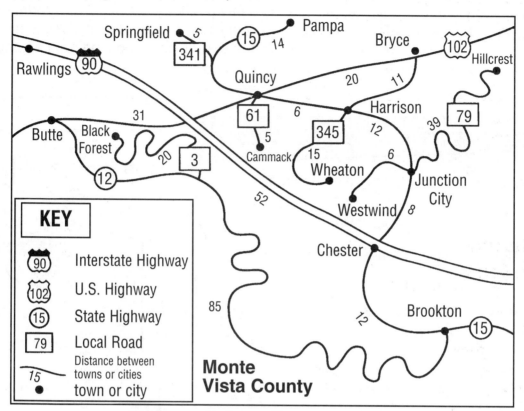

Distances Between Towns and Cities

1. You are in Butte. How far do you have to travel to
   a. Quincy? _____
   b. Pampa? _____
   c. Harrison? _____
   d. Hillcrest? _____
   e. Bryce? _____
   f. Brookton? _____

2. You are in Westwind. How far do you have to travel to
   a. Junction City? _____
   b. Chester? _____
   c. Bryce? _____
   d. Hillcrest? _____
   e. Rawlings? _____
   f. Cammack? _____

3. You are in Hillcrest. How far do you have to travel to
   a. Rawlings? _____
   b. Bryce? _____
   c. Wheaton? _____
   d. Brookton? _____
   e. Westwind? _____
   f. Pampa? _____

Challenge: Describe the route that would be fastest from Butte to Brookton.

_____

Why?_____

_____

Political Maps

One type of map that uses boundary lines is called a **political map**. A political map gives us information about county, province, state, and county boundaries as well as information about cities, towns, highways, roads, forest areas, and points of interest. Political maps also show oceans, rivers, and lakes, but they do not show the elevations of the land area as physical maps do.

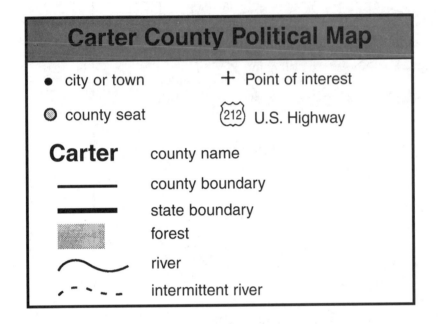

Carter County Political Map

- • city or town
- ◎ county seat
- **Carter** county name
- —— county boundary
- ▬▬ state boundary
- ▨ forest
- ～ river
- – · – · intermittent river
- ✛ Point of interest
- ⟨212⟩ U.S. Highway

Use this political map of Carter County, Montana, to answer the questions below.

1. Which sides of Montana's border does Carter County help form? _____

_____

2. What is the name of the county seat? _____

3. Through what three cities does the U.S. highway pass? _____

_____

4. Name one intermittent river in Carter County. _____

5. What is the point of interest in this county? _____

On a separate piece of paper, make a political map of the county in which you live.

Historical Maps

There is another type of map that makes use of boundary lines. These maps are called **historical maps** and show something about the history of an area.

At the time of Columbus, there were about 300 Native American tribes in North America. These tribes are often divided into seven groups: Woodland, Plains, Southwestern, California-Intermountain, Pacific Coast, Far North, and Middle American.

Use this historical map to answer questions about the Native American of early North America.

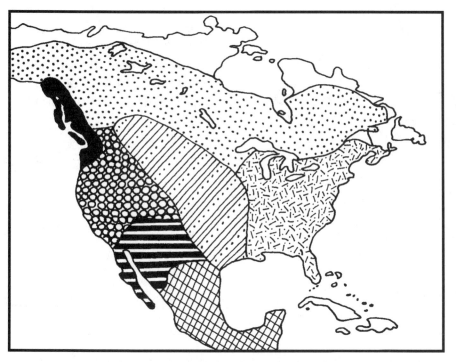

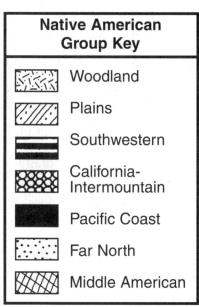

Native American Group Key

	Woodland
	Plains
	Southwestern
	California-Intermountain
	Pacific Coast
	Far North
	Middle American

1. What group of Native Americans covered the largest North American area?

_____

2. What group of Native Americans were both in Mexico and the United States?

_____

3. What group of Native Americans covered the smallest North American area?

_____

4. What Native Americans were the early inhabitants of North Dakota, South Dakota, Nebraska, and Kansas?

_____

Product Maps

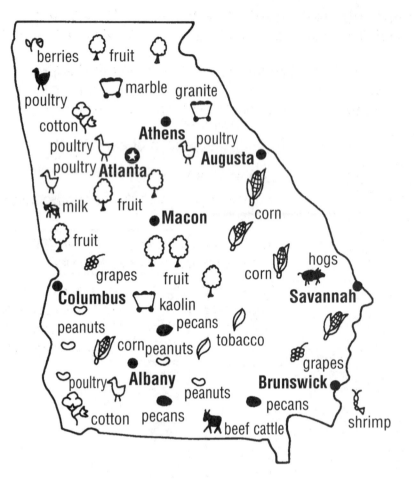

Sometimes maps can show us the types of things that are grown, raised, or mined in a certain place. These maps are called **product maps**.

Here are some of the products that are grown, raised, or mined in Georgia. Use the information on the map to answer the questions below.

1. Near what city are shrimp harvested? _____

2. What product is produced in great quantity near Macon? _____

3. What products are grown more in the southern part of Georgia than in the northern part? Name three.

    a. _____   b. _____   c. _____

4. What product is produced in the northwest corner of Georgia that is not produced in any great quantity in other locations in Georgia? _____

    _____

5. What food is grown between Augusta and Savannah? _____

6. What types of products are mined in the northern part of the state? _____

    _____

Challenge: After you have finished, use an encyclopedia or other source to find a product map of the place you live. Redraw it, selecting 10 to 20 products to draw on your map.

Population Maps

A **population map** shows the areas in which people live. This map shows the average number of people who live in certain areas of California. It is called a population density map.

Use the map to answer these questions. Write your answers on another piece of paper.

Population Density of California

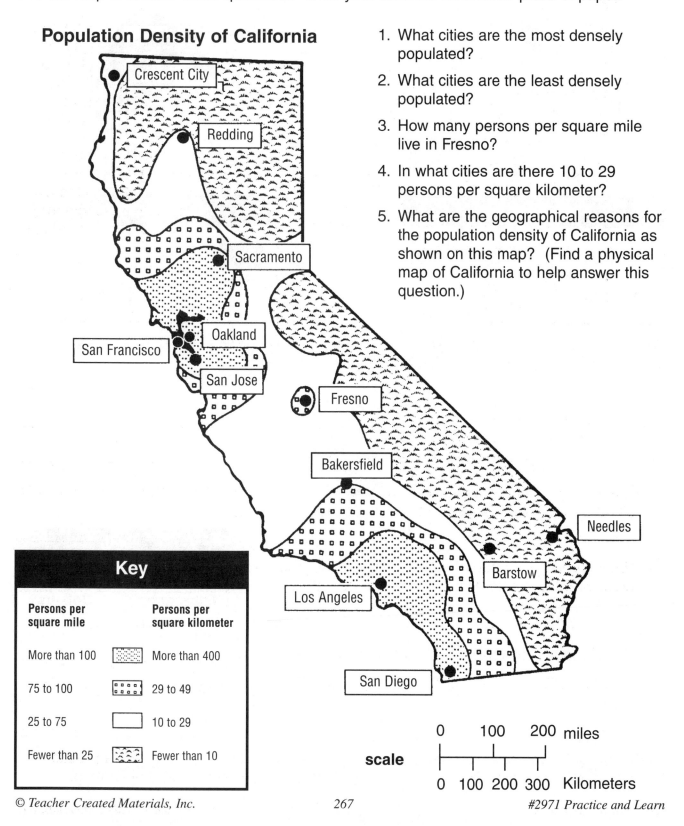

1. What cities are the most densely populated?

2. What cities are the least densely populated?

3. How many persons per square mile live in Fresno?

4. In what cities are there 10 to 29 persons per square kilometer?

5. What are the geographical reasons for the population density of California as shown on this map? (Find a physical map of California to help answer this question.)

Key

Persons per square mile		Persons per square kilometer
More than 100		More than 400
75 to 100		29 to 49
25 to 75		10 to 29
Fewer than 25		Fewer than 10

scale

0   100   200 miles

0 100 200 300 Kilometers

Weather Maps

Weather maps show what the weather of a specific area has been or could be. Weather patterns are shown on maps by using symbols or shading.

February Weather in Rainier County February, 19, 1988

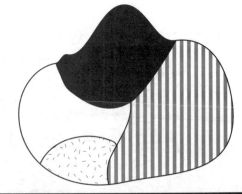

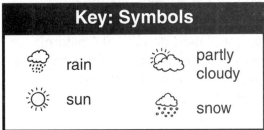

Key: Symbols

rain		partly cloudy	
sun		snow	

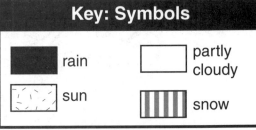

Key: Symbols

rain		partly cloudy	
sun		snow	

Weather maps can also show average temperatures in a specific area. Here is a map of the average January temperatures in Massachusetts.

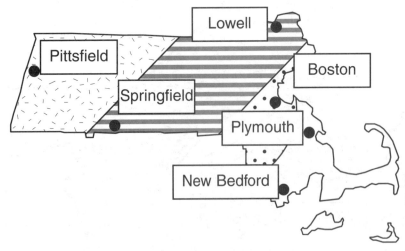

1. Which city is coldest in January? _____

2. Which cities are in the region that has the mildest winters? _____

3. What is the average January temperature in

    a. Boston? _____   b. Lowell? _____   c. Pittsfield? _____

Key

Degrees Fahrenheit		Degrees Celsius
Above 30		Above -1
26 to 30		-3 to -1
22 to 26		-6 to -3
Below 22		Below -6

It All Adds Up!

The map skills you have learned in this book all add up! Can you read this map?

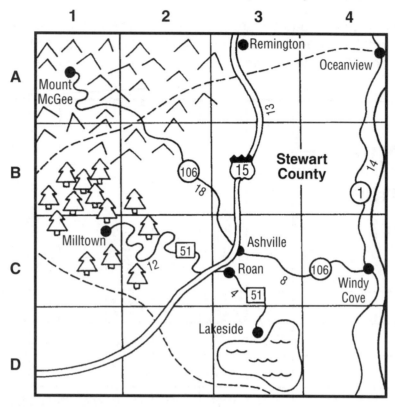

Key	● city or town	⬭ lake	🛡 interstate highway
	⋀⋀ mountains	— mileage between points	◯ state highway
	⋯ county boundary		▢ local road
	🌲🌲 forest	∿ coastline	

1. At what gridpoints are the following places:

    a. Lakeside_____   b. Mount McGee_____   c. Ashville and Roan_____

2. What gridpoints are completely out of Stewart County? _____

3. What type of road leads from Windy Cove to Mount McGee?_____

4. Lumber products might be milled in what grid points?_____

5. What cities are not in Stewart County? _____

6. How many miles is it from:

    a. Lakeside to Milltown? _____   b. Oceanview to Ashville? _____

7. State Highway 1 parallels what kind of land? _____

How Far to New York?

Distance charts show you the distance between two places if you travel by road.

This distance chart shows the road distances in miles between ten North American cities. Look at the chart carefully. Read it by using two fingers and coming together to find the distance between cities. Practice. When you are comfortable using the chart, answer the questions below.

Ten City Distance Chart	Albuquerque	Boston	Chicago	Denver	Indianapolis	Los Angeles	Miami	Montreal	New York City
Boston	2172		963	1949	906	2779	1504	318	206
Chicago	1281	963		996	181	2054	1329	828	802
Denver	417	1949	996		1058	1059	2037	1815	1771
Indianapolis	1266	906	181	1058		2073	1148	840	713
Los Angeles	807	2779	2054	1059	2073		2687	2873	2786
Miami	1938	1504	1329	2037	1148	2687		1654	1308
Montreal	2087	318	828	1815	840	2873	1654		378
New York City	1979	206	802	1771	713	2786	1308	378	
Seattle	1440	2976	2013	1307	2194	1311	3273	2685	2815

Find the distances between these cities:

1. Los Angeles and New York: _____

2. Seattle and Albuquerque: _____

3. Boston and New York: _____

4. Denver and Miami: _____

5. New York City and Chicago: _____

6. Montreal and Indianapolis: _____

7. Chicago and Miami: _____

8. Indianapolis and Denver: _____

9. Montreal and Los Angeles: _____

10. Seattle and Boston:_____

11. Chicago and Boston:_____

12. Denver and Albuquerque: _____

Tables

A **table** is a type of chart that is organized in such a way as to make information easy to find.

Read this table about the three major classifications of rocks. Use the information in the table to answer the questions at the bottom of this page.

Three Major Classifications of Rocks			
Classification	**rock**	**color**	**structure**
Igneous Rock (forms from hardened magma)	granite	white to gray, pink to red	closely arranged medium-to-coarse crystals
	obsidian	black, sometimes with brown streaks	glassy, no crystals
	pumice	grayish-white	light, fine pores, floats on water
Sedimentary Rock (formed by hardening of plant, animal, and mineral materials)	coal	shiny to dull black	brittle, in seams of layers
	limestone	white, gray, and buff to black and red	dense, forms cliffs, and may contain fossils
	shale	yellow, red, gray, green, black	dense, fine particles, soft, smells like clay
Metamorphic Rock (formed by existing rock changing because of heat or pressure)	marble	many colors, often mixed	medium-to-coarse crystals
	quartzite	white, gray, pink, and buff	big, hard, and often glassy
	schist	white, gray, red, green, black	flaky, banded, sparkles with mica

1. What is the name of the igneous rock that is black and has a glassy appearance?

_____

2. What classification of rock is most likely to contain fossils?

_____

3. To which classification do schist and marble belong?

_____

Chart the Read-a-Thon!

Students at Hudson Elementary School have been participating in a Read-a-Thon to raise money for their school library. Each student has tallied the number of books he or she has read and is ready to collect the pledge money.

This chart represents the reading and pledging of 15 students involved in the Read-a-Thon. After reading the chart, answer the questions at the bottom of the page.

Hudson Elementary School Read-a-Thon: Room 3			
Student's Name	**Total Books Read**	**Pledge per Book**	**Money Collected**
Acevedo, Jennifer	31	10¢	$3.10
Adams, Joseph	5	10¢	$.50
Barton, Michael	61	5¢	$3.05
Duran, Louis	17	15¢	$2.55
Edwards, Marylou	47	5¢	$2.35
Harrison, Trevor	11	25¢	$2.75
Lee, Rebecca	40	10¢	$4.00
Logan, Cassie	22	5¢	$1.10
Marshall, Barbara	9	50¢	$4.50
Peterson, David	102	5¢	$5.10
Ross, Kathryn	58	10¢	$5.80
Rublo, Anthony	83	5¢	$4.15
Shea, Sharon	39	10¢	$3.90
Tran, Alvan	14	10¢	$1.40
Yetter, Liz	75	5¢	$3.75
Total	614		$48.00

1. Which student read the most books?_____

2. What was the highest amount of money collected by one student? _____

3. Who had the highest pledge of money per book? _____

4. Was the person who read the most books the same as the person who collected the most money? _____

5. Was the person who had the highest pledge of money per book the same as the person who collected the most money?_____

6. What was the total number of books read by these students? _____

7. How much money did these students earn for the library? _____

Would a Read-a-Thon be a good way to raise money at your school?

Pictographs

One type of graph that gives us information is called a **pictograph**. In a pictograph, pictures are used instead of numbers.

Read this pictograph to find out the number and types of instruments sold in April at Harmony Music Store.

April Instrument Sales at Harmony Music Store	
pianos	🎹
flutes	🎵🎵
guitars	🎸🎸🎸🎸🎸🎸
drums	🥁🥁🥁
trumpets	🎺
Key: 1 instrument = 5 instruments	

1. How many of each of these instruments were sold?

   pianos _____ 5 _____   flutes _____ 10 _____   guitars _____ 30 _____

   drums _____ 15 _____   trumpets _____ 5 _____

2. How many more guitars were sold than . . .

   pianos? __ 25 _____   flutes? __ 20 _____

   drums? __ 15 _____   trumpets? 25 _____

3. Do you think the piano sales or the guitar sales brought in more money for Harmony Music Store? Explain the reason(s) for your choice.

   guitars alot of people want

   them.

Diagrams

Diagrams are pictures that are labeled so that a reader can easily learn the parts of what is pictured.

Do you know anything about guitars? Did you know there are different types of guitars? Can you describe the similarities and differences between acoustic and electric guitars?

Study these diagrams. Then answer the questions at the bottom of the page.

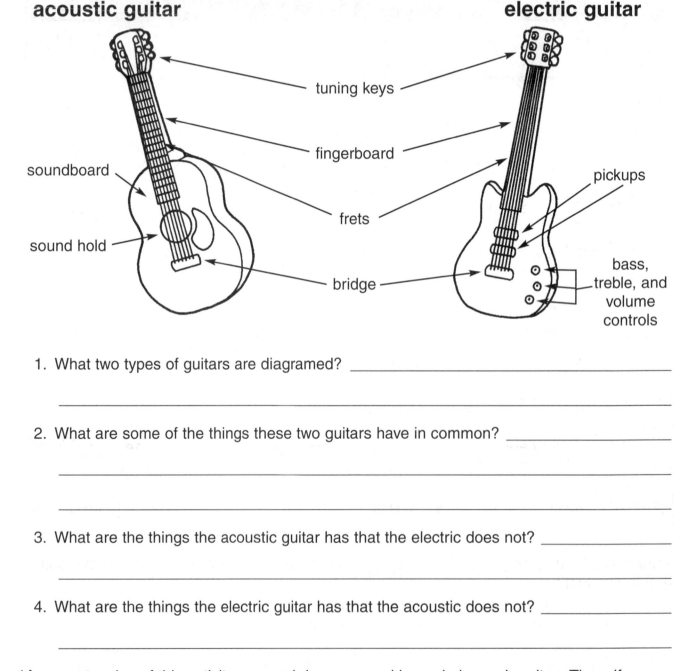

1. What two types of guitars are diagramed? _____

   _____

2. What are some of the things these two guitars have in common? _____

   _____

   _____

3. What are the things the acoustic guitar has that the electric does not? _____

   _____

4. What are the things the electric guitar has that the acoustic does not? _____

   _____

*As an extension of this activity, research how a sound is made by each guitar. Then, if possible, bring acoustic and electric guitars to class for demonstration purposes.

Ant City!

Have you ever wondered what it looks like inside an ant hill? You will get an idea from studying this cutaway diagram.

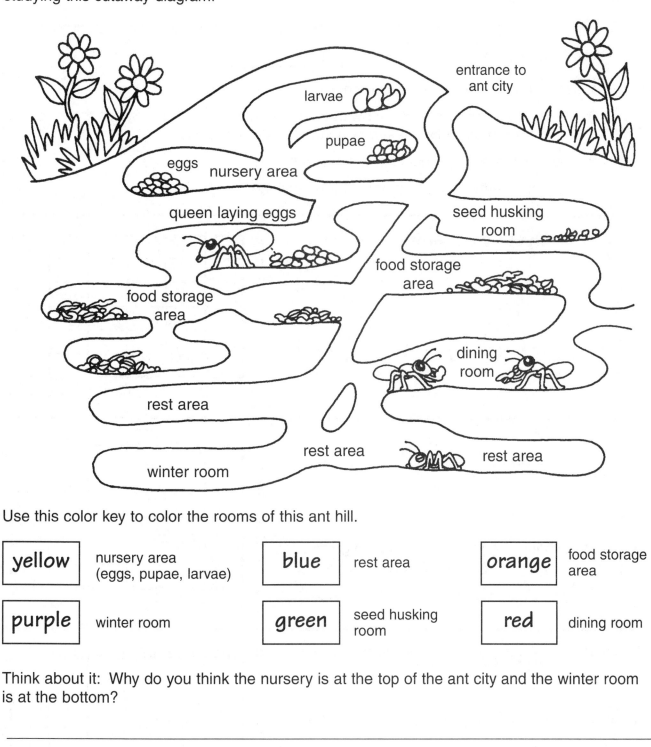

Use this color key to color the rooms of this ant hill.

yellow	nursery area (eggs, pupae, larvae)	blue	rest area	orange	food storage area
purple	winter room	green	seed husking room	red	dining room

Think about it: Why do you think the nursery is at the top of the ant city and the winter room is at the bottom?

_____

_____

_____

Graph Game

There are some letters of the alphabet hidden in these three graphs. Can you make the dots and draw the lines to find them?

Directions:

1. Begin on the left side of the graph.

2. Match the number in each pair with the number at the bottom. Match the letter in each pair with the letter on the left side of the graph.

3. Mark all the pairs with dots and connect the lines.

4. Write the name of the mystery letter on the line next to the graph.

Mystery Letter #1

Clues:

2,B   3,F   4,D   5,F   6,B

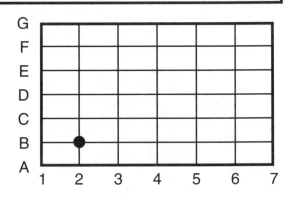

Mystery Letter #2

Clues:

2,F   3,B   4,D   5,B   6,F

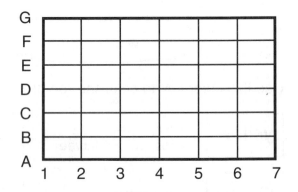

Mystery Letter #3

Clues:

3,F   4,B   5,F

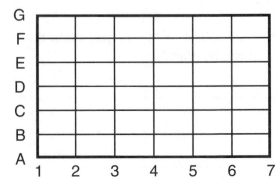

Movie Schedule

Sometimes a movie schedule is called a **timetable**. This is because the times that movies begin are listed together on a table. Look at the movie schedule. Use it to answer the questions below.

Movie	Starting Show Time
A Lad, Dan	11:00 AM, 2:00 PM, 4:30 PM
Free Billy	11:00 AM, 3:30 PM, 7:00 PM
The Sandy Lot	1:00 PM, 5:00 PM, 8:00 PM
The Mystery Garden	2:00 PM, 5:30 pm, 9:00 PM
The Adam's Farm	3:00 PM, 6:00 PM, 7:30 PM

1. Could you see *Free Billy* at 2:00 PM? No

2. If you do not get out of church until 2:00 PM, when is the earliest you can see

   The Sandy Lot? 5:00 pm

3. Is it true that three of the movies are shown in the morning? No, only two the A Lad, Dan & Free Billy

4. Name the two movies that are shown at 2:00 PM. A Lad, Dan & The mystery Garden

5. Which movies begin after 7:30 PM? The Sandy lot & The mystery Garden

6. Which movies would you like to see and at which times? Free Billy @ 7:00 pm & The Sandy lot @ 8:00 pm

Go East!

Do you know where the states of the United States are in relation to each other? Now it is your chance to find out. Go east!

This is a maze game. The object of the game is to move geographically east through the states of the United States written here. Begin at Hawaii and end at Maine. You may move one space at a time right, left, or down. You may not move upward or diagonally. Move to the space with the state that is the closest and to the east. Trace your path as you go. Have a nice trip!

Start

South Carolina	Wisconsin	North Dakota	✪ Hawaii	Washington	Alaska
Idaho	Virginia	New Jersey	Mississippi	Nevada	Oregon
Ohio	Colorado	South Dakota	Oklahoma	Wyoming	Montana
Maryland	Missouri	Illinois	Arkansas	Utah	California
Iowa	New Mexico	Kentucky	Georgia	Texas	North Carolina
Florida	Arizona	New York	West Virginia	Kansas	Louisiana
Maine ★	New Hampshire	Vermont	Nebraska	Indiana	Delaware

Finish

Go West!

Do you know where the countries of the world are in relation to each other? Now is your chance to find out. Go west!

This is a maze game. The object of the game is to move geographically west one space at a time through the countries of the world written here. Begin at Finland and end at Canada. You may not move upward or diagonally. Move to the space with the country that is closest and to the west. Trace your path as you go. Bon voyage!

Start

Russia	Spain	United States	Libya	★ Finland	Iran
Turkey	Peru	Venezuela	England	Germany	China
Nepal	Mexico	Algeria	Sudan	Japan	Brazil
Ecuador	New Zealand	Australia	Costa Rica	Thailand	Norway
Romania	Panama	Mongolia	India	Pakistan	Chile
Greece	Iraq	Sweden	Cuba	Saudi Arabia	Egypt
Chad	Canada ✪	Iceland	Ireland	France	Italy

Finish

Country and City Match

Match the city to its country by drawing a line between them.

Cities	Countries
Los Angeles	*France*
Glasgow	*South Korea*
Seoul	*United States*
Bombay	*Japan*
Nagano	*Australia*
Nice	*Israel*
Frankfurt	*Portugal*
Florence	*Ireland*
Toronto	*Brazil*
Lima	*Peru*
Rio de Janeiro	*Colombia*
Bogotá	*Egypt*
Lisbon	*South Africa*
Cairo	*Canada*
Jerusalem	*Scotland*
Copenhagen	*Italy*
Canberra	*Denmark*
Dublin	*Mexico*
Cape Town	*Germany*
Acapulco	*India*

Where Am I?

Here are clues to help you find a mystery state. When you have discovered the state, write its name on the bottom of the page.

1. I am east of California.

2. I am neither among the smallest nor the largest of the states in the United States.

3. I have a mild climate.

4. I contain all the raw materials for making steel—limestone, iron ore, and coal.

5. I am covered by forests on about two-thirds of my land.

6. I produce many chickens, eggs, and milk.

7. I am south of Michigan.

8. I have more than one famous cave.

9. I am crossed by the Tennessee River.

10. I am north of Florida.

11. I am a Southeast State.

12. I am surrounded by four states.

13. I have a belt of black clay soil that crosses me.

14. I am west of Georgia.

15. I touch the Gulf of Mexico.

I am _____!

Locate and then color the mystery state on the map below.

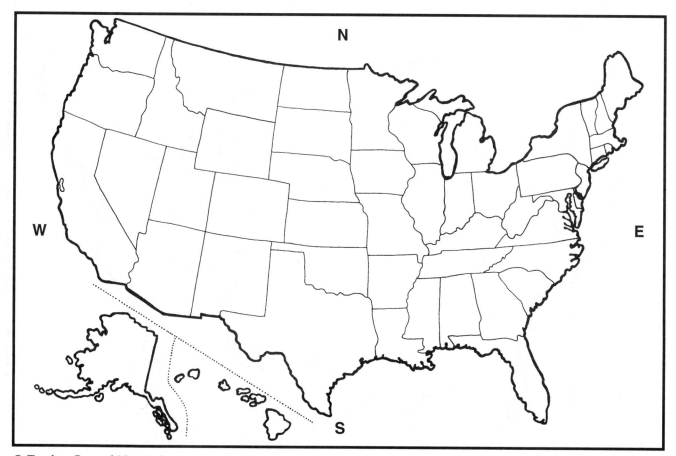

"State" My Name

Here are clues to help you find a mystery state. When you have discovered the state, write its name on the bottom of the page.

1. I am west of Virginia.

2. I am not among the smallest states in the United States.

3. I am home to buffalo, black bears, and tortoises.

4. I have a very large lake.

5. I am east of California.

6. I have rich mineral deposits, including oil shale.

7. I contain more than one national park.

8. I have snow-covered mountains.

9. I am south of Montana.

10. I am a Mountain West state.

11. I contain a huge desert.

12. I am crossed by the Colorado River.

13. I am surrounded by six states.

14. I have many famous canyons.

15. I am north of Arizona.

I am _____!

Locate and then color the mystery state on the map below.

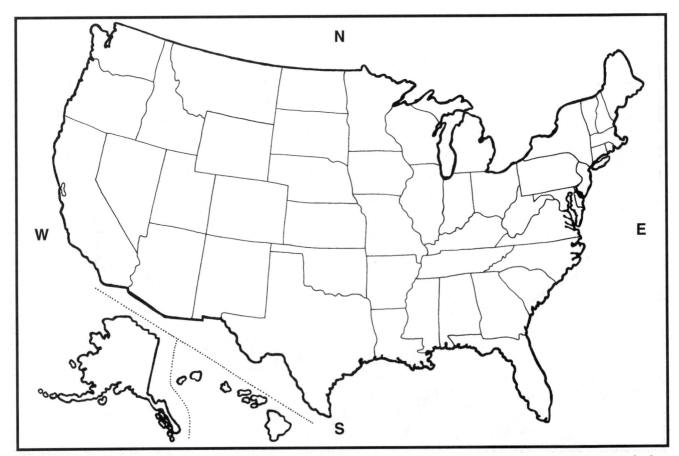

282

What Country Am I?

Here are clues to help you find a mystery country. When you have discovered the country, write its name on the bottom of the page.

1. I am in the Western Hemisphere.

2. I am south of Canada.

3. I am bordered by the Atlantic Ocean.

4. I am a leading producer of wheat.

5. I am north of Antarctica.

6. Early explorers came to find silver in my land.

7. I am a great world producer of cattle and sheep.

8. I am on the continent of South America.

9. I am bordered by the Andes Mountains.

10. I am in summer when the United States and Canada are in winter.

11. I am about a third the size of the United States.

12. I am bordered by the Uruguay River.

13. I have the highest and lowest elevations in South America.

14. Cape Horn is at my base.

15. I am east of Chile.

I am _____!

Use the map below to discover what the mystery country is.

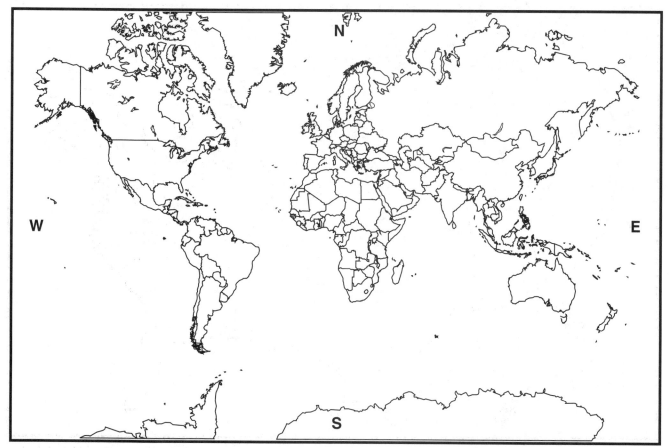

A Mystery Country

Here are clues to help you find a mystery country. When you have discovered the country, write its name on the bottom of the page.

1. I am in the Eastern Hemisphere.

2. I am not among the largest countries in the world.

3. I am west of Asia.

4. I am one of the world's leading producers and exporters of petroleum.

5. I am north of Angola.

6. Because of my nearness to the equator, I have a tropical climate.

7. I have many varied land regions.

8. I am on the continent of Africa.

9. Cacao, palm oil, and peanuts are some of my chief agricultural products.

10. I am on the west coast of Africa.

11. I rank among the world's largest nations in population.

12. Lake Chad forms part of my border.

13. I am surrounded by four countries.

14. I am crossed by the Niger River.

15. I am north of Cameroon.

I am _____!

Use the map below to discover what the mystery country is.

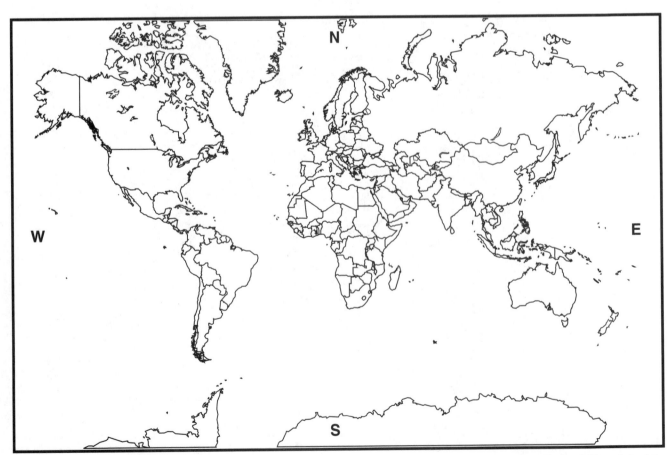

Practice & Learn
for
11 Year Olds

Nouns

Nouns are words that name a person, place, thing, or idea.

- **Persons** include both names of people and categories.

  Mr. Blue   children   policemen   teacher   girl   boy

- **Places** can name both specific and general places.

  New York   school   park   department stores   homes

- **Things** refer to objects.

  door   shoes   newspaper   table   globe

- **Ideas** tell about feelings or thoughts.

  love   pain   philosophy   care   liberty   freedom   belief   rules

A. Underline the nouns in the following sentences. The number at the end of the sentence tells how many nouns to look for.

1. Summer is a wonderful time of the year. (3)

2. The weather is hot and many children enjoy swimming. 34)

3. Most schools are closed and people have time to go on vacations. (4)

4. The days are longer and we have more hours of sunlight. (3)

5. It is wonderful to go to the pool, beach, or lake. (3)

6. My teacher, Mr. Dawson, visited the Metropolitan Museum of Art in New York City in July. (5)

7. He said that great care and concern are shown by visitors. (3)

8. My friends, Tim and Carol, went to the Statue of Liberty and to Ellis Island. (5)

9. The scent of beautiful flowers drifts across Central Park as we eat our lunch outside. (4)

10. We like to cook hamburgers on the grill and picnic in the backyard. (3)

B. Use the back of this paper to write each of the following words under the correct heading of **person**, **place**, **thing**, or **idea**.

• France	• shoelaces	• city	• loyalty	• love	• building
• happiness	• bicycles	• Ms. Litz	• glasses	• table	• fairness
• clouds	• science	• sounds	• Dr. Forest	• pain	• Texas

Verbs

Verbs are words that express action or being.

An *action verb* describes physical action, that which can be seen.

> *Example:* Tom collected stamps and coins.

Sometimes the verb expresses mental action, that which cannot be seen.

> *Example:* Candice knew all the answers on the test.

A *linking verb* joins or links the subject of a sentence with a word or words in the predicate. It tells that something *is* or *was*.

> *Example:* The pot on the stove was hot!

Common Linking Verbs include the following:

am	*be*	*feel*	*has been*	*is*	*been*	*sound*
have been	*are*	*being*	*taste*	*was*	*will be*	*look*
had been	*were*	*become*	*appear*	*seem*		

Directions: In each of the sentences below, underline the verb. Label each verb *action* or *linking*.

_____ 1. Lightning flashed across the sky.

_____ 2. The quarterback raced down the field.

_____ 3. The winner crossed the finish line.

_____ 4. The crackling fire looked beautiful!

_____ 5. The roasting marshmallows smelled delicious!

_____ 6. The hunters captured a turkey and a deer.

_____ 7. Hailstones are little ice balls.

_____ 8. Fog covered the airport, preventing the planes from landing.

_____ 9. Trucks skidded on the snow-covered highways.

_____ 10. Dew formed on the grass in the early morning.

_____ 11. The magician pulled a bouquet of flowers from the scarf.

_____ 12. Mike appears frail after his operation.

_____ 13. Kitty seems to be the fastest runner in the sixth grade.

_____ 14. The young boys became excellent ranch hands.

Tall Tale Pattern Story

Use the form below to create a tall tale. Fill in the blanks with the correct words. Then illustrate the tall tale and share it with someone.

Many years ago _____ was born in
(hero)

_____ . _____ was so big
(place)   (hero)

that he/she slept in a _____ . Each morning.
(noun)

_____ ate _____ ,
(hero)   (noun)

_____ , and _____ for breakfast. As
(noun)   (noun)

_____ grew older, he/she decided to learn to
(hero)

_____ . He/She became so good at
(verb)

_____ that he/she could _____
(verb)   (adverb)

beat anything or anybody. One day _____ found a/an
(hero)

_____ and rescued it from
(animal)

_____ . _____ named his/her new
(noun)   (hero)

friend _____ . People were amazed when they saw
(name)

_____ traveling with a/an _____
(hero)   (animal)

Then the two rescued _____ from a
(famous person)

_____ . Since then, _____
(danger)   (hero)

and _____ have become favorites of people everywhere.
(animal name)

Adjectives and Adverbs

Adjectives describe nouns and pronouns.

Adverbs modify verbs, adjectives, and other adverbs.

A. Cross out the word on the right that **cannot** be used to describe the word on the left.

1. sing   joyfully, beautiful, well, loudly
2. train   fast, yellow, electric, slowly
3. Ms. Woods   thinly, jumpy, comical, kindly
4. freedom   more powerful, limited, very, desired

B. Circle the adjectives.

1. pretty glass
2. big dog
3. green door
4. happy boy
5. thin cookie

6. round ball
7. wet towel
8. excellent work
9. broken pencil
10. smelly shoe

C. Circle the adverbs.

1. running slowly
2. turning quickly
3. quickly hit
4. falling down
5. joyfully leaping

6. writing sloppily
7. watching closely
8. sipping loudly
9. driving badly
10. throwing wildly

D. Think of three nouns and write them below. Write an adjective to go with each noun on the line next to it.

Noun	Adjective
1. _____	_____
2. _____	_____
3. _____	_____

E. Think of three verbs and write them below. Think of an adverb. Write the adverb on the line next to each verb.

Verb	Adverb
1. _____	_____
2. _____	_____
3. _____	_____

Where's My List?

A comma is used between words in a series. Three or more things together make a series.

> *Example: We will be talking today about muffins, kittens, and lollipops.*

Add the missing commas to the sentences below.

1. All birds have feathers wings and beaks.

2. My sister is sleepy grumpy and clueless.

3. I would have done my homework, but I was abducted by aliens was left in Siberia and had to wait for the Marines to rescue me.

4. I ordered a pizza with cheese pickles and sliced cherries.

5. Please go to the store and get flypaper chopsticks and kumquats.

6. I went to the door with rollers in my hair a mud mask on my face and wearing my bathrobe.

7. My dog has brown spots a short tail and fuzzy feet.

8. My little brother can't go anywhere without his blanket his stuffed duck and his rabbit's foot key chain.

9. When I go to college, I am taking a stereo a microwave and a treadmill.

10. For her birthday, Mindy wants some edible flowers sparkly socks and a pony.

✧   ✧   ✧

A comma is also used between two or more describing words (adjectives).

> *Example: A friendly, playful dog makes a good pet.*

Add the missing commas to the sentences below.

1. My rabbit has long floppy ears.

2. A large heavy sparrow could weigh 200 pounds.

3. My teacher has a green pointy nose.

4. My dad used to have curly frizzy hair.

5. A friendly playful giraffe ate all my spaghetti.

When and Where?

A comma is used when writing a date. The comma separates the date and the year. It is also used to separate the day and the date.

A. Insert commas where needed in the sentences below.
1. My parents bought their first home on January 13 1976.
2. My mom was born on March 31 1948.
3. We went to Disneyland on Tuesday August 18 and it was really crowded!
4. My brother's birthday is November 17 1973.
5. On Saturday April 19, we are flying to my grandma's house.
6. I get my tonsils out on Monday September 16 and then I can eat lots of ice cream.
7. Our puppies were born on February 14 1997.
8. It rained cats and dogs on January 18 1995.

B. Write these dates using commas correctly.
1. today's date and year_____
2. today's day and date _____
3. your birthday _____
4. your favorite day of the year (besides your birthday)_____
5. the birthdate of a member of your family (and tell who)

Use a comma between the city and state (country or province) in an address.

C. Add commas to the following sentences.
1. Yesterday, I met a girl from Canberra Australia.
2. A hurricane went on shore at Acapulco Mexico.
3. I've never been to Seattle Washington.
4. It can get very cold in Buffalo New York.
5. Yesterday, I received e-mail from Bordeaux France.
6. Many movie stars live in La Canada-Flintridge California.
7. Alexandria Virginia, is an interesting historic town.
8. You can take a great train ride in Durango Colorado.
9. Have you been on the roller coasters in St. Louis Missouri?
10. The mountains are really high in Vail Colorado.

D. Answer the following with the name of a city and state or a city and province.
1. Where were you born? _____
2. Where was your mother born? _____
3. Where do you live today? _____
4. Name where one of your grandparents lives. _____
5. Where is the last place you visited? _____

Days, Months, and Holidays

Capitalize the words on this page by changing a lowercase letter to a capital letter where it is needed. As you capitalize each **holiday**, color its first letter in the circle.

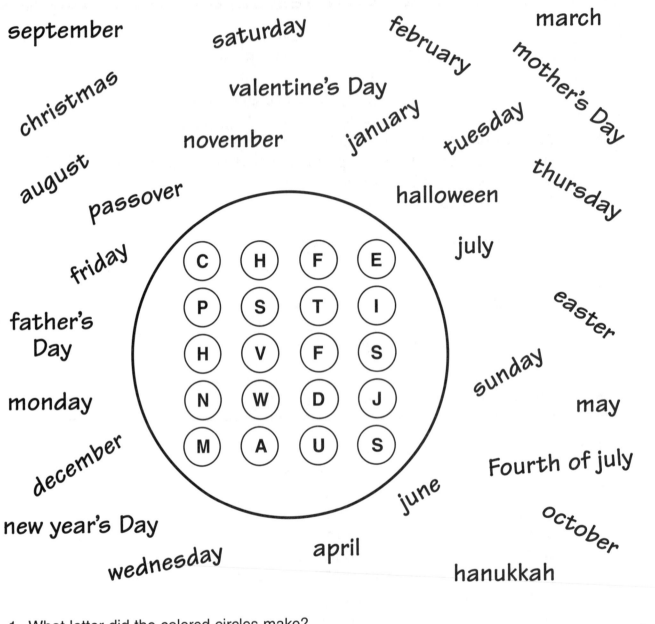

september

saturday

march

february

mother's Day

christmas

valentine's Day

january

tuesday

august

november

thursday

passover

halloween

july

friday

father's
Day

easter

sunday

monday

may

december

Fourth of july

new year's Day

june

october

wednesday

april

hanukkah

1. What letter did the colored circles make? _____

2. Write the names of two holidays that begin with this letter.

_____

3. Write the names of days of the week that begin with the same letters.

_____

4. Write the names of months that begin with the same letters.

_____

What's in a Name?

Did you know that your name is a proper noun? It is, and **you should always capitalize your first and last names and middle name if you have one**. And what about your pet snake? If you call your snake "George," "Rex," or "Samantha Slither," you should capitalize that, too. And if your stuffed animal is named "Old MacDonald" that name should be capitalized, with the M of Mac (or Mc) capitalized and the D of Donald also capitalized. Your little brother has the nickname, "Punkin"? That would also be capitalized.

Rewrite the following names so that they are properly capitalized.

1. amanda panda _____

2. jeffrey r. hardy _____

3. carlos custard appleseed _____

4. gilbert mcgillicutty _____

5. leslie q. presley _____

Do you have any pets at home? If you do, write the names of your pets (or any other pets you know) here.

_____
_____
_____
_____
_____

Here are some pets without names. Think of a name for each pet. The names can be fancy or simple, long or short, but they should all be capitalized. The first one has been done as an example.

Malcolm Angus McCollie McDuff _____ _____ _____

_____ _____ _____

Extension: Make a *Names Notebook*. In a small notebook, write all the creative names you can think of in alphabetical order. Be sure to capitalize! Keep your notebook handy. The next time you write a story, you will have lots of interesting names from which to choose.

End Marks

Every sentence must end with a punctuation mark. As you have been learning, **a sentence may end with a period, a question mark, or an exclamation point**.

- A **period** comes at the end of a sentence that tells something.

  Examples: I have a purple bicycle. Turn left at the corner.

- A **question mark** comes at the end of a sentence that asks a question.

  Examples: What color is your bicycle? Is that your house?

- An **exclamation point** comes at the end of a sentence that contains a strong feeling.

  Examples: Watch out for that car! What a wonderful surprise!

The following sentences need end marks. Think about which end punctuation each sentence needs. Then write the correct punctuation mark at the end of each sentence.

1. I have a new puppy ☐

2. I got it for my birthday ☐

3. Would you like to pet it ☐

4. My cousin has a big dog ☐

5. One time it bit me me, and it really hurt ☐

6. Have you ever been bitten by a dog ☐

7. Did you go to the doctor ☐

8. I was so mad at my cousin ☐

9. He told me he was sorry ☐

10. I'm so glad that my puppy is nice ☐

11. Watch out for mean dogs ☐

12. Don't go near them ☐

13. Can you come to my house ☐

14. We can play with my puppy ☐

15. Can you come again tomorrow ☐

Capitalization Review

It is time to see how much you have learned about capitalization. Circle all the letters below that should be capitals. (*Hint:* There are 63 of them.)

1. the first day of school is exciting.

2. freddy wilson's frog peepers hopped into mrs. woolsey's purse.

3. as i walked outside, i smelled smoke.

4. In the play, robin hood was played by lieutenant bronksy.

5. the fourth thursday in november is thanksgiving.

6. i like halloween best when it is on a saturday.

7. aunt susan went to yellowstone national park.

8. connie lives on maple street in bismark, north dakota.

9. brazil, argentina, and peru are in south america.

10. the mediterranean sea and the atlantic ocean touch spain.

11. the letter was signed, "love always, esther."

12. davis medical center opened in january last year.

13. one of the religions practiced by many african people is islam.

14. italians and germans belong to the caucasian race.

15. last tuesday ruben walked his dog spotty down tulip street to central park.

Ben Franklin

Preview the words in exercise A before reading the following selection. Then complete the exercises below.

Benjamin Franklin was a great American. He had many outstanding accomplishments in his lifetime. He was a printer, a publisher, a writer, an inventor, a scientist, a diplomat, a statesman, and an inspiration to those he met.

At age 42, Franklin decided to devote himself to the study of science. During this time, he was one of the world's greatest scientists, inventing and experimenting and loving his work. He proved that lightning was electricity and that things could be positively or negatively charged with electricity. Among the many things he made were the world's first battery, lightning rod, bifocal glasses, and an energy-efficient, wood-burning stove. However, he never patented any of his inventions. He preferred, instead, to share what he had learned freely with the world.

A. These words were used in the selection you just read. Match the words from the list on the left with their proper meaning.

_____ 1. diplomat

_____ 2. devote

_____ 3. inspiration

_____ 4. statesman

_____ 5. patent

a. official rights to the inventor

b. wise or experienced leader

c. a person who represents a country

d. give attention

e. sudden or original idea

B. Use the back of this paper to answer the following questions.

1. What are some of the many outstanding accomplishments Ben Franklin achieved in his lifetime? List three of them.

2. What did he decide to do when he was 42 years old?

3. What did he prove about lightning?

4. Did he patent any of his inventions? Why?

5. Which one of his inventions do you feel helped the world the most and why?

Our National Anthem

Preview the words in exercise A before reading the following selection. Then complete the exercises below.

In 1814, Francis Scott Key composed a poem, "The Defense of Fort McHenry," as he watched the bombardment of Ft. McHenry during the War of 1812. Later, Key's words were set to the tune of a popular English drinking song, "The Anacreaon in Heaven." Although the United States had been using the song in ceremonies for many years, it did not become the official national anthem until March 3, 1931, when President Herbert Hoover signed the bill that made "The Star-Spangled Banner" our national anthem.

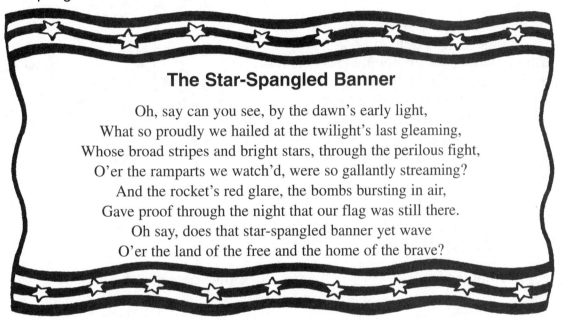

The Star-Spangled Banner

Oh, say can you see, by the dawn's early light,
What so proudly we hailed at the twilight's last gleaming,
Whose broad stripes and bright stars, through the perilous fight,
O'er the ramparts we watch'd, were so gallantly streaming?
And the rocket's red glare, the bombs bursting in air,
Gave proof through the night that our flag was still there.
Oh say, does that star-spangled banner yet wave
O'er the land of the free and the home of the brave?

A. These words were used in the selection you just read. Match the words from the list on the left with their proper meanings.

_____ 1. defense
_____ 2. bombardment
_____ 3. ceremonies
_____ 4. official
_____ 5. anthem

a. in a position of authority
b. song of patriotism or praise
c. protection from attack or harm
d. continued attacking
e. formal acts performed as a ritual

B. Use the back of this paper to answer the following questions.

1. What was the name of the poem that Francis Scott Key wrote?

2. What was happening when he wrote it?

3. When did it become the official national anthem?

4. Who was the president that signed the bill?

5. Do you think that this song is the right one for our national anthem? Explain your answer.

Morse Code

Preview the words in exercise A before reading the following selection. Then complete the exercises below.

Today, we commonly use telephones when we want to transmit a message over a long distance. However, before the use of telephones, other means of communications were used. Messages were often sent on paper. More urgent messages may have been sent by Morse code.

Morse code is a system of dashes and dots. Each combination of dashes and dots represents a different letter in the alphabet. Samuel F. B. Morse developed this language in 1835 to send messages over long distances with a telegraph machine. Morse code is still commonly used in emergencies by people today when telephone services are interrupted or unavailable.

The telegraph is used to send messages over long distances.

A. These words were used in the selection you just read. Match the words from the list on the left with their proper meanings.

_____ 1. transmit   a. series of symbols

_____ 2. interrupt   b. to send from one person to another

_____ 3. unavailable   c. to stop

_____ 4. message   d. not able to obtain or get

_____ 5. code   e. words sent from one person to another

B. Use the back of this paper to answer the following questions.

1. What symbols are used in Morse code?

2. Who developed this code?

3. Is a telephone used to send messages with Morse code?

4. Who most commonly uses Morse code today?

5. Describe when you might need to use Morse code and what you could use to send the message?

Totem Poles

Preview the words in exercise A before reading the following selection. Then complete the exercises below.

As you travel through Vancouver and Victoria, British Columbia, you can see many totem poles. Stanley Park in Vancouver and Thunderbird Park in Victoria, British Columbia, each has a wonderful collection of totem poles.

Totem poles have been used by many Native Americans as a way to record history. Tribes, clans, and families used them as a symbol. A totem pole is a carving of animals, birds, fish, plants, or other natural objects that represent a Native American tribe.

A family would place its totem pole in front of its home. At the top of the pole was the family totem or symbol. When a totem pole was erected, there was a festival called a potlatch.

A. These words were used in the selection you just read. Match the words from the list on the left with their proper meanings.

_____ 1. clan   a. something that stands for something else

_____ 2. carving   b. group of people (usually related)

_____ 3. potlatch   c. a shape made by cutting with a sharp object

_____ 4. collection   d. group of objects

_____ 5. symbol   e. festival

B. Use the back of this paper to answer the following questions.

1. Where can you find a wonderful collection of totem poles?

2. What is the purpose of totem poles?

3. What is carved on a totem pole?

4. What was put at the top of the totem pole?

5. Describe what your family's totem pole would look like. You can draw it on another piece of paper.

Frisbee™

Preview the words in exercise A before reading the following selection. Then complete the exercises below.

The Frisbee™ story began in the late 1800s with the Frisbee Pie Company in Bridgeport, Connecticut. Their pies, which came in a ten-inch-wide round tin with a raised edge and wide brim, were popular with students at nearby Yale University. At some point, pie-tin catch had become a fad among the young collegians. The fad continued into the 1950s but was changed forever with the introduction of a plastic flying dish called Flyin' Saucer invented by Walter Frederick Morrison. First marketed as the Pluto Platter, the toy's name was officially changed to Frisbee when Wham-O's president saw Yale students throwing and catching Frisbee pie plates. However, not until the 1960s did sales of the Frisbee take off. Today it remains a popular toy and sport.

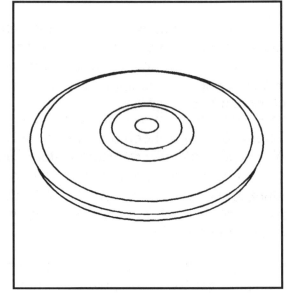

A. These words were used in the selection you just read. Match the words from the list on the left with their paper meanings.

_____ 1. fad   a. thin round object

_____ 2. collegians   b. to make something that has not been made before

_____ 3. marketed   c. something that is popular for a short time

_____ 4. disk   d. college students

_____ 5. invent   e. sold or offered for sale

B. Use the back of this paper to answer the following questions.

1. When did the Frisbee Pie Company begin?

2. What did the college students do with pie tins?

3. What name was the Flyin' Saucer marketed as before it was changed to Frisbee?

4. When did the sales of the Frisbee take off?

5. What would you have called this toy and why?

WD-40

Preview the words in exercise A before reading the following selection. Then complete the exercises below.

During the early 1950s, the aerospace industry began looking for a product to eliminate moisture from electrical circuitry and to prevent corrosion on airplanes. A satisfactory product was invented by Norman Larsen, who was the president and head chemist at the Rocket Chemical Company. His water displacement formula was developed on his fortieth try, thus the name WD-40. When it was discovered that WD-40 worked well to quiet squeaky doors and unstick stuck locks, a number of employees began sneaking the product home. In 1958, the product was made available to the public.

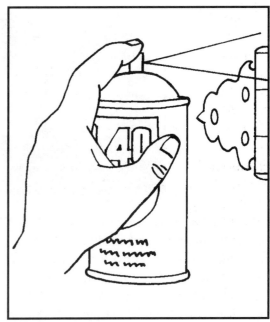

The WD-40 Company makes more than one million gallons of the lubricant each year. When astronaut John Glenn circled the earth in Friendship VII in 1964, the spacecraft was covered with WD-40 from top to bottom.

A. These words were used in the selection you just read. Match the words from the list on the left with their proper meanings.

_____ 1. corrosion

_____ 2. displacement

_____ 3. lubricant

_____ 4. astronaut

_____ 5. spacecraft

a. vehicle designed to travel into space

b. slippery substance used to lubricate parts

c. person trained to travel into space

d. act of wearing away (i.e., rusting)

e. to take the place of

B. Use the back of this paper to answer the following questions.

1. During the early 1950s, what was the aerospace industry looking for?

2. Who invented the formula later called WD-40?

3. How did it get its name?

4. What spacecraft was covered from top to bottom with this product?

5. What would you have called it and why?

Beatlemania

Preview the words in exercise A before reading the following selection. Then complete the exercises below.

Just how did four boys from Liverpool make it so big? Their story began in 1957 when John Lennon invited 15-year-old Paul McCartney to join his group, "The Quarrymen." Guitarist George Harrison and drummer Pete Best had joined the group by August 1961. In 1962, Best was replaced by Ringo Starr. After record store owner Brian Epstein became their manager, they signed with a recording company. It was not long before the Beatles became England's biggest-ever idols. Their live performances were accompanied by hordes of screaming fans. After their February, 1964, appearance on *The Ed Sullivan Show*, "The Fab Four," as they were sometimes called, became transatlantic chart-toppers. While their first album had combined pop-soul songs with some of Lennon's and McCartney's original compositions, later albums reflected the whole group's efforts.

A. These words were used in the selection you just read. Match the words from the list on the left with their proper meanings.

_____ 1. transatlantic   a. person in charge of someone's business

_____ 2. combined   b. joined together

_____ 3. compositions   c. crossing the Atlantic Ocean

_____ 4. hordes   d. works of art, literature, or music

_____ 5. manager   e. large crowds of people

B. Use the back of this paper to answer the following questions.

1. Who first started the group?

2. What was the name of the first group?

3. Who replaced Pete Best?

4. What show made them famous in America?

5. Why do you think that this group was so popular all over the world?

Butchart Gardens

Preview the words in exercise A before reading the following selection. Then complete the exercises below.

One of the most beautiful flower gardens in the world is located in Victoria, British Columbia. This garden spreads out over many acres and features a Japanese garden, a rose garden, and a sunken garden.

In most of Canada, spring-like weather does not arrive until after St. Patrick's Day on March 17. However, before spring arrives in Victoria, Flower Count Week is celebrated. During this week people all over the city go out and actually count how many flowers and buds they see. Children are given an hour off from school to help count. There are special centers to which the numbers are called, and a graph of the number of flowers counted is posted at Eaton Centre, a large shopping mall downtown.

A. Match the words from the list on the left with their proper meanings.

_____ 1. acre a. placed information for others to see

_____ 2. celebrate b. garden below the ground level

_____ 3. locate c. area of ground equal to 4,840 square yards

_____ 4. posted d. to observe a special occasion

_____ 5. sunken garden e. to find

B. Use the back of this paper to answer the following questions.

1. Where is Butchart Gardens located?

2. What are three of the types of gardens that you can find there?

3. What do people do during Flower Count Week?

4. What special privilege do children get?

5. If you could plant a garden, would it be a flower or vegetable garden? Explain your answer.

Spider-Man

Preview the words in exercise A before reading the following selection. Then complete the exercises below.

Spider-Man's real identity is Peter Parker, the freelance photographer. Peter was not born with any special powers or talents. However, when he was a teenager, he was accidentally bitten by a spider that had been exposed to huge amounts of radiation. As a result, Peter became strong and agile like a spider and was able to cling to any surface, including walls and ceilings.

He made a red and blue uniform for himself and created a mechanism for shooting a web. He decided to call himself the "Amazing Spider-Man," making sure to keep his real identity a secret. After Spider-Man's uncle was killed by a burglar, he quit his acting career and was determined to devote his life to fighting crime.

A. These words were used in the selection you just read. Match the words from the list on the left with their proper meanings.

_____ 1. freelance	a. parts that make a machine work
_____ 2. identity	b. able to move quickly
_____ 3. radiation	c. works independently
_____ 4. agile	d. who a person is
_____ 5. mechanism	e. waves or particles emitted by radioactivity.

B. Use the back of this paper to answer the following questions.

1. What is Spider-Man's true identity?

2. How did he get his special powers?

3. What did he wear when he wanted to be Spider-Man?

4. Why did he give up his career to become a full-time Spider-Man?

5. What do you think Peter's life would have been like if he had never been bitten by the spider?

Olympics in the 1920s

Preview the words in exercise A before reading the following selection. Then complete the exercises below.

The Olympic Games are the world's greatest sports contest. A tradition begun in ancient Greece in 776 B.C. and abolished in A.D. 394, the games did not begin again until 1896. Since then, the modern Olympiads have undergone numerous changes. Some sports, like rugby, have come and gone while others, like track and field, have remained constant.

During the 1920s there were two important changes in the Olympics. The now familiar Olympic flag first appeared in 1920. In 1924, the first winter Olympic games were held in Chamonix, France. Originally held in the same year as the traditional games, the schedule changed in the 1990s, with the summer and winter games held two years apart.

A. Match the words from the list on the left with their proper meanings.

_____ 1. tradition   a. first; the source

_____ 2. ancient   b. the passing of customs to the next generation

_____ 3. numerous   c. form of football

_____ 4. Rugby   d. many; a lot

_____ 5. original   e. very old

B. Use the back of this paper to answer the following questions.

1. When were the first Olympics?

2. Have they stayed the same all these years?

3. Where were the first Olympic Games held?

4. Are the winter games and summer games held in the same year?

5. What sport would you like to participate in at the Olympics and why?

Barbie™ Doll

Preview the words in exercise A before reading the following selection. Then complete the exercises below.

In 1959, the Barbie™ Doll made her debut. Today, she is the best-selling toy in American history. Her inventor is Ruth Handler, a former secretary and housewife. Ruth noticed that her daughter preferred to play with teenage dolls rather than those designed for her own age group. The problem was that the teenage dolls available at that time were paper cutouts. Ruth designed a more grown-up doll that would wear fashionable clothing and be a little girl's dream of things to come. Barbie™, named after Handler's daughter, made her debut at the 1959 New York Toy Show. A huge success, it sold $500 million worth in its first eight years. Ruth Handler went on to become vice president and then president of Mattel, Inc., the company that manufacturers Barbie™.

A. These words were used in the story you just read. Match the words on the left with their proper meanings.

_____ 1. debut   a. a good result

_____ 2. designed   b. liked better

_____ 3. fashionable   c. in the latest style

_____ 4. preferred   d. made a plan for

_____ 5. success   e. seen in public for the first time

B. Use the back of this paper to answer the following questions.

1. When did Barbie make her debut?

2. Who invented Barbie?

3. Why did she invent Barbie?

4. Who went on to become president of Mattel, Inc., the company that manufacturers Barbie?

5. Do you think Barbie is a doll that should be sold in toy stores? Explain your answer.

Hula Hoop™

Preview the words in exercise A before reading the following selection. Then complete the exercises below.

The Wham-O toy company manufactured the Hula Hoop™ in the 1950s. For six months it enjoyed great success as the Hula Hoop became the fastest-selling toy in history. Just as quickly, however, the craze seemed to die down. Every generation since then has seen a resurgence of the unusual toy. Based on a wooden hoop used by Australian youths, the plastic Hula Hoop was invented by Richard Knerr, a partner in the Wham-O toy manufacturing company.

A. These words were used in the selection you just read. Match the words on the left with their proper meanings.

_____ 1. manufactured   a. popular for a short time

_____ 2. craze   b. a circular frame

_____ 3. resurgence   c. people who grew up and lived at the same time

_____ 4. generation   d. made

_____ 5. hoop   e. having become popular again

B. Use the back of this paper to answer the following questions.

1. How long was the Hula-Hoop the fastest selling toy in history?

2. Did the craze last for a long time?

3. What was the Hula Hoop based on?

4. Who invented the Hula Hoop?

5. Invent a game you could play with the Hula Hoop. Briefly describe how to play.

The Endangered Sea Otter

Preview the words in exercise A before reading the following selection. Then complete the exercises below.

In the mid-1800s, the fur trade was thriving. Hunters up and down the West Coast were trapping and trading furs for goods. Demand for precious furs was high. Unfortunately, the sea otter was one of the animals prized for its pelt. Hunters traveled from Alaska to Southern California to capture them. As a result, the playful sea otters were hunted almost to extinction by the late 1800s. Since then, the government has taken an interest in sea otters and has placed a ban on the hunting of these creatures. Although there are still hunters who illegally poach these animals for their fur, the population of sea otters off the coast of California is increasing.

A. These words were used in the selection you just read. Match the words from the list on the left with their proper meanings.

_____ 1. thriving   a. against the law

_____ 2. endangered   b. no longer exists

_____ 3. illegally   c. group of the same kind of animal

_____ 4. extinct   d. healthy

_____ 5. species   e. to be in danger

_____ 6. pelt   f. animal skin

B. Use the back of this paper to answer the following questions.

1. What kind of trade was thriving in the mid 1800s?

2. Why did the hunters want the sea otters?

3. Why can't people hunt sea otters today?

4. What is happening to the sea otters off the coast of California today?

5. Do you think that we should be able to hunt seal otters today? Explain your reasons.

Spider-Woman

Preview the words in exercise A before reading the following selection. Then complete the exercises below.

No one knows the real identity of Spider-Woman. She kept it a well-guarded secret. She refuses to reveal her identity because she wants to protect the people she cares about from being harmed by her enemies. Unlike Spider-Man, it is unknown whether Spider-Woman was born with special powers or if she acquired them later in life.

Spider-Woman has extraordinary strength, endurance, and agility. Spider-Woman can move her body like a spider, climbing up walls and across ceilings. Spider-Woman's intuition is only average. She is not able to sense danger any better than the ordinary person. However, her psychic ability is exceptional. She can create a web by concentrating intensely and does not need any kind of device. Spider-Woman uses the web to trap criminals. One problem with the web is that it becomes increasingly weaker the further away it is from Spider-Woman. Therefore, a criminal can easily break loose if caught in the outer boundaries of the web. If Spider-Woman loses consciousness, she cannot create or maintain a web.

A. These words were used in the selection you just read. Match the words from the list on the left with their proper meanings.

_____ 1. identity   a. lines or limits where something ends

_____ 2. extraordinary   b. who a person is

_____ 3. psychic   c. able to read another's mind

_____ 4. concentrate   d. with utmost strain

_____ 5. intensely   e. beyond what is ordinary

_____ 6. boundaries   f. focus on common center

B. Use the back of this paper to answer the following questions.

1. Who is the real Spider-Woman?

2. How did she get her special powers?

3. How does she create a web?

4. Can she sense danger like an ordinary person can?

5. How can a criminal break loose from her web?

6. What super power would you add to Spider-Woman?

The Walt Disney Story

Preview the words in exercise A before reading the following selection. Then complete the exercises below.

Walter Elias Disney was born on December 5, 1901, the fourth of five children. Disney's early years were spent on a farm in Missouri, where he developed an interest in drawing.

In 1919, Disney and a friend formed an art company and made some animated cartoons.

Four years later he moved to California, where he and his brother, Roy, began Walt Disney Productions. Disney created a character he called Mortimer the Mouse. His wife, Lillian, suggested a name that was less stuffy, and Mickey was born. In 1928, with Disney providing his voice, Mickey Mouse starred in *Steamboat Willie*. The success of Mickey Mouse was only the beginning. In the thirties, Mickey acquired a number of cartoon pals, including Donald Duck, Pluto, Minnie Mouse, and Goofy. Walt Disney died in 1966, but the studio he founded continues the Disney tradition, bringing new technology to films. Disney's spirit lives on in his memorable characters and theme parks.

A. These words were used in the selection you just read. Match the words from the list on the left with the proper meanings.

_____ 1. stuffy   a. made to seem alive

_____ 2. develop   b. dull

_____ 3. founded   c. use of scientific knowledge

_____ 4. animated   d. to cause to grow; get better

_____ 5. technology   e. brought into being; established

B. Use the back of this paper to answer the following questions.

1. When was Walter Elias Disney born?

2. Where did the name Mickey Mouse come from?

3. Who did Walt go into business with to form Walt Disney Productions?

4. What was the first movie that Mickey Mouse starred in?

5. Describe a character that you would create if you had your own movie company.

The Amazon Rain Forest

Preview the words in exercise A before reading the following selection. Then complete the exercises below.

In 1971, construction began in Brazil for a major trans-Amazon highway to open up and remove areas of the rain forest for settlement and development. Huge areas of the Amazon rain forest were cut down and burned to make way for about one million new settlers. Because the large cities were so overcrowded and most people were unable to find work there, the government offered lucrative incentives to families who moved to the Amazon. Each family would be given a 240-acre piece of land, housing, and a small salary for a few months. Plans were made to build schools, health facilities, and other services. Thousands made the move but had to give up after only a few months because life in the rain forest was so difficult. The project failed, and it led to the destruction of a great deal of the Amazon rain forest. The result of this devastation was that much of the rain forest habitat was lost forever, and the soil eroded and turned into poor agricultural land.

A. These words were used in the selection you just read. Match the words from the list on the left with their proper meanings.

_____ 1. lucrative

_____ 2. facilities

_____ 3. habitat

_____ 4. incentive

_____ 5. devastation

_____ 6. agricultural

a. destruction

b. that which relates to producing crops or raising livestock

c. producing wealth, profitable

d. buildings used for activities

e. something used to make someone do better

f. place where an animal lives

B. Use the back of this paper to answer the following questions.

1. What did construction begin for in 1971?

2. What happened to large areas of the Amazon rain forest?

3. What was each family offered if they moved there?

4. What services would be available to these families?

5. Was this project a success? Explain your answer.

6. Is the rain forest important to the ecology of the rest of the world? Explain your answer.

Robin Hood

Preview the words in exercise A before reading the following selection. Then complete the exercises below.

Robin Hood is a legendary English hero whose rebellious nature made him a popular character in stories and ballads beginning sometime during the 1300s. To this day, no one knows for sure whether or not he really existed.

The legend begins when Robin Hood is rescued by a group of outlaws who live in Sherwood Forest. He finds that he has much more in common with these outlaws than anyone else so he becomes their leader. Robin Hood's followers include the beautiful Maid Marian, the love of his life; Friar Tuck, a good-hearted priest; and Little John, a seven-foot giant of a man.

Robin Hood's popularity comes from the way he fights corruption and injustice. He treats corrupt officials, such as the sheriff of Nottingham, with contempt. However, he treats women and poor people with respect. He and his band of outlaws steal from the rich and give to the poor. The commoners praise him as a hero, while authority figures proclaim him an outlaw.

A. These words were used in the selection you just read. Match the words on the left with their proper meanings.

_____ 1. legend   a. a feeling of honor

_____ 2. rebellious   b. resisting authority

_____ 3. ballads   c. dishonesty

_____ 4. commoners   d. ordinary people

_____ 5. corruption   e. poems or songs that tell a story

_____ 6. respect   f. story handed down from the past

B. Use the back of this paper to answer the following questions.

1. Who is Robin Hood?

2. Who rescues Robin Hood in the forest?

3. Who are his faithful followers?

4. How does he treat corrupt officials such as the sheriff of Nottingham?

5. How does he treat women and poor people?

6. Do you think Robin Hood was a real person? Explain your answer.

Kristi Yamaguchi

Preview the words in exercise A before reading the following selection. Then complete the exercises below.

Kristi Tsuya Yamaguchi was born in Hayward, California, in 1971. She was born with a clubfoot, but she did not let that stand in the way of her ambitions. She started skating at the age of six and was competing within two years.

When Yamaguchi was 12 years old, she started skating with Rudi Galindo. Together they won the 1985 national junior pairs championships.

In 1990, Yamaguchi and Galindo decided they wanted to concentrate on their singles careers rather than continue with their pairs skating. This gave Yamaguchi more time to devote to her singles training. As a result, her singles skating improved. She started working to make her routines more complicated. This paid off because she was able to become the world champion in figure skating in 1991 and 1992.

Yamaguchi went to Albertville, France, for the 1992 Winter Olympics. She knew that the competition was going to include many excellent skaters. She chose a routine that was technically difficult. She skated with perfection, and the judges rated her routine the highest. Yamaguchi won a gold medal. It had been 16 years since an American woman had won a gold medal in the singles event.

A. These words were used in the selection you just read. Match the words from the list on the left with their proper meanings.

_A_	1. clubfoot	a. deformity of the foot
_E_	2. concentrate	b. strong desire to achieve something
_C_	3. routine	c. a series of regular activities
_D_	4. champion	d. winner of game or contest
_B_	5. ambition	e. to direct ones thoughts on something

B. Use the back of this paper to answer the following questions.

1. Where and when was Kristi born?
   In hayward Cal. 1971
2. How old was she when she started skating?
   6
3. What did she decide to do in 1990?
   they wanted singles careers
4. What medal did she win at the 1992 Winter Olympics?
   gold
5. Would you prefer to be a singles skater or a pairs skater? Explain your answer.
   Pairs, Because you can do more tricks!!

The Greatest Airship Ever Built

Preview the words in exercise A before reading the following selection. Then complete the exercises below.

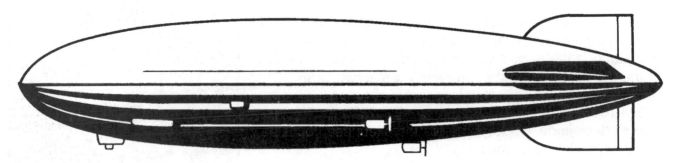

You have probably seen helium-filled blimps gracefully making their way across the sky. These ships are quiet, safe, and fuel efficient, but their cousins, the zeppelins, did not possess all of these qualities. During the 1930s, huge zeppelins more than 40 times the size of modern blimps carried passengers across the oceans.

The largest and most luxurious zeppelin ever built was the Hindenburg. A magnificent airship, it contained observation decks and private sleeping rooms and offered gourmet dining to its rich passengers.

On Monday, May 3, 1937, at 7:30 A.M. the Hindenburg began a routine journey to America. It reached America on May 6. After delays due to bad weather, it finally landed. Suddenly, there was a loud thump, and the tail section explored into flames. The fire spread rapidly throughout the rest of the craft, and within half a minute the blazing air ship was on the ground. With that unfortunate mishap, the age of the zeppelin came to a complete and abrupt halt.

A. These words were used in the selection you just read. Match the words from the list on the left with their proper meanings.

_____ 1. helium   a. a good result without waste

_____ 2. blazing   b. very splendid and comfortable

_____ 3. efficient   c. a very light gas

_____ 4. routine   d. brightly-burning flame

_____ 5. luxurious   e. regular or standard

B. Use the back of this paper to answer the following questions.

1. How much bigger were zeppelins than blimps?

2. What was the largest and most luxurious zeppelin ever built?

3. Where was the Hindenburg going in 1937?

4. What happened to the Hindenburg as it landed?

5. Would you like to ride in a blimp or zeppelin? Explain your answer.

Judy Blume

Preview the words in exercise A before reading the following selection. Then complete the exercises below.

Beginning with the introduction of her book *Are You There God? It's Me, Margaret* in 1970, Judy Blume became a leading children's author.

Judy Sussman Blume was born on February 12, 1938, in Elizabeth, New Jersey. As a child, Judy Sussman was an A student and did exactly as she was told, even though on the inside she wished she could rebel. She loved to read Nancy Drew mysteries, biographies, and horse stories but also longed to read about characters who shared problems that she and other young people were facing. She attended New York University, and in 1960, the year before she graduated, she married John W. Blume, an attorney.

Since her first book was published in 1969, Judy Blume has received awards from all over the United States. In addition to writing several juvenile fiction books, Judy Blume has written young adult and adult books. Blume also contributed to the project *Free to Be You and Me* for the Mrs. Foundation in 1974.

In recent years, Judy Blume founded KIDS Find and remains on the council of advisors for the National Coalition of Censorship.

A. These words were used in the selection you just read. Match the words from the list on the left with their proper meanings.

_____ 1. rebel   a. resist or fight authority

_____ 2. biographies   b. people who consult or give advice

_____ 3. juvenile   c. completed a course of study

_____ 4. advisors   d. childish

_____ 5. graduated   e. true stories about someone, written by another person

B. Use the back of this paper to answer the following questions.

1. What was the name of the first book that made her famous?

2. What kind of student was she as a child?

3. What kind of books did she like to read as a child?

4. Why did she change her name to Judy Blume?

5. What would be a subject for a book that you would like her to write about?

Annie Oakley

Preview the words in exercise A before reading the following selection. Then complete the exercises below.

Annie Oakley was born in 1860 in Darke County, Ohio. Her name at birth was Phoebe Ann Moses. By the age of eight, she had learned to shoot and helped her family by hunting animals for food. Annie was a professional marksman by the time she was 15. She participated in many shooting contests that took place in Cincinnati. She beat Frank Butler in a shooting match, which sparked a romance between them. Annie and Frank were married in 1876. Soon afterwards, Annie started calling herself Annie Oakley. In 1885, Annie joined Buffalo Bill's Wild West Show. She gave a fascinating performance with the assistance of her husband. She would shoot a dime that was in his hand or a cigarette that was in his mouth. Annie also did a trick during which her husband, who was standing 90 feet (27 m) away from her, threw a playing card into the air and she shot it. Annie's accuracy amazed audiences. She was often called "Little Sure Shot," a nickname that was given to her by Sitting Bull, a Sioux Indian chief.

A. These words were used in the selection you just read. Match the words from the list on the left with their proper meanings.

_____ 1. marksman   a. feelings of love toward someone

_____ 2. assistance   b. person skilled in shooting a gun or rifle

_____ 3. accuracy   c. having the power to charm

_____ 4. fascinating   d. to help

_____ 5. romance   e. freedom from error

B. Use the back of this paper to answer the following questions.

1. How did she help her family when she was eight years old?

2. How did she meet her husband?

3. Describe one of the tricks that she could do.

4. What was her nickname?

5. Why do you think that Annie's performance was so popular?

Statue of Liberty

Preview the words in exercise A before reading the following selection. Then complete the exercises below.

The Statue of Liberty has always been a symbol of welcome and a promise of freedom for immigrants to the United States of America. The statue was given to the United States by the people of France in 1884. They wanted to have it ready by the Centennial in 1876, but it was delayed because France was involved in a war with Prussia. Frédéric Bartholdi designed and sculpted the statue. He was sent to America to complete his plans. As he sailed into the harbor at Bedloe's Island, he knew that was where the statue should be. He decided to make the statue a lady as a symbol of liberty and that she would face the ocean with a greeting and a promise. He decided to call it Liberty Enlightening the World. Bartholdi talked to President Grant, and it was agreed that France would built the statue and the United States would build the base and pedestal.

The seven spikes in the statue's crown reach out to the seven seas and the seven continents. The seven spikes also stand for seven liberties.

A. These words were used in the selection you just read. Match the words from the list on the left with their proper meanings.

_____ 1. immigrants

_____ 2. sculpted

_____ 3. statue

_____ 4. spikes

_____ 5. liberties

a. long, pointed piece of metal or wood

b. people from another country

c. rights or freedoms

d. shaped or designed

e. likeness of something that has been sculpted out of another material such as clay

B. Use the back of this paper to answer the following exercises.

1. What does the Statue of Liberty symbolize?

2. Who gave the United States the statue and when?

3. Who designed it?

4. What did the designer decide to name the statue?

5. What do the seven spikes in the crown stand for?

317

A. A. Milne

7/8/01

Preview the words in exercise A before reading the following selection. Then complete the exercises below.

Alan Alexander Milne, better known as A. A. Milne, is the author of Winnie-the-Pooh stories for children. He was born on January 18, 1882, in London, England, and was the youngest of three boys. An unambitious student, he discovered writing when his brother bet him he couldn't compose a verse as well as he could. But Milne surprised his brother with a well-written poem, and the two collaborated on verse for a couple of years.

During World War I Milne joined the Royal Warwickshire Regiment, a reserve battalion, and served in France. In his spare time he was able to write his first children's book and a play to entertain the troops. When he returned to civilian life, he continued with his writing career. On August 21, 1920, his only son, Christopher Robin, was born. The book that established him as a major children's author was the 1926 story *Winnie-the-Pooh*.

Winnie, Eeyore, and Christopher Robin have become some of children's favorite storybook characters. In recent years they were immortalized on screen by the Walt Disney Company, which made its first motion picture about *Winnie-the-Pooh* in 1965.

A. These words were used in the selection you just read. Match the words from the list on the left with their proper meanings.

_C_ 1. unambitious   a. groups of soldiers

_D_ 2. collaborated   b. one section of a poem or song

_B_ 3. verse   c. not eager to succeed

_e_ 4. entertain   d. worked with someone on a project

_A_ 5. troops   e. to hold someone's attention

B. Use the back of this paper to answer the following questions.

1. How did A. A. Milne became a writer?
   his Brother said he couldnt write a
2. During World War I, what did he do in his spare time? *better verse as*
   he wrote his first kids B-day'm.
3. What book did he write in 1926?
   Winnie-the-pooh
4. Who made the first motion picture about the book written in 1926?
   walt Disney
5. What would happen if *Winnie-the-Pooh* took place in Japan? Explain your answer.
   we would never Been able to see
   him.

Constellations

Preview the words in exercise A before reading the following selection. Then complete the exercises below.

People have been using stars to guide their way and lives for centuries. Without the use of landmarks, mariners of old depended solely upon compass and stars to direct their ships. Since the stars served such an important role for people, names were given to groups of stars to help chart the night sky. We call these star groupings constellations. The constellations have been known by many different names by different groups of people. A good example of this is the Big Dipper. The Big Dipper is known as the Bear by the ancient Greeks, the Wagon by the ancient Romans, and the Plow by many European people today. To the Hindus, the Big Dipper represents the Seven Rishis.

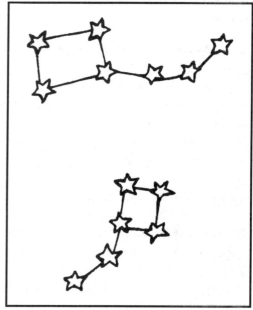

Many of the constellation names were based on ancient stories and myths. The following is a story from Greek mythology which explains the constellation Cassiopeia.

Cassiopeia claimed that she was more beautiful than the lovely sea nymphs. The nymphs became angry and complained to Poseidon, god of the sea. Poseidon decided to punish Cassiopeia for her vanity by sending a sea monster to destroy her kingdom. He then demanded that Cassiopeia's daughter be sacrificed to the sea monster. Fortunately, the young girl was rescued by Perseus before the sea monster could kill her. Cassiopeia was changed into a constellation at her death and was placed into the night sky for all to remember.

A. These words were used in the selection you just read. Match the words from the list on the left with their proper meanings.

_____ 1. mariners   a. to rely upon

_____ 2. compass   b. ones who navigate a ship

_____ 3. European   c. natives of India who believes in Hinduism

_____ 4. Hindu   d. instrument used to tell geographic locations

_____ 5. depended   e. from Europe

_____ 6. nymphs   f. female spirits who live in woods or water

B. Use the back of this paper to answer the following questions.

1. What did ancient people use the stars for?

2. What do we call star groupings?

3. What is the name of one of the constellations written about in the article?

4. What were many of the stars' names based on?

5. What did Cassiopeia think about herself?

Hercules

Preview the words in exercise A before reading the following selection. Then complete the exercises below.

Hercules is a great hero in Greek mythology. He was the son of Zeus, king of the gods of Olympia.

When Hercules was just a baby, he began showing that he had great strength by killing two serpents who were about to attack him. As he grew up, he became famous for his strength and his kindness to those in need. He learned wrestling, archery, and fencing. Although Hercules was basically a good person, he had one serious problem. He had a terrible temper. His temper was so uncontrollable that he had been banished from Thebes. Hercules was told that the only way he could make up for his behavior was to serve King Eurystheus for 12 years. During this time, Hercules was given many difficult tasks to accomplish. With strong determination, he was able to accomplish all of them

A. These words were used in the selection you just read. Match the words from the list on the left with their proper meanings.

_____ 1. banished

_____ 2. accomplish

_____ 3. mythology

_____ 4. temper

_____ 5. fencing

a. tendency to become angry

b. sport using swords

c. to carry out

d. made-up stories about people, gods, and ancestors

e. forced to leave

B. Use the back of this paper to answer the following questions.

1. Who was Hercules' father?

2. What unusual thing did Hercules do when he was just a baby?

3. What are the names of two activities that he liked to do when he was growing up?

4. Why was he banished from Thebes?

5. What did he have to do to make up for his bad behavior?

6. What lesson do you think Hercules learned from his 12-year experience?

Neil Armstrong

Preview the words in exercise A before reading the following selection. Then complete the exercises below.

Neil Alden Armstrong was born in 1930 in Wapakoneta, Ohio. During the Korean War, Armstrong was a pilot for the United States Navy. After the war, he studied at Purdue University where he graduated in 1955. Then Armstrong became a civilian test pilot for what is now called the National Aeronautics and Space Administration (NASA). In 1962, Armstrong started training to be an astronaut, making him the first civilian to join the program.

In 1966, Armstrong climbed aboard Gemini 8 to make his first flight into space. Although the mission was a success, it did encounter a serious problem. After docking the two spacecrafts, it went into a violent roll. Fortunately, he and his partner were able to deal with the crisis and safely return to Earth.

In July 1969, Armstrong was chosen as the commander of the Apollo 11 mission. People from all around the world watched as Armstrong made history on July 20, 1969, by being the first person to walk on the moon.

Armstrong retired from NASA in 1971 to become an aerospace engineering professor.

A. These words were used in the selection you just read. Match the words from the list on the left with their proper meanings.

_____ 1. aerospace   a. to meet unexpectedly

_____ 2. civilian   b. a crucial situation

_____ 3. docking   c. science that deals with space flight

_____ 4. crisis   d. guiding or coming to a dock

_____ 5. encounter   e. a person not in the armed forces

B. Use the back of this paper to answer the following questions.

1. What job did Neil Armstrong do for the Navy?

2. What was the name of the first flight that he took?

3. What was the problem they faced on the Gemini 8 flight?

4. When did he retire, and what did he do?

5. How do you think Armstrong felt about being the first person to walk on the moon? Explain your answer.

Babe Ruth

Preview the words in exercise A before reading the following selection. Then complete the exercises below.

Born in 1895, George Herman Ruth grew up on the streets of Baltimore, fending for himself, and by the age of eight had gotten into trouble. Young George was sent to a Catholic boys' home, where he played baseball. An invaluable team member, he could play just about any position.

In 1914 Ruth began his career with the Baltimore Orioles, at that time a minor league team. Later that year, Ruth joined the Boston Red Sox. There he served as a pitcher while also showing his prowess as a hitter. Because he could hit the ball harder and farther than any other team member, he held two positions—in some games he pitched and in other games he played in the outfield. By 1918, Babe Ruth was recognized as the best left-handed pitcher in baseball. He also led the American League in home runs. Boston's owner, in need of money, sold Ruth to the New York Yankees after the 1919 season. As a Yankee, Ruth concentrated solely on hitting and playing the outfield, and immediately, he shattered a number of records and brought baseball to a new level.

Formerly, baseball had been a pitcher's game, but Ruth changed all that; now it was a hitter's game. Ruth set many records that stood unchanged for years. In 1920 he broke the 1884 record of 24 home runs in one season by hitting 54. The next year he hit 59 homers and scored a total of 177 runs. In 1927 Ruth hit 60 home runs, a record that stood for 34 years. Attendance at games increased so much that the Yankees built Yankee Stadium, sometimes known as "the house that Ruth built."

A. These words were used in the selection you just read. Match the words from the list on the left with their proper meanings.

_B_	1. fending	a. superior skill or ability
_D_	2. invaluable	b. to provide for
_e_	3. concentrated	c. home runs
_F_	4. attendance	d. priceless
_A_	5. prowess	e. focused
_C_	6. homers	f. number of people at an event

B. Use the back of this paper to answer the following questions.

1. Where was George Herman Ruth born?
   Baltimore
2. What was his childhood like?
   He gotten in trouble a lot
3. During his lifetime, what positions did he play?
   Pitcher + outfield
4. What record did he break in 1920?
   the 1884 record
5. What was the other name for Yankee Stadium?
   "the house that Ruth built"
6. If you met him on the street today, what would you say to him?
   Can I have your autograph

Elvis Presley

Preview the words in exercise A before reading the following selection. Then complete the exercises below.

Elvis Presley has been called the King of rock and roll. Born on January 8, 1935, in Tupelo, Mississippi, Presley won his first talent contest when he was just eight years old. In 1954, he recorded his first song as a present for his mother. The owner of the recording service had recently started his own record company, Sun, and signed Presley as a new talent. Presley did not have much success with Sun and after a year left for RCA. Thanks in large part to television and appearances on programs such as *The Ed Sullivan Show*, Presley became a huge star all across America.

In 1955, Colonel Tom Parker became Presley's manager and signed him to RCA Records at a cost of $40,000. One year later, Presley had a number-one hit with "Heartbreak Hotel." A string of hits continued with "Hound Dog," "Don't Be Cruel," and "Love Me Tender."

Presley entered the film industry and starred in a number of musicals until he was drafted by the U.S. Army. For two years he served his country, and he was proud to do so. His return to civilian life meant a return to acting, but his singing career was not as hot as it once was. Pop artists of the sixties began to replace his now-dated style.

During the seventies, Presley started live tours, and his singing career picked up. On August 16, 1977, Elvis Presley died. He left behind an impressive 94 gold singles and over 40 gold albums. Today, he remains one of the biggest influences on 20th century pop culture and is an enduring idol in the world of rock and roll.

A. These words were used in the selection you just read. Match the words from the list on the left with their proper meanings.

1. success   a. making a strong impression
2. enduring   b. long lasting
3. manager   c. popular singers
4. drafted   d. to be selected for military service
5. pop artists   e. having achieved something
6. impressive   f. a person who is in charge of a business or person

B. Use the back of this paper to answer the following questions.

1. What did Elvis win when he was eight years old?
2. Why did he record his first song?
3. Why did he stop starring in movies?
4. How did Elvis help his career in the seventies?
5. How many albums did he make in his lifetime?
6. If Elvis were alive today, do you think you would like to go to see him in a concert? Explain your answer.

Orel Hershiser

Preview the words in exercise A before reading the following selection. Then complete the exercises below.

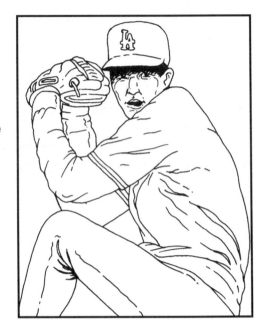

When Orel Hershiser was young, he enjoyed playing a variety of sports, such as racquetball, tennis, golf, and hockey. However, baseball was his favorite. At the age of eight, Hershiser entered a contest that was held in Yankee Stadium in New York. In the contest, he had to throw, hit, and run. He completed against boys from all across America. Hershiser came in third place.

Hershiser had a great deal of difficulty playing baseball in high school and college. In high school, he started out playing, but he was cut from the team. In college, he was not allowed to join the baseball team because his grades and his playing were not good enough. Rather than give up, Hershiser worked to improve his grades and his baseball skills. His grades went up, and he increased the speed of his pitch by five miles per hour. As a result, he made the college team.

Hershiser started playing professional baseball as a pitcher for the Los Angeles Dodgers' minor-league team. His playing ability was only fair, and he often felt discouraged. However, his coach, trainer, and manager felt Hershiser had potential so they convinced him to keep working on his pitch. That is exactly what Hershiser did, and eventually he became a starring pitcher for the major leagues.

A. These words were used in the selection you just read. Match the words from the list on the left with their proper meanings.

_____ 1. convinced   a. possibility; promise

_____ 2. variety   b. number of different kinds

_____ 3. ability   c. persuaded to do something

_____ 4. potential   d. skill

_____ 5. discouraged   e. to lack confidence or hope

B. Use the back of this paper to answer the following questions.

1. What was Orel's favorite sport as a child?

2. Did he play baseball in college?

3. Where did he start playing professional baseball?

4. Was baseball easy for him as an adult? Explain your answer.

5. Why do you think he kept on playing baseball even though he was not a great player and was often discouraged?

King Arthur

Read the following story and then complete the exercises on page 67.

King Arthur was and continues to be one of the great British heros of medieval times. Although it is believed that there really was an Arthur, the adventure stories that have been told about him for nearly 1,000 years are generally thought to be legend. According to the Latin versions of the story, King Uther Pendragon, Arthur's father was not allowed to raise Arthur himself because he had made a special pact with Merlin, a magician. As a result, Merlin raised Arthur as his own son and never told him that his father was a king.

According to the legend, there was a sword embedded in a stone that was located in a churchyard. The sword, called Excalibur, was said to be magical, and anyone who could remove it from the stone would become the king of Britain. Many nobles and knights tried to remove it, but they could not. Then Arthur tried and easily pulled Excalibur from the stone. This amazing feat proved that he was royalty, so he became Britain's king. At some point after Arthur became king, he fell in love with Princess Guinevere and married her. Although they had several castles to choose from, Arthur preferred to stay at Camelot, which was located somewhere in southern England.

Arthur tried to rule with fairness and wisdom. As a result, most knights greatly respected Arthur and wanted to serve him. They came from many countries in hopes of being chosen as a knight of the Round Table. This table was round in shape and could seat 1,600 knights without any one knight having a better seat than the others. Arthur felt that this was the best way to prevent his knights from arguing.

The legend of King Arthur tells about his many heroic adventures. He is said to have conquered most of western Europe by defeating the Roman Empire. Unfortunately, while he was away, his nephew, Mordred, captured his kingdom. When Arthur returned home, he fought and killed Mordred. Although he was victorious, he received wounds during this battle and later died. Some say that Arthur never died but was taken to the mystical island of Avalon so that his wounds would heal. Many believe that he will return someday.

King Arthur (cont.)

A. These words were used in the selection you just read. Match the words from the list on the left with their proper meanings.

_____ 1. British   a. very brave or daring

_____ 2. legend   b. the people of Great Britain

_____ 3. medieval   c. members of a royal family (i.e., king or queen)

_____ 4. embedded   d. story handed down from earlier times

_____ 5. royalty   e. relating to the Middle Ages

_____ 6. heroic   f. firmly enclosed

B. Use the space below and on the back of this paper to answer the following questions.

1. According to legend, who raised King Arthur as his own son?

2. What did Arthur do with the sword embedded in the stone?

3. What kind of ruler was King Arthur?

4. Describe the table that he had built and why he chose the shape that he did?

5. What circumstances could have caused his death?

6. What would you have done if you had been able to pull Excalibur from the stone?

_____

_____

_____

_____

_____

_____

_____

Ludwig van Beethoven

Read the selection below. When you are finished, answer the questions on page 69 and complete the activities on pages 70–72.

Ludwig van Beethoven was born in Bonn, Germany, in 1770. When he was only four years old, he was practicing on the violin and the clavier (a keyboard) for many hours each day. His father was determined to turn the boy into a musician.

He learned so quickly that he went on his first concert tour at the age of 11. When Beethoven was 17, Mozart, a great musician and composer of the time, heard him play and was impressed with his ability.

A few years later, Beethoven went to Vienna, Austria, to study with Haydn, another great musician and composer. It was not long before Beethoven was writing music, too. In his lifetime, he wrote about 300 pieces of music. Beethoven's compositions included sonatas, symphonies, concertos, and operas. (Sonatas are long musical compositions that are divided into several parts or "movements." Symphonies are sonatas written for the orchestra. Concertos are sonatas written for an instrument soloist and orchestra. Operas are plays in which the words are sung to music.)

After an illness at the age of 31, Beethoven gradually lost his hearing. Despite this terrible tragedy, he was somehow able to keep the melody or tune, the harmony of the chords, and the tempo or beat of the music inside his head. He wrote some of his most beautiful music after that time. Yet, he was never able to hear what he had written!

Toward the end of his life, Beethoven had to be turned toward the audience to see the applause because he could not hear it. He died in 1827 at the age of 57 and is considered one of the greatest composers who ever lived.

Ludwig van Beethoven (cont.)

What did you learn about Ludwig van Beethoven? Answer the following questions in complete sentences.

1. Where and when was Beethoven born? _____

2. How old was he when he began to study music?

_____

3. Who wanted him to be a musician?

_____

4. How old was Beethoven when he went on his first concert tour?

_____

5. How old was Beethoven when Mozart heard him play?

_____

6. Where did Beethoven go to study music?

_____

7. With whom did he study?

_____

8. About how many musical compositions did Beethoven write?

_____

9. What types of compositions did he write?

_____

10. What great tragedy befell Beethoven?

_____

Ludwig van Beethoven (cont.)

It is important to be able to read and spell the different words connected with the study of Beethoven. Here are some of the words you might be using.

composer	symphony	Mozart	violin
Austria	melody	concerto	Haydn
Bonn	composition	harmony	sonata
orchestra	Germany	notation	tempo
opera	piano	Vienna	musician

Using words in different ways helps you learn to read them and to spell them. Practice these skills by writing the words in alphabetical order on the lines below.

1. _____

2. _____

3. _____

4. _____

5. _____

6. _____

7. _____

8. _____

9. _____

10. _____

11. _____

12. _____

13. _____

14. _____

15. _____

16. _____

17. _____

18. _____

19. _____

20. _____

Ludwig van Beethoven (cont.)

Use these words to solve the word search.

composer	symphony	Mozart	violin
Austria	melody	concerto	Haydn
Bonn	composition	harmony	sonata
orchestra	Germany	notation	tempo
opera	piano	Vienna	musician

```
S D F G H J K P Q W E A U S T R I A X C
A C O M P O S I T I O N Z X C S T V O P
M O O N B V C A C E X Z O V I O L I N I
L M K N J H G N G F M D S T A N Q E E R
U P Y T C T R O S E R P F G A A H N H U
B O N N M E L O D Y A S O D F T H N A Y
G S T O P E R A R O M E D C V A I A Y T
A E S D F G H T K L E P M N B V C O D A
Q R W E R T Y O Q I O R H P L K J H N C
A M U S I C I A N Q U I M O Z A R T S D
A S D F G H J K L P O I U A N Y T R E W
O R C H E S T R A H A R M O N Y A S D F
Q A Z X S W E D C V F R T G B Y J U I L
```

Ludwig van Beethoven (cont.)

Imagine that you are Beethoven, the great composer. Use what you have learned from the previous selection and activities to complete this writing exercise. Write a letter to your best friend, expressing your feelings about losing your hearing while you still have so much more music to write.

Use the correct form for a personal letter and your best writing skills—grammar, punctuation, and spelling—so your readers will understand and enjoy what you have written.

Date your letter sometime in 1801, the year Beethoven suffered the loss of his hearing.

_____

_____

_____

_____

_____

_____

_____

_____

_____

_____

_____

_____

_____

_____

Addition Facts Timed Practice

When you practice basic addition facts for speed and accuracy, you improve your ability to solve problems in which addition computations are needed.

You will need a pencil and a timer with a second hand.   Set the timer . . . and go.

1. 6 + 9	2. 8 + 1	3. 8 + 9	4. 9 + 4	5. 5 + 0
6. 8 + 0	7. 5 + 9	8. 6 + 1	9. 8 + 8	10. 5 + 5
11. 7 + 6	12. 5 + 1	13. 0 + 6	14. 4 + 1	15. 4 + 4
16. 3 + 1	17. 6 + 5	18. 6 + 4	19. 7 + 0	20. 9 + 3
21. 5 + 2	22. 9 + 9	23. 4 + 2	24. 3 + 5	25. 6 + 6
26. 6 + 7	27. 6 + 8	28. 5 + 6	29. 0 + 7	30. 4 + 6
31. 9 + 6	32. 2 + 2	33. 9 + 0	34. 9 + 5	35. 0 + 1
36. 7 + 7	37. 3 + 6	38. 9 + 8	39. 7 + 3	40. 4 + 9
41. 9 + 1	42. 0 + 9	43. 3 + 9	44. 7 + 2	45. 3 + 0
46. 6 + 0	47. 5 + 3	48. 8 + 5	49. 9 + 7	50. 4 + 7

Addition Facts Timed Practice (cont.)

51. 7
    + 1

52. 8
    + 3

53.   4
    + 10

54. 4
    + 3

55. 1
    + 3

56. 2
    + 0

57. 7
    + 8

58. 3
    + 3

59. 1
    + 1

60. 6
    + 2

61. 5
    + 7

62. 2
    + 7

63. 1
    + 2

64. 8
    + 4

65. 7
    + 9

66. 0
    + 5

67. 4
    + 5

68. 7
    + 4

69. 3
    + 2

70. 1
    + 8

71. 1
    + 6

72. 1
    + 9

73. 0
    + 4

74. 8
    + 6

75. 2
    + 9

76. 2
    + 3

77. 4
    + 8

78. 5
    + 4

79. 8
    + 2

80. 1
    + 4

81. 0
    + 0

82. 3
    + 4

83. 8
    + 7

84. 3
    + 7

85. 2
    + 1

86. 0
    + 2

87. 6
    + 3

88. 1
    + 7

89. 2
    + 4

90. 3
    + 8

91. 5
    + 8

92. 2
    + 6

93. 0
    + 3

94. 1
    + 9

95. 2
    + 5

96. 0
    + 8

97. 1
    + 5

98. 2
    + 8

99. 0
    + 2

100. 7
     + 5

How long did it take you to complete the page? _____

How many did you get correct? _____

Single-Digit Addition: Three Rows

1.
```
   1
   2
 + 3
-----
   6
```

2.
```
   1
   2
 + 9
-----
  12
```

3.
```
   3
   1
 + 1
-----
   5
```

4.
```
   6
   6
 + 1
-----
  13
```

5.
```
   1
   6
 + 3
-----
  10
```

6.
```
   3
   2
 + 6
-----
  11
```

7.
```
   5
   8
 + 4
-----
  17
```

8.
```
   7
   3
 + 9
-----
  19
```

9.
```
   8
   5
 + 2
-----
  15
```

10.
```
   5
   8
 + 3
-----
  16
```

11.
```
   8
   6
 + 0
-----
  14
```

12.
```
   9
   3
 + 7
-----
  19
```

13.
```
   1
   7
 + 2
-----
  10
```

14.
```
   7
   0
 + 5
-----
  12
```

15.
```
   9
   6
 + 5
-----
  20
```

16.
```
   5
   2
 + 9
-----
  16
```

Single-Digit Addition: Four Rows

1.
```
    7
    9
    5
+   5
_____
```

2.
```
    1
    2
    2
+   1
_____
```

3.
```
    5
    4
    8
+   1
_____
```

4.
```
    5
    6
    0
+   4
_____
```

5.
```
    1
    7
    0
+   1
_____
```

6.
```
    4
    5
    7
+   1
_____
```

7.
```
    3
    6
    5
+   1
_____
```

8.
```
    7
    3
    7
+   5
_____
```

9.
```
    1
    7
    5
+   5
_____
```

10.
```
    6
    8
    8
+   1
_____
```

11.
```
    2
    6
    9
+   3
_____
```

12.
```
    8
    4
    6
+   2
_____
```

Single-Digit Addition: Eight Rows

1.
```
    7
    3
    5
    7
    9
    5
    9
 +  7
 ─────
   52
```

2.
```
    6
    8
    5
    3
    6
    8
    5
 +  8
 ─────
   49
```

3.
```
    8
    7
    4
    7
    9
    6
    8
 +  3
 ─────
   52
```

4.
```
    1
    3
    6
    3
    3
    9
    5
 +  8
 ─────
   38
```

5.
```
    3
    1
    8
    4
    5
    6
    3
 +  3
 ─────
   33
```

6.
```
    3
    8
    3
    7
    2
    1
    4
 +  7
 ─────
   35
```

7.
```
    4
    9
    5
    2
    6
    2
    7
 +  7
 ─────
   42
```

8.
```
    7
    5
    3
    8
    6
    6
    5
 +  6
 ─────
   46
```

9.
```
    9
    1
    9
    9
    2
    4
    7
 +  9
 ─────
   50
```

10.
```
    2
    7
    8
    6
    5
    1
    7
 +  2
 ─────
   38
```

11.
```
    8
    6
    4
    8
    7
    1
    8
 +  4
 ─────
   46
```

12.
```
    2
    8
    2
    1
    7
    8
    1
 +  2
 ─────
   31
```

13.
```
    6
    2
    3
    3
    6
    4
    9
 +  4
 ─────
   37
```

14.
```
    8
    7
    1
    3
    6
    7
    4
 +  4
 ─────
   40
```

15.
```
    3
    2
    5
    0
    1
    3
    8
 +  0
 ─────
   22
```

14.
```
    9
    0
    5
    2
    3
    0
    1
 +  7
 ─────
   27
```

Two Digits Plus One Digit

1.   14
   + 5

2.   16
   + 4

3.   14
   + 3

4.   47
   + 2

5.   55
   + 5

6.   52
   + 1

7.   26
   + 4

8.   68
   + 7

9.   75
   + 3

10.   82
   + 5

11.   39
   + 6

12.   60
   + 1

13.   52
   + 6

14.   20
   + 2

15.   61
   + 2

16.   15
   + 4

17.   29
   + 6

18.   79
   + 8

19.   78
   + 9

20.   48
   + 2

21.   51
   + 6

22.   37
   + 5

23.   96
   + 1

24.   48
   + 8

25.   91
   + 7

Two-Digit Addition: Two Rows

1. 36
    + 85

    121

2. 59
    + 95

    154

3. 88
    + 43

    131

4. 54
    + 40

    94

5. 55
    + 26

    81

6. 57
    + 32

    89

7. 28
    + 16

    44

8. 79
    + 41

    120

9. 35
    + 56

    91

10. 14
     + 25

     39

11. 38
     + 86

     124

12. 34
     + 13

     47

13. 65
     + 60

     125

14. 76
     + 62

     138

15. 71
     + 36

     107

16. 99
     + 97

     196

17. 43
     + 68

     111

18. 21
     + 46

     67

19. 15
     + 39

     54

20. 82
     + 45

     127

21. 73
     + 47

     120

22. 66
     + 53

     119

23. 64
     + 96

     160

24. 58
     + 77

     135

25. 61
     + 12

     73

Two-Digit Addition: Three Rows

1.
```
   76
   16
 + 77
 ____
```

2.
```
   79
   40
 + 98
 ____
```

3.
```
   64
   93
 + 34
 ____
```

4.
```
   78
   67
 + 12
 ____
```

5.
```
   42
   72
 + 18
 ____
```

6.
```
   99
   21
 + 59
 ____
```

7.
```
   48
   29
 + 34
 ____
```

8.
```
   54
   45
 + 49
 ____
```

9.
```
   12
   85
 + 91
 ____
```

10.
```
   19
   98
 + 78
 ____
```

11.
```
   82
   70
 + 29
 ____
```

12.
```
   14
   16
 + 51
 ____
```

13.
```
   69
   81
 + 68
 ____
```

14.
```
   54
   57
 + 81
 ____
```

15.
```
   68
   41
 + 78
 ____
```

16.
```
   78
   16
 + 82
 ____
```

Two-Digit Addition: Four Rows

1.   55
     77
     71
   + 63
   ‾‾‾‾‾
   266 ✬

2.   75
     72
     82
   + 71
   ‾‾‾‾‾
   300 ✬

3.   58
     16
     96
   + 12
   ‾‾‾‾‾
   182 ✬

4.   61
     52
     79
   + 73
   ‾‾‾‾‾
   265 ✬

5.   53
     36
     48
   + 45
   ‾‾‾‾‾
   182 ✬

6.   73
     87
     50
   + 36
   ‾‾‾‾‾
   246 ✬

7.   65
     62
     69
   + 16
   ‾‾‾‾‾
   212 ✬

8.   15
     71
     20
   + 42
   ‾‾‾‾‾
   148 ✬

9.   91
     99
     82
   + 86
   ‾‾‾‾‾
   358 ✬

10. 31
     88
     98
   + 86
   ‾‾‾‾‾
   303 ✬

11. 76
     96
     64
   + 12
   ‾‾‾‾‾
   248 ✬

12. 45
     17
     13
   + 16
   ‾‾‾‾‾
   91 ✬

340

Three-Digit Addition: Two Rows

1. 286
    + 612
    _____

2. 442
    + 383
    _____

3. 141
    + 931
    _____

4. 321
    + 552
    _____

5. 313
    + 675
    _____

6. 182
    + 837
    _____

7. 445
    + 891
    _____

8. 158
    + 703
    _____

9. 146
    + 243
    _____

10. 794
    + 323
    _____

11. 694
    + 396
    _____

12. 323
    + 298
    _____

13. 197
    + 646
    _____

14. 795
    + 607
    _____

15. 661
    + 351
    _____

16. 693
    + 977
    _____

17. 594
    + 229
    _____

18. 894
    + 928
    _____

19. 621
    + 346
    _____

20. 321
    + 617
    _____

21. 756
    + 492
    _____

22. 324
    + 601
    _____

23. 388
    + 235
    _____

24. 824
    + 123
    _____

25. 575
    + 739
    _____

Three-Digit Addition: Three Rows

1.   779
       864
 + 392

2.   156
       732
 + 991

3.   297
       948
 + 915

4.   862
       734
 + 367

5.   887
       228
 + 316

6.   875
       593
 + 294

7.   483
       114
 + 663

8.   879
       814
 + 582

9.   423
       384
 + 854

10.   986
       382
 + 376

11.   918
       782
 + 294

12.   893
       453
 + 276

13.   544
       218
 + 938

14.   587
       293
 + 952

15.   493
       571
 + 949

16.   224
       688
 + 111

Three-Digit Addition: Four Rows

1.
```
   757
   213
   141
 + 293
_____
```

2.
```
   414
   563
   951
 + 747
_____
```

3.
```
   486
   152
   342
 + 116
_____
```

4.
```
   775
   256
   675
 + 118
_____
```

5.
```
   954
   913
   529
 + 788
_____
```

6.
```
   495
   394
   525
 + 411
_____
```

7.
```
   994
   292
   197
 + 188
_____
```

8.
```
   181
   579
   957
 + 493
_____
```

9.
```
   555
   923
   986
 + 592
_____
```

10.
```
   288
   953
   842
 + 276
_____
```

11.
```
   885
   563
   836
 + 394
_____
```

12.
```
   384
   925
   881
 + 171
_____
```

Four-Digit Addition: Two Rows

1. 7418
    + 9921
    ⎯⎯⎯⎯

2. 5335
    + 9155
    ⎯⎯⎯⎯

3. 5721
    + 9778
    ⎯⎯⎯⎯

4. 4199
    + 1538
    ⎯⎯⎯⎯

5. 7932
    + 5284
    ⎯⎯⎯⎯

6. 4141
    + 6194
    ⎯⎯⎯⎯

7. 5425
    + 1444
    ⎯⎯⎯⎯

8. 6422
    + 9623
    ⎯⎯⎯⎯

9. 1274
    + 3411
    ⎯⎯⎯⎯

10. 7983
    + 6375
    ⎯⎯⎯⎯

11. 3323
    + 7196
    ⎯⎯⎯⎯

12. 2497
    + 4839
    ⎯⎯⎯⎯

13. 5489
    + 3121
    ⎯⎯⎯⎯

14. 6758
    + 1565
    ⎯⎯⎯⎯

15. 7788
    + 4456
    ⎯⎯⎯⎯

16. 2626
    + 5161
    ⎯⎯⎯⎯

17. 1457
    + 6296
    ⎯⎯⎯⎯

18. 6582
    + 1458
    ⎯⎯⎯⎯

19. 3951
    + 5146
    ⎯⎯⎯⎯

20. 7835
    + 4196
    ⎯⎯⎯⎯

21. 5476
    + 2939
    ⎯⎯⎯⎯

22. 1942
    + 8844
    ⎯⎯⎯⎯

23. 9255
    + 7622
    ⎯⎯⎯⎯

24. 2558
    + 4571
    ⎯⎯⎯⎯

25. 2719
    + 2447
    ⎯⎯⎯⎯

Four-Digit Addition: Three Rows

1.　　1865
　　　8935
　+　8755
　――――――

2.　　2315
　　　9165
　+　2537
　――――――

3.　　4978
　　　1918
　+　2259
　――――――

4.　　6731
　　　6579
　+　2253
　――――――

5.　　4732
　　　9287
　+　2133
　――――――

6.　　5772
　　　9105
　+　2675
　――――――

7.　　2843
　　　7503
　+　6823
　――――――

8.　　2459
　　　7737
　+　5192
　――――――

9.　　5874
　　　3316
　+　6627
　――――――

10.　　7664
　　　3491
　+　1638
　――――――

11.　　4178
　　　2877
　+　7131
　――――――

12.　　6772
　　　7966
　+　9466
　――――――

13.　　8473
　　　6825
　+　9351
　――――――

14.　　8245
　　　3306
　+　6149
　――――――

15.　　9341
　　　8816
　+　6919
　――――――

16.　　8741
　　　3687
　+　1393
　――――――

Four-Digit Addition: Four Rows

1. 5263
    5752
    7852
    + 8921

2. 7446
    2885
    7729
    + 9767

3. 6788
    4986
    2338
    + 9924

4. 8354
    2276
    8213
    + 6972

5. 6194
    1685
    3392
    + 1543

6. 8356
    9424
    3734
    + 7751

7. 3355
    8421
    5896
    + 7818

8. 7148
    5845
    2516
    + 8148

9. 9972
    4365
    7942
    + 5965

10. 1744
    5556
    1545
    + 3956

11. 3417
    7299
    8892
    + 5524

12. 6459
    5281
    4952
    + 1446

Mixed Addition Practice

1.   55
  + 21

2.   5
  + 6

3.   83
  + 37

4.   5
  + 4

5.   8
  + 7

6.   4662
  + 8

7.   18
  + 21

8.   9
  + 8

9.   85
  + 96

10.   1769
  + 9

11.   92
  + 48

12.   5
  + 14

13.   85
  + 95

14.   1839
  + 4

15.   7
  + 11

16.   7
  + 9

17.   79
  + 79

18.   88
  + 13

19.   3445
  + 4

20.   63
  + 47

Subtraction Facts Timed Practice

When you practice your basic subtraction facts for speed and accuracy, you improve your ability to solve problems in which subtraction computations are needed.

You will need a pencil and a timer with a second hand. Set the timer . . . and go.

1. 13 − 4	2. 17 − 9	3. 9 − 1	4. 15 − 9	5. 5 − 0
6. 8 − 0	7. 14 − 9	8. 7 − 1	9. 16 − 8	10. 10 − 5
11. 13 − 6	12. 6 − 1	13. 6 − 6	14. 5 − 1	15. 8 − 4
16. 4 − 1	17. 11 − 5	18. 10 − 4	19. 7 − 0	20. 12 − 3
21. 7 − 2	22. 18 − 9	23. 6 − 2	24. 8 − 5	25. 12 − 6
26. 13 − 7	27. 14 − 8	28. 11 − 6	29. 7 − 0	30. 10 − 6
31. 15 − 6	32. 4 − 2	33. 9 − 0	34. 14 − 5	35. 1 − 0
36. 14 − 7	37. 9 − 6	38. 17 − 8	39. 10 − 3	40. 13 − 9
41. 10 − 1	42. 9 − 9	43. 12 − 9	44. 9 − 2	45. 3 − 0
46. 6 − 0	47. 8 − 3	48. 13 − 5	49. 16 − 7	50. 11 − 7

7/8/01

Subtraction Facts Timed Practice (cont.)

51. 8
 − 1
 7

52. 11
 − 3
 8

53. 4
 − 0
 4

54. 7
 − 3
 4

55. 4
 − 3
 1

56. 2
 − 0
 2

57. 15
 − 8
 7

58. 6
 − 3
 3

59. 2
 − 1
 1

60. 8
 − 2
 6

61. 12
 − 7
 5

62. 9
 − 7
 2

63. 3
 − 2
 1

64. 12
 − 4
 8

65. 16
 − 9
 7

66. 5
 − 5
 0

67. 9
 − 5
 4

68. 11
 − 4
 7

69. 5
 − 2
 3

70. 9
 − 8
 1

71. 7
 − 6
 1

72. 10
 − 9
 1

73. 4
 − 4
 0

74. 14
 − 6
 8

75. 11
 − 9
 2

76. 5
 − 3
 2

77. 12
 − 8
 4

78. 9
 − 4
 5

79. 10
 − 2
 8

80. 5
 − 4
 1

81. 0
 − 0
 0

82. 7
 − 4
 3

83. 15
 − 7
 8

84. 10
 − 7
 3

85. 3
 − 1
 2

86. 11
 − 2
 9

87. 9
 − 3
 6

88. 8
 − 7
 1

89. 6
 − 4
 2

90. 11
 − 8
 3

91. 13
 − 8
 5

92. 8
 − 6
 2

93. 3
 − 3
 0

94. 1
 − 0
 1

95. 7
 − 5
 2

96. 8
 − 8
 0

97. 6
 − 5
 1

98. 10
 − 8
 2

99. 2
 − 2
 0

100. 12
 − 5
 7

How long did it take to complete the page? _____

How many did you get correct? _____

Two Digits Minus One Digit

1.
$$\begin{array}{r} 41 \\ -\ 6 \\ \hline \end{array}$$

2.
$$\begin{array}{r} 21 \\ -\ 7 \\ \hline \end{array}$$

3.
$$\begin{array}{r} 41 \\ -\ 7 \\ \hline \end{array}$$

4.
$$\begin{array}{r} 51 \\ -\ 7 \\ \hline \end{array}$$

5.
$$\begin{array}{r} 47 \\ -\ 6 \\ \hline \end{array}$$

6.
$$\begin{array}{r} 84 \\ -\ 9 \\ \hline \end{array}$$

7.
$$\begin{array}{r} 17 \\ -\ 4 \\ \hline \end{array}$$

8.
$$\begin{array}{r} 83 \\ -\ 2 \\ \hline \end{array}$$

9.
$$\begin{array}{r} 98 \\ -\ 7 \\ \hline \end{array}$$

10.
$$\begin{array}{r} 93 \\ -\ 8 \\ \hline \end{array}$$

11.
$$\begin{array}{r} 97 \\ -\ 9 \\ \hline \end{array}$$

12.
$$\begin{array}{r} 48 \\ -\ 2 \\ \hline \end{array}$$

13.
$$\begin{array}{r} 99 \\ -\ 5 \\ \hline \end{array}$$

14.
$$\begin{array}{r} 58 \\ -\ 8 \\ \hline \end{array}$$

15.
$$\begin{array}{r} 57 \\ -\ 4 \\ \hline \end{array}$$

16.
$$\begin{array}{r} 71 \\ -\ 1 \\ \hline \end{array}$$

17.
$$\begin{array}{r} 47 \\ -\ 6 \\ \hline \end{array}$$

18.
$$\begin{array}{r} 27 \\ -\ 6 \\ \hline \end{array}$$

19.
$$\begin{array}{r} 68 \\ -\ 1 \\ \hline \end{array}$$

20.
$$\begin{array}{r} 59 \\ -\ 6 \\ \hline \end{array}$$

21.
$$\begin{array}{r} 38 \\ -\ 6 \\ \hline \end{array}$$

22.
$$\begin{array}{r} 88 \\ -\ 9 \\ \hline \end{array}$$

23.
$$\begin{array}{r} 14 \\ -\ 6 \\ \hline \end{array}$$

24.
$$\begin{array}{r} 99 \\ -\ 9 \\ \hline \end{array}$$

25.
$$\begin{array}{r} 29 \\ -\ 4 \\ \hline \end{array}$$

Three Digits Minus Two Digits

1.
$$\begin{array}{r} 411 \\ -\ 51 \\ \hline \end{array}$$

2.
$$\begin{array}{r} 666 \\ -\ 41 \\ \hline \end{array}$$

3.
$$\begin{array}{r} 256 \\ -\ 37 \\ \hline \end{array}$$

4.
$$\begin{array}{r} 417 \\ -\ 68 \\ \hline \end{array}$$

5.
$$\begin{array}{r} 613 \\ -\ 32 \\ \hline \end{array}$$

6.
$$\begin{array}{r} 879 \\ -\ 56 \\ \hline \end{array}$$

7.
$$\begin{array}{r} 595 \\ -\ 62 \\ \hline \end{array}$$

8.
$$\begin{array}{r} 319 \\ -\ 72 \\ \hline \end{array}$$

9.
$$\begin{array}{r} 571 \\ -\ 37 \\ \hline \end{array}$$

10.
$$\begin{array}{r} 439 \\ -\ 99 \\ \hline \end{array}$$

11.
$$\begin{array}{r} 174 \\ -\ 56 \\ \hline \end{array}$$

12.
$$\begin{array}{r} 462 \\ -\ 81 \\ \hline \end{array}$$

13.
$$\begin{array}{r} 551 \\ -\ 94 \\ \hline \end{array}$$

14.
$$\begin{array}{r} 293 \\ -\ 31 \\ \hline \end{array}$$

15.
$$\begin{array}{r} 958 \\ -\ 28 \\ \hline \end{array}$$

16.
$$\begin{array}{r} 831 \\ -\ 67 \\ \hline \end{array}$$

17.
$$\begin{array}{r} 352 \\ -\ 13 \\ \hline \end{array}$$

18.
$$\begin{array}{r} 967 \\ -\ 88 \\ \hline \end{array}$$

19.
$$\begin{array}{r} 577 \\ -\ 44 \\ \hline \end{array}$$

20.
$$\begin{array}{r} 617 \\ -\ 22 \\ \hline \end{array}$$

21.
$$\begin{array}{r} 773 \\ -\ 95 \\ \hline \end{array}$$

22.
$$\begin{array}{r} 382 \\ -\ 25 \\ \hline \end{array}$$

23.
$$\begin{array}{r} 732 \\ -\ 75 \\ \hline \end{array}$$

24.
$$\begin{array}{r} 879 \\ -\ 53 \\ \hline \end{array}$$

25.
$$\begin{array}{r} 575 \\ -\ 22 \\ \hline \end{array}$$

Three Digits Minus Two Digits (cont.)

1. 917
   − 72

2. 241
   − 82

3. 335
   − 78

4. 918
   − 97

5. 952
   − 64

6. 274
   − 73

7. 246
   − 13

8. 783
   − 24

9. 498
   − 92

10. 485
    − 24

11. 543
    − 11

12. 568
    − 13

13. 188
    − 21

14. 237
    − 14

15. 755
    − 47

16. 681
    − 96

17. 923
    − 36

18. 266
    − 33

19. 876
    − 36

20. 864
    − 48

21. 178
    − 32

22. 834
    − 86

23. 326
    − 76

24. 779
    − 71

25. 484
    − 41

Four Digits Minus Three Digits

1. 4556
    − 343

2. 3722
    − 411

3. 2983
    − 661

4. 4349
    − 122

5. 4986
    − 813

6. 2991
    − 131

7. 4965
    − 714

8. 9589
    − 257

9. 1757
    − 145

10. 1995
    − 164

11. 5375
    − 213

12. 2558
    − 427

13. 6649
    − 344

14. 9371
    − 321

15. 7978
    − 848

16. 9356
    − 123

17. 7955
    − 321

18. 3796
    − 166

19. 7379
    − 133

20. 8976
    − 734

21. 2566
    − 332

22. 8759
    − 647

23. 7887
    − 317

24. 9998
    − 358

25. 1499
    − 328

Four Digits Minus Three Digits (cont.)

1. 9487
   − 156

2. 1896
   − 653

3. 9238
   − 121

4. 5886
   − 235

5. 8736
   − 424

6. 4648
   − 523

7. 2698
   − 247

8. 7774
   − 651

9. 9953
   − 112

10. 6697
    − 544

11. 4776
    − 735

12. 3598
    − 352

13. 1894
    − 361

14. 4758
    − 248

15. 5678
    − 348

16. 8268
    − 253

17. 6553
    − 242

18. 3497
    − 226

19. 7488
    − 314

20. 6646
    − 242

21. 4598
    − 445

22. 1416
    − 657

23. 2413
    − 766

24. 4515
    − 249

25. 7279
    − 646

Mixed Subtraction Practice

1. $\begin{array}{r} 68 \\ -\ 6 \\ \hline \end{array}$
    2. $\begin{array}{r} 53 \\ -\ 29 \\ \hline \end{array}$
    3. $\begin{array}{r} 334 \\ -\ 4 \\ \hline \end{array}$
    4. $\begin{array}{r} 794 \\ -\ 9 \\ \hline \end{array}$

5. $\begin{array}{r} 7192 \\ -\ 46 \\ \hline \end{array}$
    6. $\begin{array}{r} 8495 \\ -\ 47 \\ \hline \end{array}$
    7. $\begin{array}{r} 84 \\ -\ 9 \\ \hline \end{array}$
    8. $\begin{array}{r} 2794 \\ -\ 6 \\ \hline \end{array}$

9. $\begin{array}{r} 9689 \\ -\ 84 \\ \hline \end{array}$
    10. $\begin{array}{r} 8927 \\ -\ 5 \\ \hline \end{array}$
    11. $\begin{array}{r} 186 \\ -\ 61 \\ \hline \end{array}$
    12. $\begin{array}{r} 7851 \\ -\ 84 \\ \hline \end{array}$

13. $\begin{array}{r} 15 \\ -\ 7 \\ \hline \end{array}$
    14. $\begin{array}{r} 6688 \\ -\ 94 \\ \hline \end{array}$
    15. $\begin{array}{r} 1157 \\ -\ 9 \\ \hline \end{array}$
    16. $\begin{array}{r} 823 \\ -\ 8 \\ \hline \end{array}$

17. $\begin{array}{r} 45 \\ -\ 5 \\ \hline \end{array}$
    18. $\begin{array}{r} 861 \\ -\ 7 \\ \hline \end{array}$
    19. $\begin{array}{r} 38 \\ -\ 9 \\ \hline \end{array}$
    20. $\begin{array}{r} 76 \\ -\ 8 \\ \hline \end{array}$

Mixed Subtraction Practice (cont.)

1.
$$\begin{array}{r} 5 \\ -\ 5 \\ \hline \end{array}$$

2.
$$\begin{array}{r} 355 \\ -\ 186 \\ \hline \end{array}$$

3.
$$\begin{array}{r} 5 \\ -\ 3 \\ \hline \end{array}$$

4.
$$\begin{array}{r} 876 \\ -\ 344 \\ \hline \end{array}$$

5.
$$\begin{array}{r} 5 \\ -\ 3 \\ \hline \end{array}$$

6.
$$\begin{array}{r} 2312 \\ -\ 479 \\ \hline \end{array}$$

7.
$$\begin{array}{r} 9224 \\ -\ 667 \\ \hline \end{array}$$

8.
$$\begin{array}{r} 5792 \\ -\ 9 \\ \hline \end{array}$$

9.
$$\begin{array}{r} 433 \\ -\ 318 \\ \hline \end{array}$$

10.
$$\begin{array}{r} 7 \\ -\ 2 \\ \hline \end{array}$$

11.
$$\begin{array}{r} 333 \\ -\ 124 \\ \hline \end{array}$$

12.
$$\begin{array}{r} 7 \\ -\ 2 \\ \hline \end{array}$$

13.
$$\begin{array}{r} 742 \\ -\ 553 \\ \hline \end{array}$$

14.
$$\begin{array}{r} 3211 \\ -\ 7 \\ \hline \end{array}$$

15.
$$\begin{array}{r} 4718 \\ -\ 266 \\ \hline \end{array}$$

16.
$$\begin{array}{r} 888 \\ -\ 364 \\ \hline \end{array}$$

17.
$$\begin{array}{r} 5261 \\ -\ 5143 \\ \hline \end{array}$$

18.
$$\begin{array}{r} 9 \\ -\ 6 \\ \hline \end{array}$$

19.
$$\begin{array}{r} 3918 \\ -\ 2 \\ \hline \end{array}$$

20.
$$\begin{array}{r} 6766 \\ -\ 8 \\ \hline \end{array}$$

7/8/01

Multiplication Facts Timed Practice

When you practice basic multiplication facts for speed and accuracy, you improve your ability to solve problems in which multiplication computations are needed.

You will need a pencil and a timer with a second hand. Set the timer . . . and go.

1. $9 \times 4 = 36$
2. $3 \times 0 = 0$
3. $7 \times 3 = 21$
4. $7 \times 4 = 28$
5. $8 \times 9 = 72$

6. $6 \times 8 = 48$
7. $5 \times 7 = 35$
8. $4 \times 3 = 12$
9. $0 \times 5 = 0$
10. $6 \times 5 = 30$

11. $8 \times 1 = 8$
12. $6 \times 6 = 36$
13. $7 \times 2 = 14$
14. $3 \times 2 = 6$
15. $4 \times 2 = 8$

16. $6 \times 2 = 12$
17. $0 \times 4 = 0$
18. $3 \times 5 = 15$
19. $5 \times 1 = 5$
20. $6 \times 9 = 54$

21. $1 \times 7 = 7$
22. $4 \times 4 = 16$
23. $3 \times 7 = 21$
24. $7 \times 1 = 7$
25. $5 \times 6 = 30$

26. $4 \times 5 = 20$
27. $7 \times 6 = 56$
28. $6 \times 7 = 56$
29. $9 \times 6 = 54$
30. $1 \times 2 = 2$

31. $5 \times 5 = 25$
32. $7 \times 8 = 56$
33. $2 \times 7 = 14$
34. $6 \times 0 = 0$
35. $3 \times 1 = 3$

36. $9 \times 9 = 81$
37. $1 \times 9 = 9$
38. $6 \times 3 = 18$
39. $8 \times 3 = 24$
40. $4 \times 9 = 36$

41. $0 \times 7 = 0$
42. $1 \times 8 = 8$
43. $3 \times 9 = 27$
44. $4 \times 0 = 0$
45. $3 \times 3 = 9$

46. $5 \times 3 = 15$
47. $2 \times 3 = 6$
48. $5 \times 2 = 10$
49. $9 \times 7 = 63$
50. $2 \times 4 = 8$

Multiplication Facts Timed Practice (cont.)

51. $\begin{array}{r} 1 \\ \times\ 1 \\ \hline \end{array}$	52. $\begin{array}{r} 8 \\ \times\ 7 \\ \hline \end{array}$	53. $\begin{array}{r} 8 \\ \times\ 8 \\ \hline \end{array}$	54. $\begin{array}{r} 8 \\ \times\ 6 \\ \hline \end{array}$	55. $\begin{array}{r} 3 \\ \times\ 6 \\ \hline \end{array}$
56. $\begin{array}{r} 9 \\ \times\ 0 \\ \hline \end{array}$	57. $\begin{array}{r} 1 \\ \times\ 6 \\ \hline \end{array}$	58. $\begin{array}{r} 4 \\ \times\ 1 \\ \hline \end{array}$	59. $\begin{array}{r} 2 \\ \times\ 2 \\ \hline \end{array}$	60. $\begin{array}{r} 0 \\ \times\ 9 \\ \hline \end{array}$
61. $\begin{array}{r} 8 \\ \times\ 0 \\ \hline \end{array}$	62. $\begin{array}{r} 2 \\ \times\ 6 \\ \hline \end{array}$	63. $\begin{array}{r} 4 \\ \times\ 7 \\ \hline \end{array}$	64. $\begin{array}{r} 3 \\ \times\ 4 \\ \hline \end{array}$	65. $\begin{array}{r} 5 \\ \times\ 8 \\ \hline \end{array}$
66. $\begin{array}{r} 9 \\ \times\ 5 \\ \hline \end{array}$	67. $\begin{array}{r} 7 \\ \times\ 9 \\ \hline \end{array}$	68. $\begin{array}{r} 7 \\ \times\ 0 \\ \hline \end{array}$	69. $\begin{array}{r} 0 \\ \times\ 6 \\ \hline \end{array}$	70. $\begin{array}{r} 9 \\ \times\ 3 \\ \hline \end{array}$
71. $\begin{array}{r} 1 \\ \times\ 3 \\ \hline \end{array}$	72. $\begin{array}{r} 9 \\ \times\ 1 \\ \hline \end{array}$	73. $\begin{array}{r} 2 \\ \times\ 9 \\ \hline \end{array}$	74. $\begin{array}{r} 6 \\ \times\ 4 \\ \hline \end{array}$	75. $\begin{array}{r} 4 \\ \times\ 6 \\ \hline \end{array}$
76. $\begin{array}{r} 8 \\ \times\ 4 \\ \hline \end{array}$	77. $\begin{array}{r} 3 \\ \times\ 8 \\ \hline \end{array}$	78. $\begin{array}{r} 7 \\ \times\ 7 \\ \hline \end{array}$	79. $\begin{array}{r} 5 \\ \times\ 9 \\ \hline \end{array}$	80. $\begin{array}{r} 8 \\ \times\ 5 \\ \hline \end{array}$
81. $\begin{array}{r} 5 \\ \times\ 0 \\ \hline \end{array}$	82. $\begin{array}{r} 6 \\ \times\ 1 \\ \hline \end{array}$	83. $\begin{array}{r} 2 \\ \times\ 0 \\ \hline \end{array}$	84. $\begin{array}{r} 9 \\ \times\ 8 \\ \hline \end{array}$	85. $\begin{array}{r} 1 \\ \times\ 0 \\ \hline \end{array}$
86. $\begin{array}{r} 0 \\ \times\ 3 \\ \hline \end{array}$	87. $\begin{array}{r} 1 \\ \times\ 4 \\ \hline \end{array}$	88. $\begin{array}{r} 8 \\ \times\ 2 \\ \hline \end{array}$	89. $\begin{array}{r} 5 \\ \times\ 4 \\ \hline \end{array}$	90. $\begin{array}{r} 4 \\ \times\ 8 \\ \hline \end{array}$
91. $\begin{array}{r} 0 \\ \times\ 0 \\ \hline \end{array}$	92. $\begin{array}{r} 0 \\ \times\ 1 \\ \hline \end{array}$	93. $\begin{array}{r} 9 \\ \times\ 2 \\ \hline \end{array}$	94. $\begin{array}{r} 1 \\ \times\ 1 \\ \hline \end{array}$	95. $\begin{array}{r} 7 \\ \times\ 5 \\ \hline \end{array}$
96. $\begin{array}{r} 0 \\ \times\ 2 \\ \hline \end{array}$	97. $\begin{array}{r} 2 \\ \times\ 8 \\ \hline \end{array}$	98. $\begin{array}{r} 1 \\ \times\ 5 \\ \hline \end{array}$	99. $\begin{array}{r} 0 \\ \times\ 8 \\ \hline \end{array}$	100. $\begin{array}{r} 2 \\ \times\ 5 \\ \hline \end{array}$

How long did it take you to complete the pages? _____

How many did you get correct? _____

Two Digits Times One Digit

1.   42
     X 9

2.   99
     X 8

3.   32
     X 9

4.   15
     X 6

5.   73
     X 8

6.   81
     X 5

7.   45
     X 1

8.   88
     X 7

9.   88
     X 2

10.   33
     X 7

11.   75
     X 5

12.   92
     X 6

13.   18
     X 2

14.   76
     X 4

15.   81
     X 7

16.   25
     X 9

17.   18
     X 6

18.   18
     X 2

19.   48
     X 3

20.   35
     X 2

21.   18
     X 5

22.   98
     X 5

23.   96
     X 9

24.   25
     X 6

25.   68
     X 4

Two Digits Times One Digit (cont.)

1. 11
   X 4

2. 91
   X 3

3. 69
   X 4

4. 59
   X 5

5. 26
   X 4

6. 17
   X 3

7. 42
   X 6

8. 97
   X 3

9. 22
   X 2

10. 71
    X 4

11. 12
    X 7

12. 26
    X 3

13. 25
    X 7

14. 85
    X 3

15. 58
    X 5

16. 97
    X 4

17. 18
    X 9

18. 33
    X 1

19. 86
    X 3

20. 16
    X 6

21. 65
    X 7

22. 38
    X 7

23. 43
    X 8

24. 24
    X 8

25. 95
    X 3

Two Digits Times Two Digits

1. 35
   X 22

2. 23
   X 77

3. 11
   X 44

4. 58
   X 53

5. 94
   X 55

6. 48
   X 67

7. 74
   X 35

8. 91
   X 88

9. 11
   X 51

10. 53
    X 73

11. 93
    X 34

12. 99
    X 82

13. 47
    X 62

14. 12
    X 93

15. 28
    X 45

16. 78
    X 99

17. 87
    X 29

18. 32
    X 76

19. 71
    X 66

20. 39
    X 28

21. 18
    X 29

22. 61
    X 56

23. 31
    X 23

24. 59
    X 22

25. 75
    X 97

Two Digits Times Two Digits (cont.)

1. 16
    X 98

2. 44
    X 88

3. 36
    X 74

4. 98
    X 31

5. 16
    X 36

6. 37
    X 98

7. 77
    X 54

8. 29
    X 49

9. 47
    X 82

10. 92
    X 19

11. 67
    X 56

12. 39
    X 76

13. 82
    X 34

14. 59
    X 44

15. 96
    X 24

16. 91
    X 71

17. 73
    X 77

18. 22
    X 87

19. 29
    X 77

20. 98
    X 48

21. 95
    X 31

22. 36
    X 75

23. 58
    X 71

24. 73
    X 95

25. 82
    X 52

Three Digits Times One Digit

1. 385
X 8

2. 775
X 5

3. 252
X 5

4. 617
X 9

5. 599
X 9

6. 467
X 6

7. 214
X 6

8. 991
X 2

9. 155
X 6

10. 202
X 5

11. 641
X 6

12. 869
X 2

13. 908
X 2

14. 854
X 5

15. 144
X 6

16. 588
X 6

17. 301
X 2

18. 683
X 9

19. 331
X 8

20. 458
X 8

21. 532
X 9

22. 121
X 9

23. 957
X 7

24. 859
X 2

25. 474
X 5

Three Digits Times One Digit (cont.)

1. 283
    X 7

2. 346
    X 6

3. 923
    X 8

4. 796
    X 2

5. 596
    X 4

6. 811
    X 5

7. 231
    X 8

8. 206
    X 6

9. 179
    X 6

10. 853
    X 3

11. 682
    X 8

12. 117
    X 9

13. 636
    X 2

14. 884
    X 9

15. 929
    X 4

16. 393
    X 1

17. 346
    X 7

18. 802
    X 5

19. 597
    X 1

20. 955
    X 8

21. 864
    X 2

22. 832
    X 4

23. 273
    X 8

24. 375
    X 3

25. 681
    X 5

Three Digits Times One Digit (cont.)

1. 283
    X 9

2. 746
    X 6

3. 985
    X 1

4. 123
    X 6

5. 224
    X 4

6. 783
    X 7

7. 486
    X 9

8. 735
    X 3

9. 797
    X 8

10. 453
    X 4

11. 514
    X 2

12. 733
    X 6

13. 709
    X 6

14. 998
    X 6

15. 261
    X 1

16. 536
    X 5

17. 228
    X 1

18. 651
    X 5

19. 192
    X 3

20. 765
    X 6

21. 166
    X 3

22. 572
    X 7

23. 109
    X 1

24. 641
    X 9

25. 646
    X 7

Three Digits Times Two Digits

1. 911
    X 41

2. 748
    X 63

3. 128
    X 41

4. 667
    X 36

5. 843
    X 38

6. 156
    X 76

7. 497
    X 22

8. 898
    X 33

9. 473
    X 72

10. 444
    X 86

11. 971
    X 24

12. 691
    X 84

13. 903
    X 93

14. 621
    X 85

15. 692
    X 45

16. 459
    X 56

17. 133
    X 69

18. 333
    X 15

19. 794
    X 17

20. 638
    X 25

21. 775
    X 27

22. 315
    X 43

23. 671
    X 52

24. 489
    X 52

25. 592
    X 13

Three Digits Times Two Digits (cont.)

1. 261
    X 71

2. 243
    X 17

3. 951
    X 31

4. 785
    X 66

5. 864
    X 25

6. 232
    X 19

7. 235
    X 69

8. 871
    X 92

9. 785
    X 98

10. 637
    X 44

11. 693
    X 77

12. 967
    X 27

13. 928
    X 37

14. 822
    X 51

15. 346
    X 46

16. 165
    X 81

17. 724
    X 45

18. 644
    X 84

19. 783
    X 63

20. 278
    X 26

21. 323
    X 32

22. 937
    X 15

23. 827
    X 31

24. 812
    X 39

25. 372
    X 55

Mixed Multiplication Practice

1. $\begin{array}{r} 9 \\ \times\ 5 \\ \hline \end{array}$
2. $\begin{array}{r} 27 \\ \times\ 6 \\ \hline \end{array}$
3. $\begin{array}{r} 46 \\ \times\ 8 \\ \hline \end{array}$
4. $\begin{array}{r} 9 \\ \times\ 3 \\ \hline \end{array}$

5. $\begin{array}{r} 32 \\ \times\ 69 \\ \hline \end{array}$
6. $\begin{array}{r} 3 \\ \times\ 2 \\ \hline \end{array}$
7. $\begin{array}{r} 5 \\ \times\ 54 \\ \hline \end{array}$
8. $\begin{array}{r} 31 \\ \times\ 5 \\ \hline \end{array}$

9. $\begin{array}{r} 4 \\ \times\ 15 \\ \hline \end{array}$
10. $\begin{array}{r} 4 \\ \times\ 97 \\ \hline \end{array}$
11. $\begin{array}{r} 76 \\ \times\ 92 \\ \hline \end{array}$
12. $\begin{array}{r} 46 \\ \times\ 5 \\ \hline \end{array}$

13. $\begin{array}{r} 5 \\ \times\ 34 \\ \hline \end{array}$
14. $\begin{array}{r} 1 \\ \times\ 9 \\ \hline \end{array}$
15. $\begin{array}{r} 47 \\ \times\ 79 \\ \hline \end{array}$
16. $\begin{array}{r} 28 \\ \times\ 5 \\ \hline \end{array}$

17. $\begin{array}{r} 8 \\ \times\ 11 \\ \hline \end{array}$
18. $\begin{array}{r} 8 \\ \times\ 7 \\ \hline \end{array}$
19. $\begin{array}{r} 57 \\ \times\ 2 \\ \hline \end{array}$
20. $\begin{array}{r} 5 \\ \times\ 7 \\ \hline \end{array}$

Mixed Multiplication Practice (cont.)

1. 125
   X 69
   _____

2. 28
   X 91
   _____

3. 783
   X 62
   _____

4. 8
   X 7
   _____

5. 5
   X 5
   _____

6. 347
   X 3171
   _____

7. 238
   X 98
   _____

8. 878
   X 98
   _____

9. 55
   X 35
   _____

10. 718
    X 61
    _____

11. 4883
    X 737
    _____

12. 269
    X 47
    _____

13. 9
    X 6
    _____

14. 81
    X 89
    _____

15. 9
    X 3
    _____

16. 43
    X 68
    _____

17. 378
    X 99
    _____

18. 4
    X 3
    _____

19. 3
    X 4
    _____

20. 5
    X 9
    _____

Division Facts Timed Practice

When you practice basic division facts for speed and accuracy, you improve your ability to solve problems in which division computations are needed.

You will need a pencil and a timer with a second hand. Set the timer . . . and go.

1. $1 \overline{)5}$ 2. $8 \overline{)56}$ 3. $2 \overline{)16}$ 4. $3 \overline{)21}$ 5. $6 \overline{)30}$

6. $9 \overline{)72}$ 7. $9 \overline{)54}$ 8. $3 \overline{)9}$ 9. $4 \overline{)20}$ 10. $6 \overline{)0}$

11. $7 \overline{)28}$ 12. $5 \overline{)40}$ 13. $2 \overline{)10}$ 14. $4 \overline{)28}$ 15. $1 \overline{)4}$

16. $2 \overline{)18}$ 17. $5 \overline{)0}$ 18. $8 \overline{)48}$ 19. $2 \overline{)14}$ 20. $5 \overline{)25}$

21. $3 \overline{)6}$ 22. $6 \overline{)42}$ 23. $3 \overline{)27}$ 24. $6 \overline{)54}$ 25. $7 \overline{)14}$

26. $2 \overline{)12}$ 27. $8 \overline{)64}$ 28. $6 \overline{)24}$ 29. $8 \overline{)0}$ 30. $1 \overline{)3}$

31. $5 \overline{)45}$ 32. $2 \overline{)8}$ 33. $8 \overline{)32}$ 34. $4 \overline{)12}$ 35. $9 \overline{)81}$

36. $3 \overline{)18}$ 37. $8 \overline{)72}$ 38. $7 \overline{)63}$ 39. $9 \overline{)45}$ 40. $9 \overline{)63}$

Division Facts Timed Practice (cont.)

41. $8 \overline{)8}$ 42. $9 \overline{)36}$ 43. $4 \overline{)32}$ 44. $1 \overline{)1}$ 45. $5 \overline{)15}$

46. $6 \overline{)18}$ 47. $7 \overline{)7}$ 48. $5 \overline{)30}$ 49. $2 \overline{)0}$ 50. $5 \overline{)10}$

51. $8 \overline{)24}$ 52. $1 \overline{)9}$ 53. $1 \overline{)3}$ 54. $7 \overline{)35}$ 55. $4 \overline{)16}$

56. $3 \overline{)0}$ 57. $4 \overline{)24}$ 58. $1 \overline{)0}$ 59. $6 \overline{)36}$ 60. $4 \overline{)8}$

61. $5 \overline{)35}$ 62. $4 \overline{)36}$ 63. $9 \overline{)27}$ 64. $3 \overline{)12}$ 65. $2 \overline{)6}$

66. $4 \overline{)0}$ 67. $6 \overline{)12}$ 68. $1 \overline{)6}$ 69. $6 \overline{)48}$ 70. $3 \overline{)3}$

71. $7 \overline{)0}$ 72. $9 \overline{)9}$ 73. $7 \overline{)56}$ 74. $8 \overline{)40}$ 75. $7 \overline{)42}$

76. $1 \overline{)7}$ 77. $8 \overline{)16}$ 78. $5 \overline{)20}$ 79. $3 \overline{)24}$ 80. $3 \overline{)15}$

81. $7 \overline{)21}$ 82. $1 \overline{)8}$ 83. $9 \overline{)18}$ 84. $5 \overline{)5}$ 85. $6 \overline{)6}$

86. $4 \overline{)4}$ 87. $9 \overline{)0}$ 88. $2 \overline{)4}$ 89. $7 \overline{)49}$ 90. $2 \overline{)2}$

How long did it take you to complete this practice? _____

How many did you get correct? _____

One Digit Divided by One Digit

1. $2\overline{)7}$
2. $5\overline{)7}$
3. $3\overline{)4}$
4. $1\overline{)5}$

5. $3\overline{)6}$
6. $3\overline{)8}$
7. $2\overline{)4}$
8. $3\overline{)4}$

9. $6\overline{)9}$
10. $4\overline{)9}$
11. $3\overline{)7}$
12. $1\overline{)4}$

13. $5\overline{)6}$
14. $1\overline{)6}$
15. $3\overline{)9}$
16. $5\overline{)8}$

17. $4\overline{)4}$
18. $4\overline{)7}$
19. $2\overline{)2}$
20. $1\overline{)9}$

One Digit Divided by One Digit *(cont.)*

1. $1 \overline{)4}$ 2. $3 \overline{)8}$ 3. $7 \overline{)7}$ 4. $2 \overline{)8}$

5. $5 \overline{)7}$ 6. $5 \overline{)8}$ 7. $2 \overline{)7}$ 8. $3 \overline{)6}$

9. $7 \overline{)9}$ 10. $4 \overline{)6}$ 11. $1 \overline{)7}$ 12. $6 \overline{)9}$

13. $4 \overline{)7}$ 14. $3 \overline{)7}$ 15. $4 \overline{)9}$ 16. $7 \overline{)8}$

17. $1 \overline{)4}$ 18. $1 \overline{)6}$ 19. $2 \overline{)3}$ 20. $3 \overline{)5}$

Two Digits Divided by One Digit

1. $1 \overline{)19}$ 2. $5 \overline{)56}$ 3. $3 \overline{)81}$ 4. $8 \overline{)77}$

5. $3 \overline{)32}$ 6. $4 \overline{)85}$ 7. $4 \overline{)24}$ 8. $1 \overline{)93}$

9. $7 \overline{)38}$ 10. $2 \overline{)54}$ 11. $4 \overline{)67}$ 12. $3 \overline{)62}$

13. $6 \overline{)94}$ 14. $2 \overline{)42}$ 15. $7 \overline{)66}$ 16. $2 \overline{)44}$

17. $9 \overline{)13}$ 18. $4 \overline{)58}$ 19. $9 \overline{)82}$ 20. $5 \overline{)67}$

Two Digits Divided by One Digit (cont.)

1. $5 \overline{)25}$ 2. $4 \overline{)19}$ 3. $8 \overline{)94}$ 4. $9 \overline{)97}$

5. $5 \overline{)44}$ 6. $4 \overline{)61}$ 7. $5 \overline{)49}$ 8. $8 \overline{)71}$

9. $3 \overline{)62}$ 10. $5 \overline{)69}$ 11. $4 \overline{)46}$ 12. $5 \overline{)82}$

13. $2 \overline{)92}$ 14. $2 \overline{)75}$ 15. $3 \overline{)76}$ 16. $7 \overline{)92}$

17. $7 \overline{)53}$ 18. $8 \overline{)22}$ 19. $2 \overline{)67}$ 20. $6 \overline{)71}$

Three Digits Divided by One Digit

1. $2 \overline{)884}$

2. $3 \overline{)933}$

3. $2 \overline{)539}$

4. $7 \overline{)868}$

5. $1 \overline{)725}$

6. $6 \overline{)187}$

7. $2 \overline{)467}$

8. $3 \overline{)399}$

9. $7 \overline{)946}$

10. $5 \overline{)854}$

11. $9 \overline{)818}$

12. $6 \overline{)476}$

13. $8 \overline{)418}$

14. $6 \overline{)282}$

15. $3 \overline{)572}$

16. $4 \overline{)766}$

17. $9 \overline{)962}$

18. $4 \overline{)489}$

19. $5 \overline{)814}$

20. $6 \overline{)725}$

Three Digits Divided by One Digit (cont.)

1. 7) 295

2. 6) 668

3. 8) 641

4. 7) 391

5. 9) 163

6. 9) 839

7. 4) 157

8. 3) 159

9. 8) 398

10. 4) 474

11. 7) 658

12. 3) 563

13. 3) 251

14. 6) 553

15. 1) 515

16. 7) 323

17. 6) 234

18. 2) 839

19. 2) 436

20. 9) 969

Three Digits Divided by One Digit (cont.)

1. $9 \overline{)331}$ 2. $9 \overline{)229}$ 3. $9 \overline{)231}$ 4. $4 \overline{)317}$

5. $3 \overline{)326}$ 6. $4 \overline{)514}$ 7. $6 \overline{)398}$ 8. $4 \overline{)699}$

9. $6 \overline{)661}$ 10. $4 \overline{)739}$ 11. $2 \overline{)711}$ 12. $3 \overline{)577}$

13. $8 \overline{)622}$ 14. $5 \overline{)238}$ 15. $5 \overline{)175}$ 16. $7 \overline{)483}$

17. $6 \overline{)798}$ 18. $3 \overline{)653}$ 19. $9 \overline{)839}$ 20. $6 \overline{)468}$

Three Digits Divided by Two Digits

1. $47 \overline{) 454}$　　2. $77 \overline{) 456}$　　3. $85 \overline{) 783}$　　4. $35 \overline{) 263}$

5. $36 \overline{) 736}$　　6. $19 \overline{) 656}$　　7. $31 \overline{) 561}$　　8. $82 \overline{) 627}$

9. $77 \overline{) 715}$　　10. $33 \overline{) 533}$　　11. $78 \overline{) 957}$　　12. $81 \overline{) 525}$

13. $43 \overline{) 855}$　　14. $63 \overline{) 139}$　　15. $49 \overline{) 223}$　　16. $89 \overline{) 942}$

17. $41 \overline{) 434}$　　18. $62 \overline{) 384}$　　19. $73 \overline{) 436}$　　20. $69 \overline{) 374}$

Three Digits Divided by Two Digits (cont.)

1. $26\overline{)235}$ 2. $43\overline{)519}$ 3. $22\overline{)137}$ 4. $18\overline{)895}$

5. $16\overline{)921}$ 6. $82\overline{)881}$ 7. $35\overline{)209}$ 8. $17\overline{)921}$

9. $28\overline{)777}$ 10. $55\overline{)801}$ 11. $42\overline{)841}$ 12. $53\overline{)207}$

13. $19\overline{)221}$ 14. $15\overline{)822}$ 15. $21\overline{)625}$ 16. $25\overline{)927}$

17. $12\overline{)225}$ 18. $18\overline{)355}$ 19. $62\overline{)994}$ 20. $17\overline{)631}$

Three Digits Divided by Two Digits (cont.)

1. $72 \overline{)\ 672}$ 2. $69 \overline{)\ 531}$ 3. $57 \overline{)\ 242}$ 4. $32 \overline{)\ 834}$

5. $91 \overline{)\ 787}$ 6. $68 \overline{)\ 921}$ 7. $88 \overline{)\ 318}$ 8. $94 \overline{)\ 599}$

9. $49 \overline{)\ 895}$ 10. $24 \overline{)\ 656}$ 11. $26 \overline{)\ 684}$ 12. $81 \overline{)\ 956}$

13. $58 \overline{)\ 658}$ 14. $36 \overline{)\ 578}$ 15. $19 \overline{)\ 246}$ 16. $15 \overline{)\ 678}$

17. $64 \overline{)\ 667}$ 18. $71 \overline{)\ 241}$ 19. $33 \overline{)\ 358}$ 20. $89 \overline{)\ 441}$

Changing Improper Fractions to Mixed Numbers

Write each of these improper fractions as a mixed number. Simplify where possible.

1. $\dfrac{7}{4}$ 2. $\dfrac{15}{7}$ 3. $\dfrac{12}{5}$ 4. $\dfrac{7}{5}$

5. $\dfrac{5}{3}$ 6. $\dfrac{16}{9}$ 7. $\dfrac{10}{3}$ 8. $\dfrac{14}{13}$

9. $\dfrac{12}{11}$ 10. $\dfrac{9}{2}$ 11. $\dfrac{4}{3}$ 12. $\dfrac{7}{2}$

13. $\dfrac{13}{8}$ 14. $\dfrac{6}{5}$ 15. $\dfrac{8}{3}$ 16. $\dfrac{5}{4}$

17. $\dfrac{16}{5}$ 18. $\dfrac{19}{10}$ 19. $\dfrac{15}{12}$ 20. $\dfrac{7}{6}$

21. $\dfrac{12}{9}$ 22. $\dfrac{9}{6}$ 23. $\dfrac{5}{2}$ 24. $\dfrac{16}{12}$

25. $\dfrac{18}{11}$ 26. $\dfrac{9}{5}$ 27. $\dfrac{9}{8}$ 28. $\dfrac{6}{4}$

29. $\dfrac{8}{7}$ 30. $\dfrac{9}{7}$ 31. $\dfrac{11}{5}$ 32. $\dfrac{6}{5}$

33. $\dfrac{14}{9}$ 34. $\dfrac{3}{2}$ 35. $\dfrac{5}{4}$ 36. $\dfrac{18}{13}$

37. $\dfrac{7}{6}$ 38. $\dfrac{9}{8}$ 39. $\dfrac{19}{8}$ 40. $\dfrac{7}{2}$

Converting Mixed Numbers to Improper Fractions

Write each of the mixed numbers as an improper fraction.

1. $4\frac{4}{5}$
2. $3\frac{1}{5}$
3. $2\frac{5}{7}$
4. $7\frac{1}{3}$
5. $9\frac{1}{4}$

6. $1\frac{5}{7}$
7. $9\frac{1}{2}$
8. $9\frac{4}{5}$
9. $2\frac{5}{8}$
10. $9\frac{3}{5}$

11. $4\frac{6}{8}$
12. $1\frac{6}{9}$
13. $8\frac{3}{9}$
14. $7\frac{5}{8}$
15. $8\frac{3}{6}$

16. $5\frac{8}{9}$
17. $2\frac{5}{6}$
18. $4\frac{3}{5}$
19. $3\frac{4}{6}$
20. $1\frac{4}{5}$

21. $4\frac{2}{6}$
22. $9\frac{8}{9}$
23. $7\frac{1}{6}$
24. $1\frac{1}{3}$
25. $4\frac{2}{3}$

26. $5\frac{3}{6}$
27. $8\frac{3}{7}$
28. $6\frac{3}{9}$
29. $3\frac{2}{4}$
30. $6\frac{1}{8}$

31. $9\frac{1}{3}$
32. $7\frac{1}{9}$
33. $2\frac{3}{6}$
34. $8\frac{1}{2}$
35. $9\frac{6}{7}$

36. $1\frac{5}{8}$
37. $6\frac{3}{4}$
38. $5\frac{7}{8}$
39. $8\frac{1}{9}$
40. $6\frac{4}{5}$

Adding Fractions

Add the fractions and write your answer in simplest form where possible.

1. $1\frac{1}{2}$
    $+ 1\frac{1}{2}$

2. $2\frac{1}{3}$
    $+ 1\frac{1}{3}$

3. $5\frac{1}{6}$
    $+ 2\frac{2}{6}$

4. $1\frac{1}{8}$
    $+ \frac{3}{8}$

5. $6\frac{1}{9}$
    $+ \frac{2}{9}$

6. $3\frac{2}{3}$
    $+ 1\frac{1}{3}$

7. $5\frac{1}{4}$
    $+ \frac{2}{4}$

8. $9\frac{1}{2}$
    $+ 1\frac{1}{2}$

9. $2\frac{1}{6}$
    $+ 1\frac{2}{6}$

10. $4\frac{2}{3}$
    $+ 3\frac{1}{3}$

11. $2\frac{1}{8}$
    $+ 1\frac{2}{8}$

12. $7\frac{1}{7}$
    $+ 1\frac{3}{7}$

13. $2\frac{2}{8}$
    $+ 3\frac{1}{8}$

14. $13\frac{1}{3}$
    $+ 1\frac{2}{3}$

15. $22\frac{4}{5}$
    $+ \frac{1}{5}$

16. $101\frac{1}{6}$
    $+ 33\frac{2}{6}$

Adding Fractions (cont.)

Add the fractions and write your answer in simplest form where possible.

1. $\dfrac{2}{3}$
   $+ \dfrac{7}{8}$

2. $\dfrac{7}{8}$
   $+ \dfrac{5}{7}$

3. $\dfrac{1}{3}$
   $+ \dfrac{2}{6}$

4. $\dfrac{4}{5}$
   $+ \dfrac{7}{8}$

5. $\dfrac{3}{5}$
   $+ \dfrac{3}{9}$

6. $\dfrac{4}{5}$
   $+ \dfrac{3}{9}$

7. $\dfrac{1}{6}$
   $+ \dfrac{4}{5}$

8. $\dfrac{6}{7}$
   $+ \dfrac{2}{3}$

9. $\dfrac{7}{9}$
   $+ \dfrac{2}{8}$

10. $\dfrac{1}{9}$
    $+ \dfrac{3}{5}$

11. $\dfrac{4}{5}$
    $+ \dfrac{8}{9}$

12. $\dfrac{7}{8}$
    $+ \dfrac{2}{5}$

13. $\dfrac{4}{6}$
    $+ \dfrac{4}{5}$

14. $\dfrac{4}{7}$
    $+ \dfrac{1}{6}$

15. $\dfrac{7}{9}$
    $+ \dfrac{2}{7}$

16. $\dfrac{5}{9}$
    $+ \dfrac{6}{8}$

Adding Fractions (cont.)

Add the fractions and write your answer in simplest form where possible.

1. $\frac{4}{7}$
   $+ \frac{2}{4}$

2. $\frac{7}{8}$
   $+ \frac{2}{4}$

3. $\frac{3}{8}$
   $+ \frac{4}{9}$

4. $\frac{4}{5}$
   $+ \frac{2}{3}$

5. $\frac{2}{8}$
   $+ \frac{3}{8}$

6. $\frac{1}{2}$
   $+ \frac{5}{7}$

7. $\frac{3}{4}$
   $+ \frac{1}{3}$

8. $\frac{3}{7}$
   $+ \frac{2}{8}$

9. $\frac{4}{5}$
   $+ \frac{5}{9}$

10. $\frac{3}{8}$
    $+ \frac{2}{3}$

11. $\frac{6}{7}$
    $+ \frac{1}{2}$

12. $\frac{2}{7}$
    $+ \frac{6}{7}$

13. $\frac{1}{6}$
    $+ \frac{2}{3}$

14. $\frac{1}{6}$
    $+ \frac{1}{5}$

15. $\frac{5}{8}$
    $+ \frac{5}{7}$

16. $\frac{1}{5}$
    $+ \frac{6}{7}$

Adding Fractions (cont.)

Add the fractions and write your answer in simplest form where possible.

1. $\quad 1\frac{5}{9}$
$+\ 5\frac{2}{4}$

2. $\quad 3\frac{3}{4}$
$+\ 9\frac{4}{8}$

3. $\quad 6\frac{2}{5}$
$+\ 6\frac{1}{5}$

4. $\quad 3\frac{4}{6}$
$+\ 4\frac{7}{9}$

5. $\quad 1\frac{3}{9}$
$+\ 9\frac{6}{9}$

6. $\quad 9\frac{1}{9}$
$+\ 1\frac{5}{8}$

7. $\quad 1\frac{8}{9}$
$+\ 5\frac{6}{7}$

8. $\quad 2\frac{3}{7}$
$+\ 7\frac{7}{9}$

9. $\quad 1\frac{1}{3}$
$+\ 2\frac{7}{8}$

10. $\quad 6\frac{2}{6}$
$+\ 1\frac{2}{4}$

11. $\quad 2\frac{3}{9}$
$+\ 6\frac{2}{8}$

12. $\quad 5\frac{2}{6}$
$+\ 4\frac{3}{7}$

13. $\quad 2\frac{4}{6}$
$+\ 3\frac{5}{6}$

14. $\quad 8\frac{2}{9}$
$+\ 8\frac{4}{6}$

15. $\quad 2\frac{5}{9}$
$+\ 5\frac{3}{8}$

16. $\quad 6\frac{1}{5}$
$+\ 9\frac{5}{6}$

Subtracting Fractions

Subtract the fractions and write your answer in simplest form where possible.

1. $\frac{4}{12}$
   $-\frac{3}{12}$

2. $\frac{7}{8}$
   $-\frac{2}{8}$

3. $\frac{13}{16}$
   $-\frac{7}{16}$

4. $\frac{3}{6}$
   $-\frac{1}{6}$

5. $\frac{5}{6}$
   $-\frac{1}{6}$

6. $\frac{2}{3}$
   $-\frac{2}{3}$

7. $\frac{9}{10}$
   $-\frac{1}{10}$

8. $\frac{5}{8}$
   $-\frac{1}{8}$

9. $\frac{3}{4}$
   $-\frac{1}{4}$

10. $\frac{2}{5}$
    $-\frac{1}{5}$

11. $\frac{10}{11}$
    $-\frac{2}{11}$

12. $\frac{9}{10}$
    $-\frac{3}{10}$

13. $\frac{9}{10}$
    $-\frac{8}{10}$

14. $\frac{11}{16}$
    $-\frac{7}{16}$

15. $\frac{7}{12}$
    $-\frac{3}{12}$

16. $\frac{13}{14}$
    $-\frac{12}{14}$

Subtracting Fractions (cont.)

Subtract the fractions and write your answer in simplest form where possible.

1. $\dfrac{4}{7}$
   $-\dfrac{1}{2}$

2. $\dfrac{6}{9}$
   $-\dfrac{2}{5}$

3. $\dfrac{4}{5}$
   $-\dfrac{7}{9}$

4. $\dfrac{7}{9}$
   $-\dfrac{1}{3}$

5. $\dfrac{3}{4}$
   $-\dfrac{2}{9}$

6. $\dfrac{5}{8}$
   $-\dfrac{3}{7}$

7. $\dfrac{5}{7}$
   $-\dfrac{1}{3}$

8. $\dfrac{2}{7}$
   $-\dfrac{1}{5}$

9. $\dfrac{1}{5}$
   $-\dfrac{1}{8}$

10. $\dfrac{5}{6}$
    $-\dfrac{2}{6}$

11. $\dfrac{2}{3}$
    $-\dfrac{2}{4}$

12. $\dfrac{5}{8}$
    $-\dfrac{5}{9}$

13. $\dfrac{5}{6}$
    $-\dfrac{1}{6}$

14. $\dfrac{7}{9}$
    $-\dfrac{1}{3}$

15. $\dfrac{8}{9}$
    $-\dfrac{7}{8}$

16. $\dfrac{5}{8}$
    $-\dfrac{2}{6}$

Multiplying Fractions

Multiply the fractions and write your answer in simplest form where possible.

1. $\dfrac{2}{4} \times \dfrac{2}{5}$

2. $\dfrac{4}{9} \times \dfrac{5}{6}$

3. $\dfrac{1}{6} \times \dfrac{3}{5}$

4. $\dfrac{4}{8} \times \dfrac{2}{3}$

5. $\dfrac{4}{7} \times \dfrac{4}{9}$

6. $\dfrac{8}{9} \times \dfrac{3}{4}$

7. $\dfrac{3}{8} \times \dfrac{6}{8}$

8. $\dfrac{1}{8} \times \dfrac{4}{9}$

9. $\dfrac{4}{8} \times \dfrac{4}{5}$

10. $\dfrac{3}{4} \times \dfrac{1}{2}$

11. $\dfrac{2}{3} \times \dfrac{7}{9}$

12. $\dfrac{7}{8} \times \dfrac{2}{6}$

13. $\dfrac{6}{9} \times \dfrac{5}{9}$

14. $\dfrac{1}{6} \times \dfrac{3}{6}$

15. $\dfrac{2}{5} \times \dfrac{3}{9}$

16. $\dfrac{4}{9} \times \dfrac{3}{4}$

17. $\dfrac{4}{7} \times \dfrac{3}{4}$

18. $\dfrac{1}{7} \times \dfrac{2}{5}$

19. $\dfrac{4}{5} \times \dfrac{1}{3}$

20. $\dfrac{1}{6} \times \dfrac{4}{9}$

21. $\dfrac{7}{9} \times \dfrac{4}{7}$

22. $\dfrac{1}{4} \times \dfrac{2}{6}$

23. $\dfrac{3}{6} \times \dfrac{3}{8}$

24. $\dfrac{2}{3} \times \dfrac{3}{4}$

Multiplying Fractions (cont.)

Multiply the fractions and write your answer in simplest form where possible.

1. $\frac{4}{7} \times \frac{6}{9}$

2. $\frac{4}{5} \times \frac{1}{2}$

3. $\frac{8}{9} \times \frac{1}{6}$

4. $\frac{1}{5} \times \frac{1}{4}$

5. $\frac{3}{9} \times \frac{5}{6}$

6. $\frac{3}{8} \times \frac{5}{9}$

7. $\frac{2}{5} \times \frac{5}{7}$

8. $\frac{7}{8} \times \frac{2}{8}$

9. $\frac{5}{6} \times \frac{7}{8}$

10. $\frac{2}{3} \times \frac{3}{9}$

11. $\frac{8}{9} \times \frac{7}{9}$

12. $\frac{4}{9} \times \frac{2}{9}$

13. $\frac{6}{9} \times \frac{1}{4}$

14. $\frac{4}{7} \times \frac{2}{6}$

15. $\frac{1}{3} \times \frac{3}{4}$

16. $\frac{4}{6} \times \frac{5}{9}$

17. $\frac{1}{2} \times \frac{2}{4}$

18. $\frac{3}{8} \times \frac{1}{6}$

19. $\frac{5}{7} \times \frac{3}{6}$

20. $\frac{5}{9} \times \frac{2}{5}$

21. $\frac{2}{3} \times \frac{4}{8}$

22. $\frac{7}{8} \times \frac{1}{3}$

23. $\frac{1}{2} \times \frac{2}{8}$

24. $\frac{3}{5} \times \frac{1}{9}$

Dividing Fractions

Divide the fractions and write your answer in simplest form where possible.

1. $\dfrac{1}{5} \div \dfrac{4}{8}$　　2. $\dfrac{3}{9} \div \dfrac{1}{7}$　　3. $\dfrac{2}{7} \div \dfrac{4}{5}$　　4. $\dfrac{3}{5} \div \dfrac{7}{9}$

5. $\dfrac{5}{9} \div \dfrac{4}{6}$　　6. $\dfrac{1}{7} \div \dfrac{4}{9}$　　7. $\dfrac{3}{6} \div \dfrac{4}{5}$　　8. $\dfrac{1}{8} \div \dfrac{2}{5}$

9. $\dfrac{4}{5} \div \dfrac{7}{8}$　　10. $\dfrac{3}{8} \div \dfrac{7}{8}$　　11. $\dfrac{2}{4} \div \dfrac{3}{5}$　　12. $\dfrac{1}{8} \div \dfrac{6}{9}$

13. $\dfrac{1}{7} \div \dfrac{3}{7}$　　14. $\dfrac{8}{9} \div \dfrac{4}{7}$　　15. $\dfrac{1}{2} \div \dfrac{5}{6}$　　16. $\dfrac{1}{5} \div \dfrac{4}{5}$

17. $\dfrac{3}{8} \div \dfrac{2}{6}$　　18. $\dfrac{4}{6} \div \dfrac{1}{2}$　　19. $\dfrac{2}{6} \div \dfrac{1}{5}$　　20. $\dfrac{1}{4} \div \dfrac{5}{6}$

21. $\dfrac{9}{10} \div \dfrac{3}{5}$　　22. $\dfrac{5}{9} \div \dfrac{2}{6}$　　23. $\dfrac{4}{5} \div \dfrac{3}{7}$　　24. $\dfrac{4}{9} \div \dfrac{2}{6}$

Dividing Fractions (cont.)

Divide the fractions and write your answer in simplest form where possible.

1. $\dfrac{3}{4} \div \dfrac{1}{8}$

2. $\dfrac{8}{9} \div \dfrac{2}{3}$

3. $\dfrac{2}{6} \div \dfrac{4}{7}$

4. $\dfrac{3}{4} \div \dfrac{4}{6}$

5. $\dfrac{5}{6} \div \dfrac{5}{9}$

6. $\dfrac{1}{2} \div \dfrac{1}{6}$

7. $\dfrac{6}{7} \div \dfrac{5}{6}$

8. $\dfrac{7}{8} \div \dfrac{2}{9}$

9. $\dfrac{7}{8} \div \dfrac{3}{4}$

10. $\dfrac{1}{8} \div \dfrac{5}{8}$

11. $\dfrac{4}{7} \div \dfrac{6}{9}$

12. $\dfrac{2}{6} \div \dfrac{1}{5}$

13. $\dfrac{5}{9} \div \dfrac{4}{7}$

14. $\dfrac{2}{9} \div \dfrac{2}{9}$

15. $\dfrac{4}{8} \div \dfrac{5}{6}$

16. $\dfrac{3}{9} \div \dfrac{3}{5}$

17. $\dfrac{6}{8} \div \dfrac{2}{3}$

18. $\dfrac{5}{6} \div \dfrac{2}{3}$

19. $\dfrac{1}{5} \div \dfrac{3}{8}$

20. $\dfrac{3}{4} \div \dfrac{7}{9}$

21. $\dfrac{6}{7} \div \dfrac{4}{7}$

22. $\dfrac{1}{8} \div \dfrac{2}{8}$

23. $\dfrac{2}{4} \div \dfrac{6}{9}$

24. $\dfrac{2}{9} \div \dfrac{7}{8}$

Dividing Fractions (cont.)

Divide the fractions and write your answer in simplest form where possible.

1. $\dfrac{1}{8} \div \dfrac{2}{3}$

2. $\dfrac{5}{8} \div \dfrac{6}{8}$

3. $\dfrac{8}{9} \div \dfrac{3}{9}$

4. $\dfrac{1}{7} \div \dfrac{6}{9}$

5. $\dfrac{3}{8} \div \dfrac{2}{6}$

6. $\dfrac{5}{6} \div \dfrac{4}{7}$

7. $\dfrac{4}{5} \div \dfrac{4}{6}$

8. $\dfrac{5}{9} \div \dfrac{4}{9}$

9. $\dfrac{1}{2} \div \dfrac{7}{9}$

10. $\dfrac{4}{9} \div \dfrac{2}{3}$

11. $\dfrac{3}{6} \div \dfrac{6}{8}$

12. $\dfrac{3}{8} \div \dfrac{1}{3}$

13. $\dfrac{3}{4} \div \dfrac{1}{2}$

14. $\dfrac{3}{4} \div \dfrac{1}{3}$

15. $\dfrac{4}{9} \div \dfrac{3}{9}$

16. $\dfrac{5}{8} \div \dfrac{1}{8}$

17. $\dfrac{8}{9} \div \dfrac{2}{4}$

18. $\dfrac{7}{8} \div \dfrac{4}{8}$

19. $\dfrac{1}{2} \div \dfrac{3}{4}$

20. $\dfrac{4}{6} \div \dfrac{6}{7}$

21. $\dfrac{1}{8} \div \dfrac{3}{4}$

22. $\dfrac{6}{9} \div \dfrac{2}{6}$

23. $\dfrac{7}{8} \div \dfrac{4}{5}$

24. $\dfrac{1}{4} \div \dfrac{1}{4}$

Greater Than and Less Than

Complete each problem to show greater than or less than. (Write > or < in the spaces.)

1. 14 _____ 49   2. 91 _____ 47   3. 34 _____ 72

4. 98 _____ 39   5. 86 _____ 22   6. 57 _____ 73

7. 27 _____ 38   8. 48 _____ 39   9. 98 _____ 78

10. 57 _____ 51   11. 46 _____ 65   12. 16 _____ 69

13. 43 _____ 33   14. 44 _____ 87   15. 61 _____ 41

16. 37 _____ 49   17. 46 _____ 31   18. 95 _____ 54

19. 36 _____ 54   20. 32 _____ 24   21. 42 _____ 86

22. 24 _____ 42   23. 74 _____ 83   24. 29 _____ 76

25. 33 _____ 66   26. 42 _____ 67   27. 34 _____ 46

28. 22 _____ 52   29. 62 _____ 22   30. 89 _____ 32

31. 69 _____ 64   32. 64 _____ 41   33. 22 _____ 82

Pictographs

One type of graph that gives us information is called a *pictograph*. In a pictograph, pictures are used instead of numbers.

Read this pictograph to find out the number and types of pets sold in April at Harmony Pet Store.

April Pet Sales at Harmony Pet Store	
birds	
fish	
dogs	
cats	
rabbits	
Key: 1 picture = 5 pets	

1. How many of each of these animals were sold?

   birds _____   fish _____   dogs _____   cats _____   rabbits _____

2. How many more dogs were sold than each of the following?

   birds _____   fish _____   cats _____   rabbits _____

3. Which category of animals do you think brought in more money for Harmony Pet Store? Explain the reason(s) for your choice.

   _____

   _____

   _____

   _____

   _____

Chocolate Consumers of the World

There are chocolate lovers all over the world! Listed below are some of the major chocolate-consuming countries of the world. Beside each country is the average number of pounds/kilograms (lbs/kg) of chocolate eaten per person each year. (Metric conversions, rounded to the nearest tenth, are listed for those using metric measurement.)

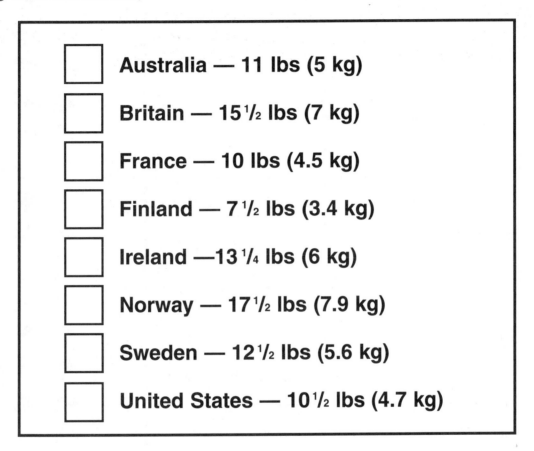

☐ **Australia — 11 lbs (5 kg)**

☐ **Britain — 15 ½ lbs (7 kg)**

☐ **France — 10 lbs (4.5 kg)**

☐ **Finland — 7 ½ lbs (3.4 kg)**

☐ **Ireland —13 ¼ lbs (6 kg)**

☐ **Norway — 17 ½ lbs (7.9 kg)**

☐ **Sweden — 12 ½ lbs (5.6 kg)**

☐ **United States — 10 ½ lbs (4.7 kg)**

Activity

A pictograph is a graph in which pictures or symbols represent information. The graph's key shows the value that each symbol or picture represents. The key on page 155 indicates that one chocolate candy symbol represents one pound of chocolate for each person in a year. Create a pictograph on the "Chocolate Consumers of the World" chart on page 155.

Directions

1. Arrange the countries in order from 1-8, with 1 representing the country that consumes the most chocolate and 8 representing the country with the least amount of chocolate consumed. Write the order in the boxes above. Copy the countries (in order) on the chart on page 155.

2. Cut out the correct number of candies from the bottom of page 155 to represent each country's chocolate consumption. (Use the key to determine how many chocolates to cut out.)

3. Complete the pictograph by gluing the correct number of chocolates next to each country. (Be sure to use half of a chocolate to represent ½ pound, one quarter of a chocolate to show ¼ of a pound, etc. Do the same for kilograms.)

Chocolate Consumers of the World (cont.)

Chocolate Consumption*

Country							

Key: * Each candy represents 1 pound (.45 kg) per person per year.

Circle Graphs

One type of graph that gives us information is called a *circle graph*. In a circle graph, you can show how things are divided into the parts of a whole.

Shown in this circle graph are the types and amounts of fruit sold at a produce stand in a week in July.

Fruits Sold at O'Henry's Fruit Stand

July 1 to July 7

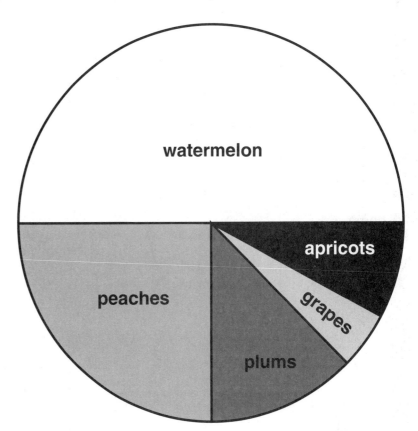

1. What fruit sold the most at O'Henry's Fruit Stand?_____

2. What fruit sold the least?_____

3. Rank the order of the fruits that were sold. Number 1 will be the fruit that sold the most and number 5 the least.

   1. _____   2. _____   3. _____

   4. _____   5. _____

4. Circle the correct fraction.

   Watermelon was $\frac{1}{2}$ $\frac{1}{4}$ $\frac{1}{8}$ of all the fruits sold.

   Peaches were $\frac{1}{2}$ $\frac{1}{4}$ $\frac{1}{8}$ of all the fruits sold.

   Plums were $\frac{1}{2}$ $\frac{1}{4}$ $\frac{1}{8}$ of all the fruits sold.

5. Which of the fruits represented on the circle graph is your favorite?

_____

Slices

In a *circle graph*, all the parts must add up to be a whole. Think of the parts as a pieces that add up to one whole pie.

Look at the circle graph below that shows what Chris did at home between 4 P.M. and 5 P.M. on November 5.

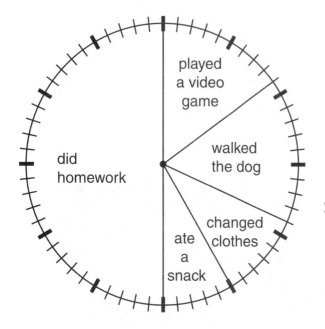

1. How many minutes did Chris spend on the following things?

   doing homework   _____

   eating a snack   _____

   changing clothes   _____

   playing a video game _____

   walking the dog   _____

2. How did you figure out the number of minutes Chris did things?

   _____

   _____

   _____

Make a circle graph that shows what you did during one of your after school hours.

did homework   _____

played a video game   _____

walked the dog   _____

changed clothes   _____

ate a snack   _____

Write the title of your graph here.

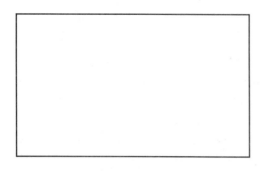

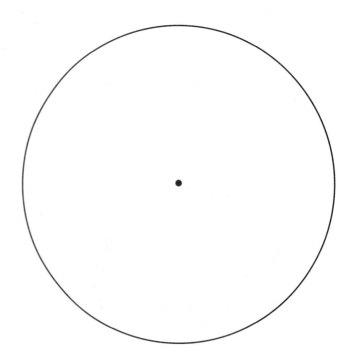

Bar Graphs

One type of graph that gives us information is called a *bar graph*. A bar graph shows us many different types of things by the height or length of the bars.

Sam has to plan ahead to store food for the winter months. The graphs below show two ways Sam could organize his food. Use the graphs to answer the questions.

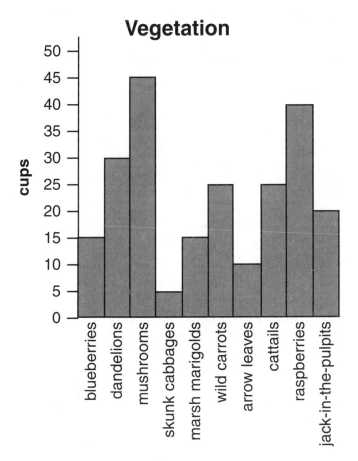

Vegetation

(**Hint:** 2 cups = 1 pint; 2 pints = 1 quart)

1. How many cups of cattails does Sam have? _____

2. How many cups of berries are there? _____

3. How many quarts of raspberries have been stored? _____

4. There are 10 cups of arrow leaves. How many more cups of dandelions than arrow leaves are there? _____

5. How many pints of jack-in-the-pulpits are there? _____

6. If Sam made bread and used one pint of cattails to make flour, how many cups would he have left? _____

7. Which plant has Sam stored the least amount of? _____

8. Which plant has Sam stored the greatest amount of? _____

9. If Sam ate half his store of wild carrots by January, how many cups would he have left for the spring months? _____

(**Hint:** 16 ounces = 1 pound)

1. How many pounds of squirrel are there? _____

2. How many ounces of rabbit meat does Sam have stored? _____

3. How many more pounds of venison than fish are there? _____

4. If Sam used 24 ounces of turtle to make soup, how many pounds would he have left? _____

5. How many pounds of meat does Sam have in all? _____

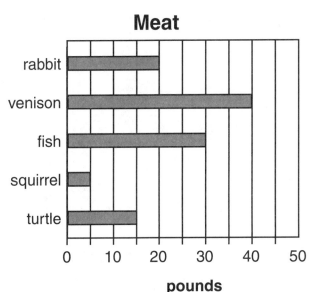

Meat

Using Distance Charts

Distance charts show you the distance between two places if you travel by road.

How Far to New York?

This distance chart shows the miles between 10 North American cities. Look at the chart carefully. Read it by locating the two cities and moving one finger across and one finger down until the two fingers come together to show the distance between cities. Practice. When you are comfortable using the chart, answer the questions below.

Ten-City Distance Chart	Albuquerque	Boston	Chicago	Denver	Indianapolis	Los Angeles	Miami	Montreal	New York City
Boston	2172		963	1949	906	2779	1504	318	206
Chicago	1281	963		996	181	2054	1329	828	802
Denver	417	1949	996		1058	1059	2037	1815	1771
Indianapolis	1266	906	181	1058		2073	1148	840	713
Los Angeles	807	2779	2054	1059	2073		2687	2873	2786
Miami	1938	1504	1329	2037	1148	2687		1654	1308
Montreal	2087	318	828	1815	840	2873	1654		378
New York City	1979	206	802	1771	713	2786	1397	378	
Seattle	1440	2976	2013	1307	2194	1131	3273	2685	2815

Find the distances between these cities.

1. Los Angeles and New York _____

2. Seattle and Albuquerque _____

3. Boston and New York City _____

4. Denver and Miami _____

5. New York City and Chicago _____

6. Montreal and Indianapolis _____

7. Chicago and Miami _____

8. Indianapolis and Denver _____

9. Montreal and Los Angeles _____

10. Seattle and Boston _____

11. Chicago and Boston _____

12. Denver and Albuquerque _____

Interpreting Charts

Students at Hudson Elementary School have been participating in a Read-a-Thon to raise money for their school library. Each student has tallied the number of books he or she has read and is now ready to collect the pledge money.

This chart represents the reading and pledges of 15 students involved in the Read-a-Thon. After reading the chart, answer the questions at the bottom of the page.

Hudson Elementary School Read-a-Thon: Room 3			
Student's Name	**Total Books Read**	**Pledge per Book**	**Money Collected**
Acevedo, Jennifer	31	10¢	$3.10
Adams, Joseph	5	10¢	$ .50
Barton, Michael	61	5¢	$3.05
Duran, Louis	17	15¢	$2.55
Edwards, Marylou	47	5¢	$2.35
Harrison, Trevor	11	25¢	$2.75
Lee, Rebecca	40	10¢	$4.00
Logan, Cassie	22	5¢	$1.10
Marshall, Barbara	9	50¢	$4.50
Peterson, David	102	5¢	$5.10
Ross, Kathryn	58	10¢	$5.80
Rublo, Anthony	83	5¢	$4.15
Shea, Sharon	39	10¢	$3.90
Tran, Alvin	14	10¢	$1.40
Yetter, Liz	75	5¢	$3.75
TOTAL	**614**	——	**$48.00**

1. Which student read the most books?_____

2. What was the highest amount of money collected by one student? _____

   Which student?_____

3. Who had the highest pledge of money per book? _____

4. Was the person who read the most books the same as the person who collected the most money? _____

5. Was the person who had the highest pledge of money per book the same as the person who collected the most money?_____

6. What was the total number of books read by these students? _____

7. How much money did these students earn for the library? _____

Would a Read-a-Thon be a good way to raise money at your school? _____

Using Chart Information

How much do you weigh? Your weight depends upon where you are. If you are in orbit around Earth, far away from Earth's gravitational pull, you would be weightless and would float. Mass is the amount of matter that makes up an object. The gravitational pull depends upon mass. Even a pencil has mass. Thus, it has a gravitational pull, but since it is far less than Earth's mass, it falls to the ground when you drop it.

If you were to visit planets and moons with more or less mass than Earth's, a scale would show you weighed a different amount than you do on Earth. Complete the chart to find out how much you would weigh on the planets in our solar system and on the Moon.

Planet	Surface Gravity		Your Weight on Earth	New Weight
Mercury	.38	x		
Venus	.90	x		
Earth	1.00	x		
Mars	.38	x		
Jupiter	2.64	x		
Saturn	1.13	x		
Uranus	.89	x		
Neptune	1.13	x		
Pluto	.06	x		
Earth's Moon	.17	x		

Using Chart Information (cont.)

Make a graph to show the results of the calculations from your data-capture sheet (page 161).

MY WEIGHT ON THE PLANETS AND THE MOON

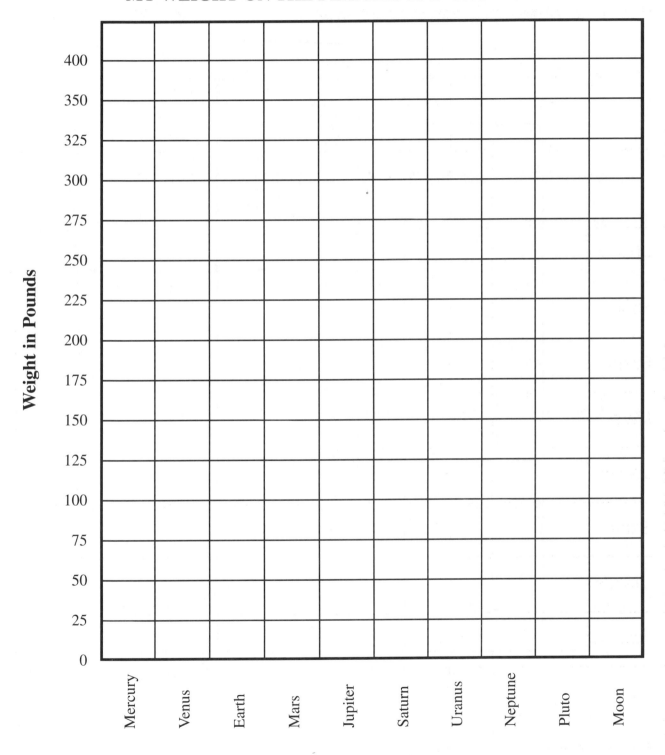

Weight in Pounds

400
350
325
300
275
250
225
200
175
150
125
100
75
50
25
0

Mercury — Venus — Earth — Mars — Jupiter — Saturn — Uranus — Neptune — Pluto — Moon

Location

Locating Points on a Graph

Jim earned a terrific prize for winning first place in the community talent show. The prize he won is spelled out in this graph.

Find the points on the graph that are identified below. Can you discover what Jim won? Each point you find will give you a letter of the hidden prize.

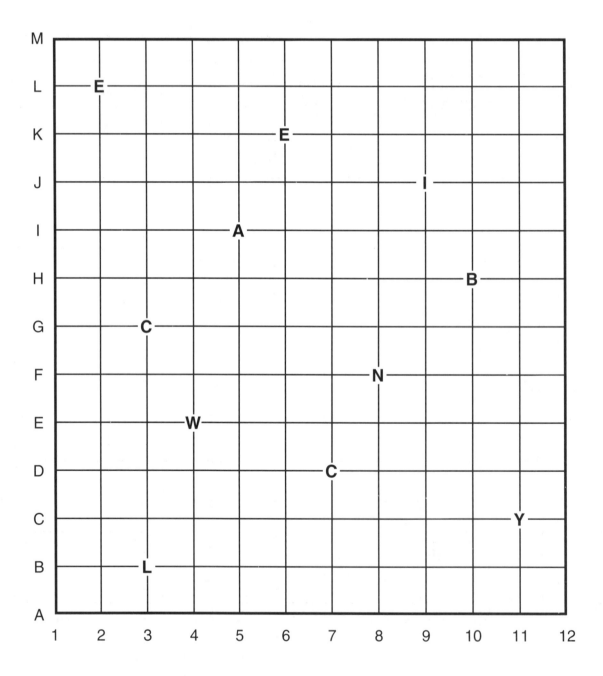

$\overline{\quad}$ $\overline{\quad}$ $\overline{\quad}$ $\overline{\quad}$ $\overline{\quad}$ $\overline{\quad}$ $\overline{\quad}$ $\overline{\quad}$ $\overline{\quad}$ $\overline{\quad}$ $\overline{\quad}$
I,5   F,8   L,2   E,4   H,10 J,9 G,3 C,11 D,7 B,3 K,6

Finding Coordinates on a Graph

How Do You Make a Hot Dog Stand?

The answer to this riddle is written in a special code at the bottom of this page. Each pair of numbers stands for a point on the graph. Write the letter shown at the point near the intersection of each pair of numbers. Read numbers across and then up. The letters will spell out the answer to the riddle.

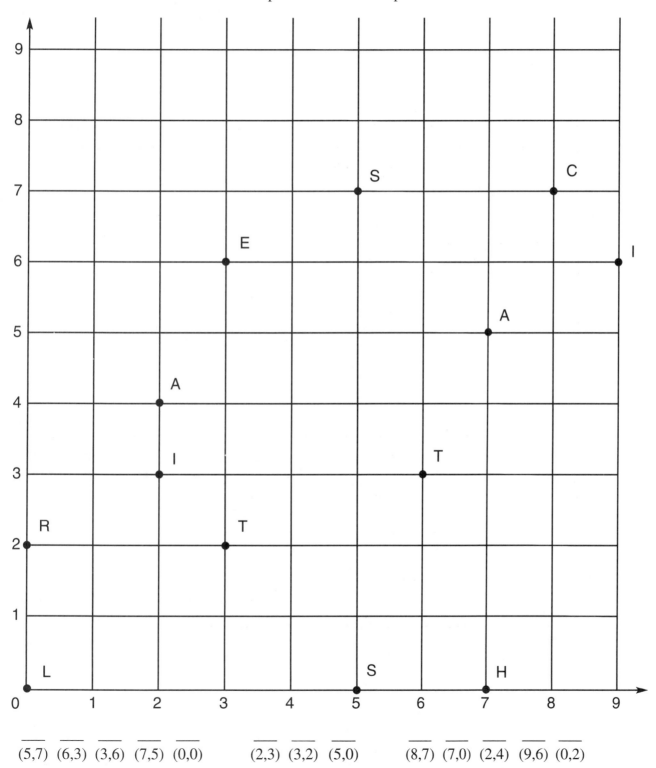

‾‾ ‾‾ ‾‾ ‾‾   ‾‾ ‾‾ ‾‾   ‾‾ ‾‾ ‾‾ ‾‾
(5,7) (6,3) (3,6) (7,5) (0,0)   (2,3) (3,2) (5,0)   (8,7) (7,0) (2,4) (9,6) (0,2)

Simple Addition Word Problems

Read each word problem and then answer the questions.

1. Daniel bought 2 candy bars at 47 cents each. How much did he spend?	2. Laura had 92 cents. She wanted to buy a 35 cent juice and a 49 cent hog dog. How much did she spend? How much change does she receive?
3. Jim put his pennies into 2 small boxes. He put 1396 pennies into each box. How many pennies did he have?	4. The Wilson's drove their car 10,483 miles one year and 19,768 miles the next year. How far did they drive during the two years?
5. Robyn had 296 marbles in one box and 187 marbles in another box. How many marbles did she have?	6. In 1959, the population of Happyville was 28,746. During the next 20 years the population increased by 19,658. What was the population then?
7. Russell bought 4 bags of chips at 60 cents each, 2 sodas at 35 cents each and 2 cookies at 25 cents each. How much did he spend?	8. Tamra wanted to go bowling. She rented shoes for $10.00, paid for 2 games at $2.00 a game and bought one soda for $0.35. How much did she spend?
9. Kristen had 12 red socks, 27 green socks, 13 blue socks and 32 pink socks. How many socks did she have?	10. Paul has 75 rocks in his collection. His Uncle Joe has 139 and wants to give them to Paul. How many will he then have?

Addition and Subtraction Word Problems

Read the following problems. Circle the important facts you need to solve them. Use the space provided to find the solution to each problem.

1. There were 76 students in a school jog-a-thon. Twenty-six of them were in 3rd grade, 28 of them were in 4th grade, and 22 of them were in 5th grade.

   a. How many 4th- and 5th-grade students were in the jog-a-thon? _____

   b. Which grade had the most students in the jog-a-thon? _____

2. The jog-a-thon route covered 150 kilometers. There were 4 rest stops for the runners. Niki ran 52 kilometers and stopped at the second rest stop.

   a. How much further does Niki have to run to complete the route? _____

   b. Had she gone at least half the distance? _____

3. Melita's team wanted to collect a total of $325.00. They collected $208.75 from the jog-a-thon and $76.20 from a candy sale.

   a. How much money did they collect? _____

   b. Would they collect more money from 3 candy sales than from 1 jog-a-thon? _____

4. Twenty team members had lunch together at the third rest stop. They had traveled 70 kilometers. Thirteen team members drank milk with their lunch and the rest drank grape juice.

   a. How many team members drank grape juice? _____

   b. How many students did not drink grape juice? _____

5. Bill, Holly, and Katie collected contributions from their neighbors. Bill collected $13.78, Holly collected $16.85, and Katie collected $12.34.

   a. How much more did Holly collect than Bill? _____

   b. How much did Holly and Katie collect together? _____

6. To get ready, Carol bought new shoes for $36.00 and a new water bottle for $1.36. Her mom gave her $47.00 to spend.

   a. How much did she spend for the shoes and water bottle? _____

   b. How much more were the shoes than the water bottle? _____

Multiplication and Division Word Problems

Read each problem and then answer the questions.

The Bailey family runs a small market that not only sells but also grows fresh fruit and vegetables. They sell gardening tools, seeds, and plants. They help their customers with questions about picking which plants to grow and how to best care for them.

1. Two hundred fifteen watermelon seeds were planted in the ground. Five seeds were planted in each small hole. How many small holes were there?	2. The gardeners at Bailey's Market planted 48 onions in each of 12 rows. How many onions were planted?
3. A clerk sold Garrett a rake for $7.75 and a shovel for $13.77. He paid half and had his brother pay the other half. How much did each pay?	4. Tim bought 2,000 carrot seeds on Monday and 3,985 seeds on Tuesday. He needs to plant all of the seeds. He plants 7 seeds in each hole. How many holes will he have when he is done?
5. Randy planted 7 rows of corn and each row had 8 plants in it. He needed to wrap them into 4 bundles. How many bundles would he have?	6. Two customers each bought 25 potatoes for a pot luck supper. They made 10 pots of stew and used all of the potatoes. How many potatoes did they use in each stew?
7. Each seed packet cost $.79. Robyn bought 9 of them. How much did she spend?	8. Each seed packet has 135 seeds in it. Robyn will need to plant 15 seeds in a row. How many rows will she plant?
9. What will be the total cost of 2 bags of grapes at $2.00 each, 1 bag of potatoes at $1.99 each, and 4 baskets of strawberries at $3.46 each?	10. The workers need to move the display case that has the apples in it. There are 6 different kinds of apples. Each bin has 44 apples in it. How many apples are there in the display case?

Division Word Problems

Read each problem and then answer the questions.

1. You deliver 630 newspapers each week. You deliver the same amount each day. How many papers do you deliver each day?

2. You have a roll of film that will take 24 pictures. How many rolls would you need to take 108 pictures?

3. Patti has 396 gum balls and 12 friends to share them with. How many will each friend get?

4. You have collected 3,960 pennies in an old pickle jar. You have 22 friends that you want to give them to. How many would each friend receive?

5. Doug has 657 decals in his desk drawer. He wants to split them among his 9 friends. How many would each one receive?

6. Chris has 5,987 soccer cards. He wants to sell them in packages of 24. How many packages would he have? Would he have any left over. If so, how many?

7. Mike collects rocks. He has 627 in his collection. He wants to store them in 8 boxes. How many will he have in each box? How many will be left over?

8. Cathy was organizing her photographs and found that she had 156 vacation pictures. If she arranges eight pictures on a photo album page, how many pages will she need?

9. Susan's grandmother was making cookies for Susan's classroom. She made 90 cookies. There are 29 students in Susan's class and one teacher. How many cookies would each person get?

10. The pet store had 78 birds that they had to put in 13 cages. How many birds would be in each cage?

Cardinal Points

There are four directions that are of prime importance when we learn our way around the world in which we live. These directions are north, south, east, and west, and they are sometimes referred to as the four cardinal points. Cardinal points are shown on maps by the use of a compass rose.

There are several ways to make a compass rose.

North and south indicators are often longer than east and west indicators.

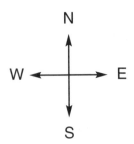

Fill in the direction words that are missing.

1. north west ←→ east _____	2. _____ west ←→ east south
3. north _____ ←→ east south	4. north west ←→ _____ south
5. _____ west ←→ east _____	6. north _____ ←→ _____ south
7. north _____ ←→ _____ _____	8. _____ _____ ←→ _____ _____

Through the Squares

Can you find your way through the squares by following the directions? Color your path as you go. Write your name in the square where you finish.

1. Start above the square marked start here.

2. Go south 5 squares.

3. Go east 2 squares.

4. Go north 3 squares.

5. Go east 4 squares.

6. Go south 2 squares.

7. Go west 3 squares.

8. Go south 3 squares.

9. Go west 4 squares.

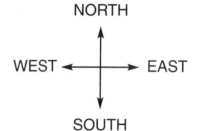

Start here.

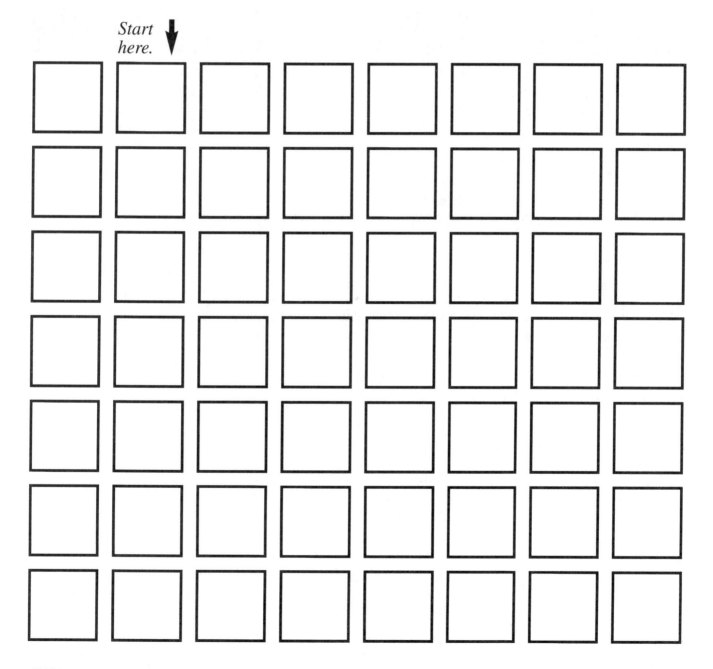

Scale

Map makers can make things on a map larger or smaller than they really are. They can do this by using a map scale. A map scale shows us a way to measure distance. We are told by the scale what kind of measurement equals what kind of distance.

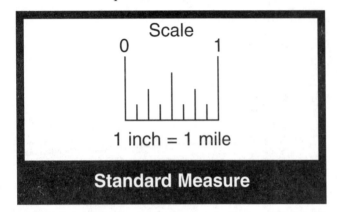

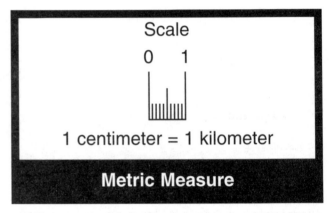

Look at this scale. One inch represents one mile. A road five miles long can be shown on the map as five inches. A road 10 miles long can be shown as 10 inches.

Look at this scale. One centimeter stands for 1 kilometer. A road five kilometers long can be shown on the map as five centimeters. A road 10 kilometers long can be shown as 10 centimeters.

Directions

Use the scales on this page to complete the activities below.

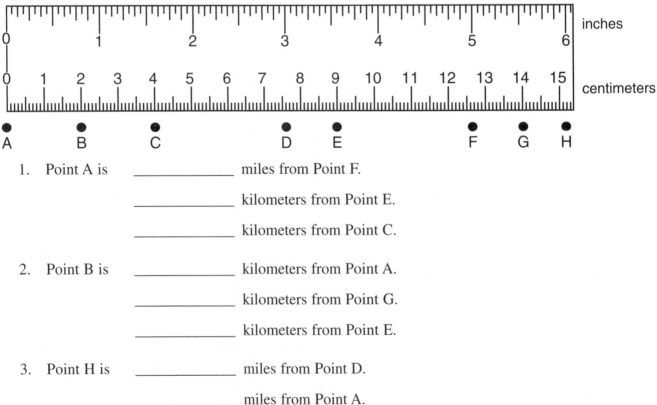

1. Point A is _____ miles from Point F.

   _____ kilometers from Point E.

   _____ kilometers from Point C.

2. Point B is _____ kilometers from Point A.

   _____ kilometers from Point G.

   _____ kilometers from Point E.

3. Point H is _____ miles from Point D.

   _____ miles from Point A.

   _____ miles from Point F.

How Far?

Directions

Use this map scale and metric ruler to answer the distance questions on this page.

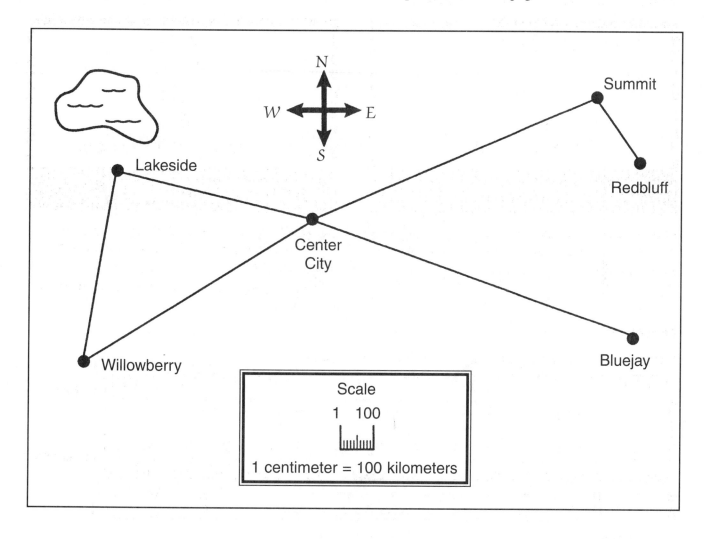

1. Center City is _____ kilometers from Bluejay.

2. Summit is _____ kilometers from Redbluff.

3. Willowberry is _____ kilometers from Lakeside.

4. Bluejay is _____ kilometers from Lakeside.

5. Summit is _____ kilometers from Center City.

6. Center City is _____ kilometers from Lakeside.

7. Willowberry is _____ kilometers from Summit.

8. Center City is _____ kilometers from Willowberry.

7/13/06

How to Measure

When you measure distances using a map scale, you can measure several different ways. The easiest and most accurate way is to use a standard-measure or metric-measure ruler.

You can also use a piece of string, paper, the joints of your fingers, a pencil or pen, or other things that could help you mark size.

Once you have chosen your measurement, place it along the imaginary or real line between the distances you want to measure.

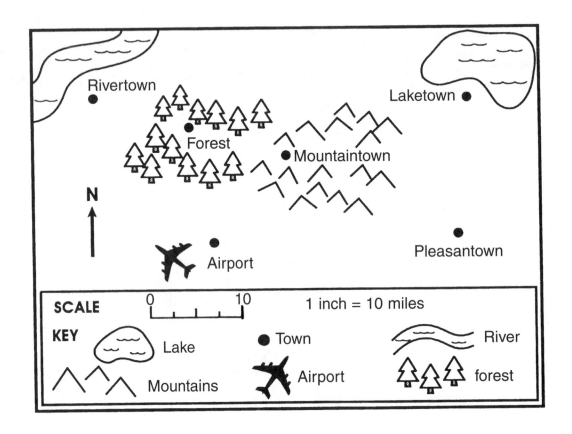

Directions

Find the distance in miles between the following places:

1. Rivertown and the airport _20 miles_

2. Mountaintown and the forest _10 miles_

3. Rivertown and Laketown _40 miles_

4. Mountaintown and Pleasantown _20 miles_

5. Laketown and Mountaintown _20 miles_

6. Rivertown and the forest _10 miles_

The Equator and Hemispheres

The earth is divided into two parts by an imaginary line called the equator. The part of the earth that is north of the equator is called the Northern Hemisphere. The part of the earth that is south of the equator is called the Southern Hemisphere.

The equator is like an imaginary line that divides the sphere of the earth into two half spheres, or hemispheres.

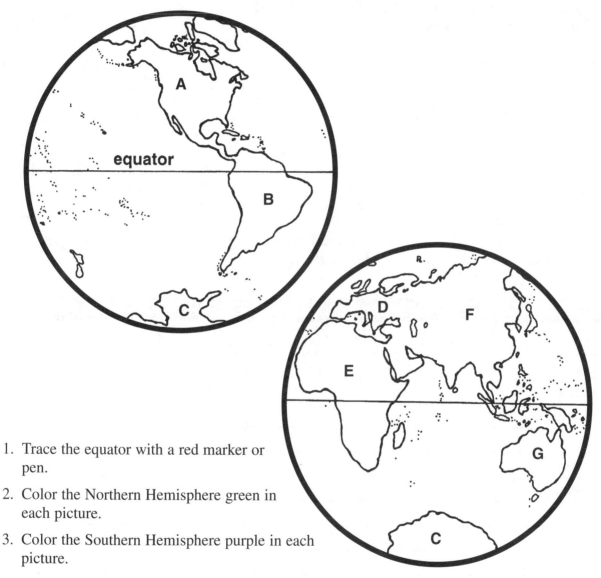

1. Trace the equator with a red marker or pen.

2. Color the Northern Hemisphere green in each picture.

3. Color the Southern Hemisphere purple in each picture.

4. Match the letters below to their locations on the maps above. Write the names of the continents next to their matching letters.

A. _____   E. _____

B. _____   F. _____

C. _____   G. _____

D. _____

Where Is It?

7/1/0[?]

[Use the] hemisphere maps on this page to help you locate the correct hemispheres for the places listed below.

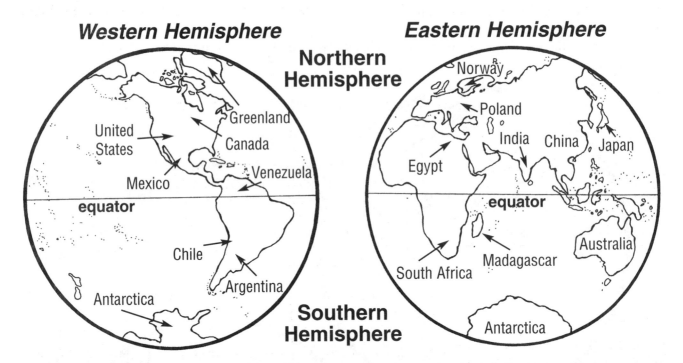

Western Hemisphere

Eastern Hemisphere

Northern Hemisphere

Southern Hemisphere

Hemisphere Location Chart		
Place	Hemisphere (Northern or Southern)	Hemisphere (Eastern or Western)
1. South Africa	S	E
2. Norway	N	E
3. Venezuela	N	W
4. Canada	N	W
5. Japan	N	E
6. Mexico	N	W
7. China	N	E
8. Egypt	N	E
9. United States	N	W
10. Argentina	S	W
11. Poland	N	E
12. Greenland	N	W
13. India	N	E
14. Chile	S	W
15. Madagascar	S	E
16. Australia	S	E

Latitude and Longitude

You can find places in the world by knowing how to read latitude and longitude lines. **Latitude** and **longitude** lines (also called **meridian** lines) are imaginary lines that divide the earth. You have already learned one of these lines—the equator. The equator is the main line of latitude. The **prime meridian** is the main line of longitude.

Latitude

Latitude lines run from west to east. They measure distances north and south of the equator.

The equator cuts the world into north and south latitude. The equator is marked 0 degrees. The latitude lines north of the equator are marked N (degrees north) and the latitude lines south of the equator are marked S (degrees south).

Longitude

Longitude lines run from north to south, pole to pole. They measure distances west and east of the prime meridian.

The prime meridian cuts the world into west and east longitudes. The longitude lines west of the prime meridian are marked W (degrees west) and the longitude lines east of the prime meridian are marked E (degrees east)

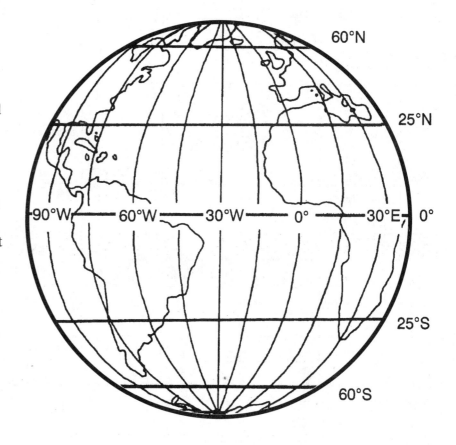

1. Which lines run from west to east? _____

2. Which lines run from north to south? _____

3. The equator is a line of (latitude or longitude)_____.

4. The prime meridian is a line of (latitude or longitude) _____.

419

Latitude and Longitude (cont.)

The intersection of the Earth's latitude and longitude lines from a grid. All of these lines have degree markings. If you know the degrees of latitude and longitude of a certain place, you can easily find it on a map.

The map of Colorado below shows the latitude and longitude lines that divide the state. Use the map to complete the activity at the bottom of the page.

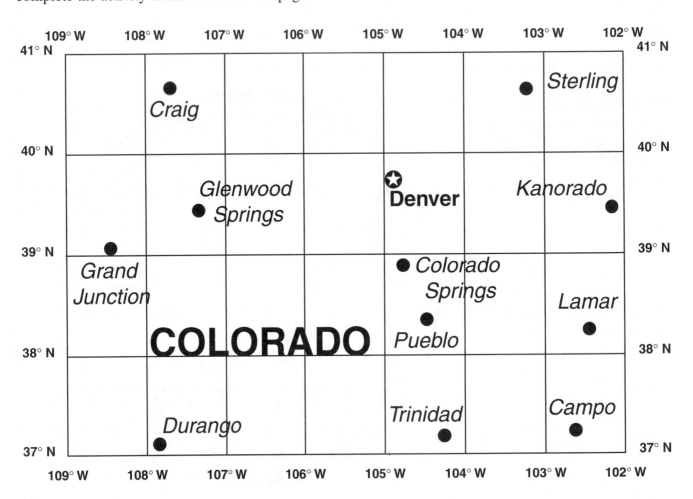

Which city is near each of these latitude/longitude lines?

1. 39°N, 108°W? _Grand Junction_

2. 41°N, 103°W? _Sterling_

3. 40°N, 105°W? _Denver_

4. 38°N, 102°W? _Lamar_

5. 37°N, 108°W? _Durango_

6. 39°N, 105°W? _Colorado Springs_

7. 39°N, 107°W? _Glenwood Springs_

8. 37°N, 103°W? _Campo_

9. 41°N, 108°W? _Craig_

10. 39°N, 102°W? _Lamar_

Continents and Oceans

Use the following map to answer the questions on this page.

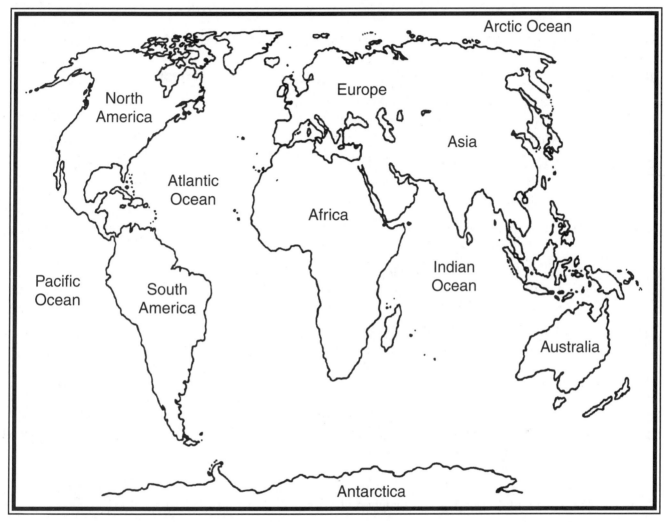

1. The largest areas of land in the world are called continents. There are seven continents. Which continent do you live on?

   _____

2. The largest areas of water in the world are called oceans. There are four main oceans. Which ocean is closest to you?

   _____

3. What are the names of the seven continents?

   _____   _____

   _____   _____

   _____   _____

4. What are the names of the four major oceans?

   _____   _____

   _____   _____

Time Line of World Events, 1933-1945

Use your knowledge of World War II and research skills to match the event with the correct date.

Event

_____ 1. General Montgomery leads the Allies to a victory over the Axis troops in North Africa.

_____ 2. The Germans take over Austria.

_____ 3. Adolf Hitler becomes the leader of Germany.

_____ 4. Japanese planes bomb the United States naval base at Pearl Harbor.

_____ 5. The Japanese attack China.

_____ 6. Germany surrenders (V-E Day) and Japan surrenders (V-J Day).

_____ 7. Japan takes over the Philippines.

_____ 8. Poland is invaded by German and Soviet troops.

_____ 9. The Allies send invasion forces to Normandy, France.

_____ 10. Franklin D. Roosevelt is re-elected as president of the United States for a third term.

Date

A. 1940

B. 1933

C. 1945

D. 1941

E. 1944

F. 1937

G. 1938

H. 1939

I. 1942

J. 1943

Now, use the dates and events that you matched above to construct a time line for World War II.

Time Line of World Events, 1933–1945

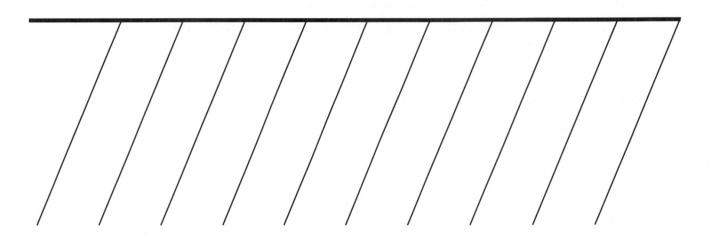

422

Practice & Learn
for
12 Year Olds

Homophones

Circle the word which best completes the sentence.

1. (Where, Wear) are you going this afternoon?

2. (There, Their, They're) are (eight, ate) students absent today.

3. John broke his (tow, toe) while skateboarding.

4. The youngster has (groan, grown) three inches over the year, according to the pediatrician.

5. (Would, Wood) you like to spend this weekend visiting your grandparents in Florida?

6. Pamela could not decide (which, witch) (role, roll) to eat for lunch.

7. The (hair, hare) on the dog's (tail, tale) was singed in the fire.

8. Do you (know, no) how to (sew, so) on the sewing machine?

9. The (air, heir) that we breathe is a renewable resource that still needs to be conserved.

10. The (rode, road) leading to the (steal, steel) mill is filled with potholes from the winter storms.

11. (Too, To, Two) many ships have been lost at (see, sea) in the Bermuda Triangle.

12. At the (fair, fare) grounds a (pair, pare, pear) of diamond earrings was found.

13. Do you (hear, here) the sound of the (planes, plains) as they approach the runway of the airport?

14. (For, Four) hundred wild (boars, bores) stampeded across the grasslands.

15. (There, They're, Their) going to be (seen scene) by the doctor in a few minutes.

16. Who will play the (roll, role) of the (witch, which) in the Halloween play?

Subjects and Predicates

Every sentence has two parts: the *subject* and the *predicate*. The *complete subject,* all the words that tell *whom* or *what* the sentence is about, is the part about which something is said. The *complete predicate,* all the words that tell what the subject *does* or *did* or what the subject *is* or *was,* is the part of the sentence usually following the subject.

Examples

Subject	**Predicate**
The tall sailing vessel	*docked at the long pier.*
Many of the trees	*are losing their leaves.*
Spring flowers	*are beautiful signs of a new season.*

Directions: Draw one line under the complete subject and two lines under the complete predicate.

Example: The winner of the competition was awarded a trophy.

1. The snow was falling heavily during the night, depositing one foot on the ground.

2. The streets and highways were closed for many hours.

3. All the schools in the area had delayed opening for two hours.

4. Most of the elementary school students did not attend school at all.

5. Many high school students were stranded on an overturned bus.

6. A helicopter and an ambulance transported the injured students to the hospital.

7. Another major storm pounded the area, dumping another four feet of snow.

8. The board of education decided to close the schools for two weeks.

9. At first the children enjoyed ice skating, building snowmen, and sledding.

10. The regular school year was extended for two weeks into the month of July.

11. The Little League baseball game schedule was revised and altered.

12. The local pools and beaches changed their lifeguard schedules.

13. Many vacation plans needed to be adjusted or cancelled.

14. The highlight of the summer, the county fair, continued as planned.

Simple Subjects and Predicates

The *simple predicate* of a sentence is the most important word or words of the complete predicate. The simple predicate is the *verb* of the sentence. *Action verbs* tell about an action, while *linking* or *state-of-being verbs* tell that something is or was.

> *Example:*   Rain <u>fell</u> from the sky. Johnny <u>skateboarded</u> to the park. (action)
> Baseball <u>is</u> the national pastime. The dark sky <u>looked</u> threatening. (linking)

The *simple subject* is the most important word or words in the complete subject. The simple subject is also referred to as the *subject of the verb*. It is usually a noun or pronoun. The simple subject answers the question *who* or *what*. To find the subject, locate the verb first and then ask who or what.

> *Example:*   The funny clowns at the circus performed three times.
> Verb: *performed*
> Who or what performed? *clowns*

Directions: Draw *one line* under the *complete predicate*. Then circle the simple predicate or verb.

Example: The frightened dog (barked) at the stranger.

1. The heart is the strongest muscle in the body.
2. The brain is enclosed in the skull.
3. The optic nerve attaches the eye to the brain.
4. The boy broke his femur during the basketball game.
5. The baby could distinguish color at an early age.

Directions: Draw *one line* under the *simple subject* and *two lines* under the <u>simple predicate</u> or <u>verb</u>.
Example: The little <u>kitten</u> <u>sipped</u> the warm milk.

1. Crossword puzzles help develop vocabulary.
2. The clues in these puzzles are definitions.
3. Sometimes students check the dictionary.
4. Maryanne always keeps the dictionary by her side.
5. The cryptogram is another type of word game.
6. This word puzzle has words in code.
7. A word search puzzle includes hidden words.
8. The puzzle solver hunts for the hidden word or words.
9. Some children like to make up their own codes.
10. Summertime is a good time to read and exercise.
11. Michael and Joe join the reading program at their local library.
12. Joan read 20 books last summer.
13. Heather was the first-place winner in the swim competition.
14. The lifeguards awarded her a trophy and a plaque.
15. The librarian distributed certificates to all "reading buddies."

Subjects in Different Positions

The subject is usually at the beginning of a declarative sentence, or statement. That word order is considered *natural*. However, sometimes the subject follows the verb. Then the word order is called *inverted*. To find the subject in an inverted word order sentence, first find the verb. Then ask *who* or *what* before the verb.

> *Example:* **Natural**—The soccer game lasted two hours yesterday.
> Verb: *lasted* Who or what lasted? (game) The subject of *lasted* is *game*.
> **Inverted**—Onto the field dashed the players.
> Verb: *dashed* Who or what dashed? (players) The subject of *dashed* is *players*.

When a sentence begins with *here* or *there*, the subject usually follows the verb.

> *Example:* Here are the golf balls.
> Verb: *are* Who or what are? (golf balls) The subject of *are* is *golf balls*.

Directions: In the sentences below, draw <u>one line</u> under the subject and <u>two lines</u> under the simple predicate or verb. On the line to the right, write *natural* or *inverted* to describe the word order.

1. Here is the equipment for the game. _____

2. Along the coast are twenty humpback whales. _____

3. With a smile on her face, Susan greeted the guests. _____

4. Into the cage climbed the tiger. _____

Interrogative, exclamatory, and imperative sentences may also have unusual word order. To find the subject in an interrogative or exclamatory sentence, change the word order to a declarative sentence.

Interrogative Sentence: Do some trees lose their leaves in autumn?

Declarative Sentence: Some trees do lose their leaves in autumn.

> **Verb:** *do lose*   **Subject:** *trees*

Exclamatory Sentence: What a great game they played!

Declarative Sentence: They played a great game.

> **Verb:** *played*   **Subject:** *they*

An imperative sentence, or command, does not usually contain a subject. The subject is understood to be you. (You) *Close the garage.* (You) *Brush your teeth.*

If a person is named in an imperative sentence, then the name is the subject.

Mark, walk the dog.   *Mark* is the subject.

Subjects in Different Positions (cont.)

Directions: In the sentences below, draw a line under the subject of the verb. If the subject is understood, write (*you*) after the sentence.

1. Please turn the computer off. _____

2. What a wonderful time we had at the party! _____

3. Did you throw a no-hitter during the baseball game? _____

4. Which animals were in the dark and dreary cave? _____

5. Buckle your safety belt before we start the car. _____

6. Draw a map of your bedroom. _____

7. Did your relatives visit for the Fourth of July? _____

8. Did priests make calendars in ancient Babylon and Egypt? _____

9. Jessica, please pass the candy to all the children. _____

10. How many goals did Sam score in the soccer game? _____

11. What a lovely mural is on the subway wall! _____

12. When were the pyramids built in Egypt? _____

Nouns

Nouns are words that name a person, place, thing, or idea.

- **Persons** include both names of people and categories.

  Mr. Blue   children   policemen   teacher   girl   boy

- **Places** can name both specific and general places.

  New York   school   park   department stores   homes

- **Things** refer to objects.

  door   shoes   newspaper   table   globe

- **Ideas** tell about feelings or thoughts.

  love   pain   philosophy   care   liberty   freedom   belief   rules

Directions: Underline the nouns in the following sentences. The number at the end of the sentence tells how many nouns to look for.

1. Summer is a wonderful time of the year. (3)

2. The weather is hot and many children enjoy swimming. (3)

3. Most schools are closed and people have time to go on vacations. (4)

4. The days are longer and we have more hours of sunlight. (3)

5. It is wonderful to go to the pool, beach, or lake. (3)

6. My teacher, Mr. Dawson, visited the Metropolitan Museum of Art in New York City in July. (5)

7. He said that great care and concern are shown by visitors. (3)

8. My friends, Tim and Carol, went to the Statue of Liberty and to Ellis Island. (5)

9. The scent of beautiful flowers drifts across Central Park as we eat our lunch outside. (4)

10. We like to cook hamburgers on the grill and picnic in the backyard. (3)

Directions: Place each of the following words under the correct heading of person, place, thing, or idea.

- France
- happiness
- clouds
- shoelaces
- bicycles
- science
- city
- Ms. Litz
- sounds
- loyalty
- glasses
- Dr. Forest
- love
- table
- pain
- building
- fairness
- Texas

Person	Place	Thing	Idea
Ms. Litz	France	happiness	happiness
Dr. Forest	Building	clouds	science
	City	shoelaces	loyalty
	Texas	Bicycles	rain love
		sounds table	pain

Common and Proper Nouns

Common nouns are words that name any person, place, or thing. They begin with small letters.

Examples: house   buildings   statues   city   country

Proper nouns are words that name specific people, places, or things. These words begin with a capital letter.

Examples: White House   Empire State Building   Statue of Liberty   San Francisco   United States

Directions: In the following sentences, put one line under each common noun and two lines under each proper noun.

1. The first president of the United States was George Washington.

2. The Eiffel Tower is a tourist attraction in Paris.

3. John Glenn is well known as a famous astronaut.

4. There are many famous bridges such as the Golden Gate Bridge in California and the George Washington Bridge in New York.

5. The Space Needle is a tourist attraction in Seattle, Washington.

Directions: Match each common noun in column A with a proper noun in column B.

Column A	Column B
_____ 1. city	A. Bingo
_____ 2. river	B. *Titanic*
_____ 3. building	C. Asia
_____ 4. movie	D. Dallas
_____ 5. newspaper	E. French
_____ 6. game	F. Mississippi
_____ 7. continent	G. *New York Times*
_____ 8. ocean	H. Twin Towers
_____ 9. people	I. Pacific
_____ 10. ship	J. *The Little Mermaid*

Directions: Write the letter *C* by each word that is a common noun. If the word is a proper noun, label it with the letter *P*.

1. Mr. Brown _____

2. sun _____

3. king _____

4. King Charles _____

5. Mickey Mouse _____

6. Mt. Olympus _____

7. Nile River _____

8. table _____

9. president _____

10. Aunt Nellie _____

Singular and Plural Nouns

Singular nouns name only one person, one place, or one thing.
> *Example:* dog   house   child

Plural nouns name two or more persons, places, or things.
> *Example:* dogs   houses   children

A. Most plurals are formed by adding the letter *s* to the noun.
> *Example:* dog—dogs

B. If the last two letters of a noun are a vowel (*a, e, i, o, u*) plus the letter *y*, just add the letter *s*.
> *Example:* key—keys

C. If the last two letters of a noun end in a consonant and the letter *y*, change the y to *i* and add the letters *es*.
> *Example:* baby—babies

D. If a noun ends with the letter *f* (or sometimes *fe*), change it to the letter *v* and add *es*.
> *Example:* elf—elves

E. If the last two letters of the noun end in a vowel (*a, e, i, o, u*) plus the letter *o*, just add the letter *s*.
> *Example:* patio—patios

F. If the last two letters end in a consonant and the letter *o*, add the letters *es*.
> *Example:* tomato—tomatoes

G. If a noun ends with *s, z, sh, ch,* or *x,* add the letters *es*.
> *Example:* box—boxes

Directions: Write the plural form of each word.

1. fox   _____
2. knife   _____
3. apple   _____
4. stereo _____

5. lady   _____
6. family _____
7. monkey _____
8. giraffe _____

Directions: In the following sentences label each underlined word (S) singular or (P) plural.

1. The <u>zookeeper</u> must keep all the <u>animals</u> clean and healthy.
2. Three <u>men</u> used <u>axes</u> to chop the <u>trees</u> down in the <u>forest</u>.
3. The <u>man</u> and <u>woman</u> waited patiently for the next <u>bus</u> to arrive.
4. <u>Cars</u> waited for the <u>children</u> to cross the street.
5. <u>Ponies</u>, <u>monkeys</u>, <u>lions</u>, and <u>bears</u> are attractions at the <u>circus</u>.
6. <u>Leaves</u> fall off <u>trees</u> in autumn.
7. The busy <u>bee</u> buzzes around the beautiful <u>flowers</u> before landing.
8. <u>Flashes</u> of lightning lit the evening <u>sky</u> before a <u>bolt</u> struck the <u>benches</u>.
9. <u>People</u> on <u>farms</u> usually live in rural <u>areas</u>.
10. People in a large <u>city</u> live in a metropolitan <u>area</u>.

Possessive Nouns

Possessive nouns are nouns that are written to show ownership.

    A. *Singular nouns* show ownership when an apostrophe plus *s* ('s) are added at the end of the word.
        Example: This book belongs to Dina.
                   This is *Dina's* book.

    B. Plural nouns that end with the letter *s* show ownership when an apostrophe is added after the ending letter *s*.
        Example: These toys belong to the boys.
                   These are the *boys'* toys.

    C. Plural nouns that do not end with the letter *s* show ownership when an apostrophe plus *s'* is added at the end of the word.
        Example: This bus belongs to the children.
                   This is the *children's* bus.

Directions: Write each underlined word in the possessive form.

1. <u>Mr. Briggs</u> house was the largest on the block.   _____

2. The <u>mens</u> coats were hanging in the front closet.   _____

3. The <u>birds</u> nest was on the fifth branch of the tree.   _____

4. My <u>sisters</u> plant grew taller than mine.   _____

5. When the <u>puppies</u> collars slipped off, we put them on again. _____

6. We found the <u>mouses</u> cheese was left uneaten.   _____

7. The <u>libraries</u> checkout systems were not working today.   _____

8. <u>Womens</u> clothing is located on the second floor.   _____

9. <u>Freds</u> ride arrived earlier than expected.   _____

10. Mary tuned the <u>guitars</u> strings before each song.   _____

Directions: Underline the correct possessive in each of the following sentences.

1. All of the (girls, girl's girls') bookbags were placed on the chairs.

2. The (teachers, teacher's, teachers') notebook contained all the marks for her class.

3. The (babys, baby's, babies') cries in the hospital nursery woke everyone up.

4. All (players, player's, players') hats were new and clean before the game started.

5. The largest (deers, deer's, deers') tracks were easily seen in the freshly fallen snow.

Directions: Write the singular and plural possessive forms for each noun.

Noun	*Singular Possessive*	*Plural Possessive*
1. cat	_____	_____
2. mouse	_____	_____
3. runner	_____	_____

Noun Abbreviations

Abbreviations are shortened forms of words, usually nouns. The abbreviation of a proper noun is written with a capital letter. Periods usually follow an abbreviation.

Directions: Write the abbreviations for the following words.

Days of the Week

Sunday_____

Monday_____

Tuesday_____

Wednesday_____

Thursday_____

Friday_____

Saturday_____

Months of the Year

January_____

February_____

March_____

April_____

May_____

June_____

July_____

August_____

September_____

October_____

November_____

December_____

Titles

Mister_____

Doctor_____

Reverend_____

President_____

Senator_____

Governor_____

Captain_____

General_____

Professor_____

Junior_____

Senior_____

Streets

Drive_____

Avenue_____

Road_____

Boulevard_____

Parkway_____

Highway_____

Street_____

Place_____

Lane_____

Places

Fort_____

Mountain_____

River_____

National Park_____

States
(Use zip code abbreviations—no periods.)

New York_____

New Jersey_____

California_____

Texas_____

Wisconsin_____

Illinois_____

Kentucky_____

General

Celsius_____

Fahrenheit_____

United States Navy_____

District Attorney_____

Subject Pronouns

Pronouns are words that are used to take the place of a noun in a sentence.

Subject pronouns are used to take the place of one or more of the nouns in the subject.

    A. Singular Subject Pronouns: B. Plural Subject Pronouns:

       I   *you*   *he*   *she*   *it*   *we*   *you*   *they*

Examples: Mary and Tom went shopping at the mall.

                  Mary and he went shopping at the mall.

                  She and he went shopping at the mall.

Subject pronouns are used after a state-of-being (linking) verb.

Example: The winners of the race were Tom and Mary.

              The winners of the race were Tom and she.

              The winners of the race were he and she.

Directions: Choose the correct subject pronoun in each of the following sentences.

1. The tallest children in the class are Sally and (I, me).

2. (We, Us) girls decorated the room for the surprise party.

3. Tom and (him, he) will pick up the soda before coming.

4. (They, Them) said that they will be late arriving.

5. The hostesses at the party will be Karen and (she, her).

6. (She, her) and (I, me) will come early to help you.

7. The first guests to arrive were Craig and (him, he).

8. (They, us) said the party was fun.

Directions: Use the correct subject pronoun in place of the words in parentheses.

1. Steffanie and _____ like to go to the museum on Sunday afternoons. (Christine)

2. Christine and _____ made dinner for the whole family. (Kevin)

3. _____ is a beautiful instrument if played well. (the piano)

4. The singers were _____ and I. (John)

5. _____ are scheduled to play basketball on Saturday. (Bob, Larry, Phil, Jack)

Directions: Rewrite this sentence twice. The first time, substitute only one subject pronoun. The next time, substitute two subject pronouns.

Carl and Mike like to water-ski in the summer. _____

_____

Possessive and Reflexive Pronouns

Possessive pronouns show ownership.

A. Singular Possessive Pronouns:

    my   *mine*   *your*   *yours*   *his*   *hers*   *its*

B. Plural Possessive Pronouns:

    our   *ours*   *your*   *yours*   *their*   *theirs*

Reflexive pronouns refer to the subject of the sentence and end with *self* or *selves*.

A. Singular Reflexive Pronouns:

    myself   *yourself*   *himself*   *herself*   *itself*

B. Plural Reflexive Pronouns:

    ourselves   *yourselves*   *themselves*

Directions: Underline the possessive pronouns in the following sentences.

1. My bicycle is the green one in front of Katie's house.

2. The science book is mine, not yours.

3. Your brother can run faster than mine.

4. She had her hair cut at the new salon in town.

5. My mother bought our new shirts at the shopping mall on Thursday.

6. How far away is his house from the school bus stop?

7. Their house is painted white and has green shutters.

8. The children placed their cookies on the kitchen table.

Directions: Complete each of the following sentences with the correct reflexive pronoun. Use the list at the top of the page to help you.

1. They treated _____ to an ice-cream sundae at the soda shop.

2. "We should treat _____ to a good movie tonight."

3. Beth reminded _____ that she had forgotten her math book.

4. Will considers _____ to be the best hockey player on the team.

5. The coach told his players, "Don't upset _____ , or you will not play well."

6. The little girl said that she didn't want her mother to help her get dressed because she could do it _____ .

7. We can call Sarah, or you can call her _____ .

8. We recognized _____ in our class graduation picture.

Object Pronouns

Object pronouns are used to replace nouns.

   A. Singular Object Pronouns:
      me   you   him   her   it

   B. Plural Object Pronouns:
      us   you   them

Object pronouns can be used as the *direct object* in a sentence. This happens when the word receives the action sent to it by the verb.

   Example: John threw it.
                John saw him and her.

The verb in the first sentence is *threw.* "It" is the word that received the action. The question you can ask to help find the direct object is "What was thrown?" The answer to this is "it."

The verb in the second sentence is *saw.* What was seen? The answer is *him* and *her.* In this case, there are two answers which make it a *compound object.*

Object pronouns can also be used as the object of the preposition in prepositional phrases.

   Example: Sue and Ellen came with him.

In this sentence *him* is the object in the prepositional phrase *with him.*

Directions: Underline the object pronouns in each of the following sentences.

   1. Polly cried all day about it.

   2. Her mother helped her look for the missing book.

   3. Please help Tim and him with the groceries.

   4. Did you see them at the store?

   5. Herb joined us on the checkout line.

   6. I asked her and him about the game.

   7. The teacher gave me the part in the play.

   8. You will see us in the play.

Directions: Insert an object pronoun in the blank in each of the following sentences.

   1. He found _____ seated in the front of the auditorium. (singular)

   2. Would you tell Philip about _____ part in the school play. (singular)

   3. We saved _____ some seats. (plural)

   4. They must give _____ the tickets to the movie. (plural)

   5. I bought the popcorn for _____ . (singular)

   6. Did you make arrangements with him or _____ ? (singular)

Pronouns and Antecedents

Pronouns are words that are used to take the place of nouns.

Antecedents are words to which the pronouns refer.

A. Antecedents are nouns (or sometimes other pronouns) in the sentence.

B. Antecedents usually come before the pronoun in the same sentence.

C. Antecedents sometimes appear in the sentence just before the one with the pronoun.

Singular Pronouns:

I	me	mine	you	your	yours	he
she	it	him	her	his	hers	its

Plural Pronouns:

we	us	our	ours	you	your
yours	they	them	their	theirs	

Examples:

1. Evan took great care growing his garden. (*His* refers to the antecedent noun *Evan*).

2. Carl tumbled down the hill. He was badly bruised. (*He* refers to the antecedent *Carl*.)

Directions: Underline the pronoun and circle its antecedent.

1. Wanda said the library is not far from where she works.

2. Biking is fun. It is usually done in warm weather.

3. Craig and Bill came in at three o'clock. They were playing football.

4. Carla said she didn't feel well.

5. Louise said her mother would be home soon.

6. Bob and Jim set everything up for their party.

Directions: Supply the correct pronoun in the following sentences.

1. Jennifer and Betty brought _____ books with them.

2. The library was not open. The sign said _____ was closed on Sunday.

3. The sale at the store ended before Hal got there. _____ was very disappointed.

4. Debra felt that _____ project was the best in the class.

5. Margo and Katie took _____ walk at the same time every evening.

6. Wendy liked the way _____ looked in her new dress.

7. Baseball players must practice to keep _____ skills sharp.

8. Jack took the last shot in the basketball game. _____ scored the winning point.

Indefinite Pronouns

Indefinite pronouns are words that do not refer to a specific person or to a specific thing.

A. Singular Indefinite Pronouns:

another	*everything*	*each*	*anybody*	*everyone*
someone	*anything*	*one*	*nobody*	*anyone*
either	*someone*	*everybody*	*neither*	*no one*

B. Plural Indefinite Pronouns:

several	*many*	*few*	*both*

Directions: Underline each indefinite pronoun in the following sentences.

1. Everybody brought his own chair to the outdoor concert.

2. Neither has come with a camera.

3. I don't know if anyone can bring a lunch.

4. Each was given a ticket when he or she paid.

5. Somebody agreed to hold her flowers during the performance.

Directions: Choose the correct pronoun for the indefinite pronoun that is its antecedent.

Example: Everyone missed (their, his) cue to come onto the stage.
                 Everyone is the antecedent, and *his* is the correct pronoun because *everyone* is
                 singular and the pronoun must agree with its antecedent.

1. I am sure that no one will be willing to pay that much money for (his, their) entry fee.

   Antecedent: _____

   Pronoun: _____

2. One of my friends said that (she, her) read that book last month.

   Antecedent: _____

   Pronoun: _____

3. Each of the children in my family has (his, her, his or her, its, their) own set of roller blades.

   Antecedent: _____

   Pronoun: _____

4. Either of the movie critics can make (their, his, his or her) own choice about the best movie.

   Antecedent: _____

   Pronoun: _____

Verbs

Verbs are words that express action or being.

An *action verb* describes physical action, that which can be seen.

   Example: Tom collected stamps and coins.

Sometimes the verb expresses mental action, that which cannot be seen.

   Example: Candice knew all the answers on the test.

A *linking verb* joins or links the subject of a sentence with a word or words in the predicate. It tells that something *is* or *was*.

   Example: The pot on the stove was hot!

Common Linking Verbs:

am	*be*	*feel*	*has been*	*is*	*been*	*sound*
have been	*are*	*being*	*taste*	*was*	*will be*	*look*
had been	*were*	*become*	*appear*	*seem*		

Directions: In each of the sentences below, underline the verb. Label each verb *action* or *linking*. If the verb is an action verb, write *PA* for physical action or *MA* for mental action.

_____   1. Lightning flashed across the sky.

_____   2. The quarterback raced down the field.

_____   3. The winner is the first person to cross the finish line.

_____   4. The crackling fire looked beautiful!

_____   5. The roasting marshmallows smelled delicious!

_____   6. The hunters captured a turkey and a deer.

_____   7. Hailstones are little ice balls.

_____   8. Fog covered the airport, preventing the planes from landing.

_____   9. Trucks skidded on the snow-covered highways.

_____   10. Dew formed on the grass in the early morning.

_____   11. The magician pulled a bouquet of flowers from the scarf.

_____   12. Mike appears frail after his operation.

_____   13. Kitty seems to be the fastest runner in the sixth grade.

_____   14. The young boys became excellent ranch hands.

Main Verbs and Helping Verbs

A *verb* is one word or a group of words. If there are two or more that make up the verb, the last word is the *main verb*. It expresses action or being. The *helping verb* is the verb that helps the main verb express the action.

> *Example:* is walking, are racing

The helping verb and the main verb are sometimes separated by other words in the sentence.

> *Example:* Can chickens *fly*? Joseph *must* not *have heard* the doorbell.

The most common helping verbs are forms of *be*, *have*, and *do*.

be—*am, is, are, was, were, will be*
have—*have, has, had*
do—*do, does, did*
Other common helpers—*could, should, would, can, must*

Directions: In the sentences below, underline the verbs. Then write the parts of the verb in the correct columns. The first example has been completed for you.

	Helping Verb(s)	Main Verb
1. Lois has sketched a scene of the trees.	has	sketched
2. Have you ever visited the White House?		
3. A senator is elected for a term of six years.		
4. A president can serve for two elected terms.		
5. What will be needed for the experiment?		
6. The farmer has planted three acres of corn.		
7. The children were dressed in costumes.		
8. The pool has been closed all week.		
9. The beaches will reopen on Saturday.		
10. The planes are circling the airport now.		
11. The criminal could not control his temper.		
12. Have you ever collected dolls?		
13. Valerie will be going to the zoo tomorrow.		
14. The Tigers have won the tournament.		

Verb Tenses

Tense is time expressed by a verb. The tense tells whether the action or state of being takes place in the present, past, or future.

The present tense tells about action or state of being happening now. Sometimes *s* or *es* is added to the base word when the subject is singular.

    Example: I play the flute. I am on vacation. She likes Jello.

The past tense tells about action or state of being that has been completed. Most past-tense regular verbs end in *d* or *ed*. Others change their spelling.

    Example: The boy climbed the tree. He was in the park. She sang a song.

The future tense tells about action or state of being that will take place at some time in the future. The helping verbs *will* or *shall* are used with the main verb.

    Example: The bus will arrive in one hour. I shall be on it.

Directions: Underline the verb in each sentence. Label the verb tense *present, past,* or *future.*

_____   1. Will the airplane take off on time?

_____   2. The flight left Kennedy Airport at 11:00 A.M.

_____   3. Jordan landed at 2:00 P.M. in Fort Lauderdale.

_____   4. The plane ride was bumpy and uncomfortable.

_____   5. The pilot steers the plane to the terminal.

_____   6. Now Jordan waits for his baggage.

_____   7. Jordan meets his grandparents and drives home.

_____   8. The rain beats heavily on the windshield.

_____   9. According to the forecast, the sun will shine in the morning.

_____ 10. Jordan and his grandfather played golf every morning.

Directions: Complete the sentences with the correct indicated tense of each italicized verb in parentheses.

11. The sun _____ in the east every morning. (*rise,* present)

12. The astronauts' spacesuits _____ them from the cold and heat. (*protect,* past)

13. NASA _____ a new weather satellite. (*launch,* past)

14. The next space shuttle _____ Earth for many years. (*circle,* future)

15. Once many herds of buffalo _____ this country. (*roam,* past)

Verbs with Direct and Indirect Objects

A *direct object* is the word in the sentence that receives any action from the verb.

> *Example:* *The dog caught the ball.*
> The verb is *caught*.
> What was caught? (*ball*)

Ball is the direct object because it receives the action of the verb. You may find it helpful to first find the verb and then ask "what?"

Directions: Put two lines under the verb and one line under the direct object.

1. Mom drove us to the mall.

2. John asked for the book, and the librarian brought it.

3. Dad read the newspaper before dinner.

4. We picked apples from the tree.

5. The teacher collected the papers.

6. They found us asleep in front of the television.

An *indirect object* tells if something was done for someone or to someone. This is the indirect object of the sentence.

> *Example:* *Martha brought him a book.*
> The verb is *brought*.
> The direct object is *book*. (Brought what?)

The indirect object answers the question *for whom*? (him) *Him* is the indirect object. Indirect objects always come before the direct object.

Directions: Answer the questions to find the direct and indirect objects in the following sentences.

1. Mom bought us a new CD.

   A. What is the verb? _____

   B. What is the direct object? _____

   C. For whom or to whom is something being done? _____ is the indirect object.

2. Please send him this letter.

   A. What is the verb? _____

   B. What is the direct object? _____

   C. For whom or to whom is something being done? _____ is the indirect object.

Verbs and Predicate Adjectives

Every sentence has two parts. One part is the complete subject, and the other part is the complete predicate. The predicate of the sentence contains the verb, also known as the simple predicate. Two types of verbs can be used. One is an action verb, and the other is a linking verb, also known as the state-of-being verb. An adjective that comes after a state-of-being verb and modifies the subject is called a *predicate adjective*.

> *Example:* The child was tired.
> *Child* is the subject.
> *Tired* describes the child and comes after the predicate *was*.

Directions: After each sentence, write the *subject, predicate* and *predicate adjective* on the lines provided. Be alert that some of these sentences are inverted, so the predicates (and predicate adjectives) will come before the subjects rather than after.

Sentence	Subject	Predicate	Predicate Adjective(s)
1. The soup was hot and delicious.			
2. The room was dark and cool.			
3. Famous throughout the world is the Statue of Liberty.			
4. Fierce and cold was the wind.			
5. We felt happy after getting our gifts.			
6. Jodi felt relaxed after reading her book.			
7. The lights in the store windows are colorful.			
8. The game was unbelievable.			
9. The train whistle sounds low.			
10. Cool and chilling was the rain.			

Directions: Complete the following sentences.

1. The cake was _____ .

2. The sky seemed _____ .

3. Old and worn was _____ .

4. Loud and noisy is _____ .

5. The song is _____ .

Principal Parts of Regular Verbs

The three main forms of a verb are its *principal parts.* The principal parts are the *present,* the *past,* and the *past participle.*

The **present part** of the verb is its present tense. To form the future tense, just add *will* or *shall* to the present part.

The **past part** of the verb is its past tense. Add *d, ed,* or change a *y* to an *i* if preceded by a consonant.

The **past participle** is always used with a helping verb such as *have, has, had, was, has been, had been, will have, should have been, could have been.*

Present	Past	Past Participle
walk(s)	walked	(have, has, had) walked
study(s)	studied	(have, has, had) studied
rub(s)	rubbed	(have, has, had) rubbed

Directions: Write the past and past participle for each of the following verbs.

	Present	Past	Past Participle
1. rush	_____	_____	_____
2. ruin	_____	_____	_____
3. pass	_____	_____	_____
4. try	_____	_____	_____
5. grade	_____	_____	_____
6. provide	_____	_____	_____
7. slip	_____	_____	_____

Directions: Complete each sentence with a correct form of the verb in parentheses. Then write the name of the principal part used.

8. Many kinds of animals _____ Africa's plains. (roam) _____

9. Monkeys have always _____ trees in the jungle. (climb) _____

10. Crocodiles _____ in Africa's rivers. (live) _____

11. Elephants have been _____ for their tusks. (kill) _____

12. Last year the children _____ gazelles. (study) _____

Irregular Verbs

Irregular verbs are verbs that do not add *d* or *ed* to the past or past participle forms. Changes are made to the spelling of the present tense to form the past or past participle.

Present	Past	Past Participle (have, has, had)	Present	Past	Past Participle (have, has, had)
come(s)	came	come	begin(s)	began	begun
run(s)	ran	run	ring(s)	rang	rung
go(es)	went	gone	drink(s)	drank	drunk
do(es)	did	done	swim(s)	swam	swum
see(s)	saw	seen	fall(s)	fell	fallen
say(s)	said	said	eat(s)	ate	eaten
bring(s)	brought	brought	fly(ies)	flew	flown
think(s)	thought	thought	know(s)	knew	known
sell(s)	sold	sold	ride(s)	rode	ridden
catch(es)	caught	caught	write(s)	wrote	written
tear(s)	torn	torn	take(s)	took	taken
freeze(s)	froze	frozen	grow(s)	grew	grown
break(s)	broke	broken	give(s)	gave	given
choose(s)	chose	chosen	wear(s)	wore	worn
speak(s)	spoke	spoken	steal(s)	stole	stolen
throw(s)	threw	thrown	teach(es)	taught	taught

Irregular Verbs *(cont.)*

Directions: Circle the correct form of the irregular verb in the parentheses.

1. John F. Kennedy (say, said) in a speech, "Ask not what your country can do for you; ask what you can do for your country."

2. The tortoise and the hare (ran, run) in a race.

3. The teacher has (chose, chosen) a new book for the class to read.

4. How many bases were (stole, stolen) last year?

5. Redwood trees (grow, grown) to great heights.

6. R. L. Stine has (wrote, written) many thrillers and mystery stories for young adults.

7. Who (took, taken) a trip in a time machine?

8. The hailstones have (fell, fallen) from the sky for 60 minutes.

9. The flock of birds (flown, flew) south for the winter.

10. The explorers nearly (froze, frozen) to death in Antarctica.

Directions: Complete each sentence with the correct form of the verb in parentheses.

11. Last week the children _____ a rainbow after the rain stopped. (see)

12. Have you ever _____ a horse in a rodeo? (ride)

13. Babe Ruth's home run record was _____ in 1998. (break)

14. The pond _____ last week during the storm. (freeze)

15. Has the dog _____ yet today? (eat)

16. The guidance counselor _____ good advice to the students. (give)

17. Many cities _____ tremendously during the nineteenth century. (grow)

18. The outfielder _____ the ball to win the game. (catch)

Irregular Verbs *(cont.)*

Directions: Write the correct form of the verb in parentheses.

1. The winning team was _____ a trophy and a cash prize. (give)

2. Mozart had _____ how to compose music at the age of five. (know)

3. Which languages are _____ in Canada? (speak)

4. The fabric on the couch was _____ by the movers. (tear)

5. My uncle _____ the New York Marathon in three hours. (run)

6. *The Wizard of Oz* was _____ by L. Frank Baum after telling stories to his children. (write)

7. John Glenn has _____ on two space missions during his lifetime. (go)

Directions: Write the principal parts of these verbs.

Present	Past	Past Participle
1. go		
2. come		
3. throw		
4. eat		
5. fly		
6. forget		
7. begin		
8. buy		
9. hear		

Directions: Circle the sets of principal parts that are correct.

1. go(es), went, went
2. come(s), came, come
3. bring(s), brang, brought
4. drink(s), drank, drunken
5. take(s), taked, took
6. grow(s), grew, grown
7. steal(s), stealed, stole
8. see(s), saw, saw
9. say(s), said, said
10. run(s), ran, run
11. teach(es), teached, taught
12. forget(s), forgot, forgot
13. sing(s), sang, sung
14. know(s), knew, known
15. ride(s), road, rode
16. throw(s), threw, thrown
17. choose(s), chose, chosed
18. fly(s), flew, flew
19. do(es), did, done
20. eat(s), ate, ate

Confusing Verbs

Some verbs tend to be confusing. It is important to recognize the differences in meanings between the confusing sets of verbs.

Lay/Lie: *Lay* means "to put" or "to place." Principal parts: *lay, laid,* (have or has) *laid*

Lie means "to rest" or "to recline." Principal parts: *lie, lay,* (have or has) *lain*

Leave/Let: *Leave* means "to depart" or "let be." Principal parts: *leave, left,* (have or has) *left*

Let means "to permit." Principal parts: *let, let,* (have or has) *let*

Learn/Teach: *Learn* means "to understand." Principal parts: *learn, learned,* (have or has) *learned*

Teach means "to explain." Principal parts: *teach, taught,* (have or has) *taught*

Raise/Rise: *Raise* means "to hoist or lift." Principal parts: *raise, raised,* (have or has) *raised*

Rise means "to get or go up." Principal parts: *rise, rose,* (have or has) *risen*

Set/Sit: *Set* means "to place or put down." Principal parts: *set, set,* (have or has) *set*

Sit means "to rest." Principal parts: *sit, sat,* (have or has) *sat*

May/Can: *May* means "to have permission."

Can means "to be able to."

Directions: Circle the correct verb in parentheses.

1. (Can, May) I bring a camera into the museum?
2. The body builder (may, can) press two hundred pounds.
3. The foundation of the new stadium was (lay, laid) by the workers.
4. I (lie, lay) in bed at night, dreaming of becoming a move star.
5. The trains (left, let) on time this morning.
6. (Let, Leave) the boys carry the books to the car.
7. (Leave, Let) the keys to the car on the table by the door.
8. Please (set, sat) the chairs around the table.
9. Michael Jordan (sat, set) with the championship basketball team at the awards dinner.
10. The flag is (raised, risen) at school each morning by the custodians.
11. The sun (raises, rises) later in the winter.
12. The students (raised, rose) important issues at the meeting.
13. The price of theater tickets has (risen, rose) in recent years.
14. You can (learn, teach) to play tennis if you practice.
15. Girls were (learned, taught) how to spin and weave during the colonial period.
16. Animal trainers (learn, teach) the dolphins to do tricks.
17. Helen Keller (learned, taught) how to read, speak, and write from Ann Sullivan.
18. Merlin (taught, learned) King Arthur about the magical powers of the sword.
19. (Let, Leave) the meat marinate in the refrigerator overnight.
20. (May, Can) a laser beam repair eye damage?

Subject-Verb Agreement

A subject and a verb in a sentence must agree in *number*. If the subject is singular, the verb must be singular. If a subject is plural, the verb must be plural. This is called *agreement in number.*

The letter *s* is usually added to a verb when a subject is singular. (Notice that this reverses the usual practice for nouns.)

> *Example:* The teacher defines the words for the class.
> *Teacher* is singular, and *defines* is singular.

The letter *s* is usually dropped from a verb when a subject is plural.

> *Example:* The teachers define the words for the class.
> *Teachers* is plural, and *define* is plural.

Directions: Decide if the subject is singular or plural and then choose the verb that agrees in number.

1. The boy (hold, holds) the bat tightly.

2. Policemen (protect, protects) citizens.

3. The librarian (place, places) the books on shelves.

4. They always (cross, crosses) the street at the corner.

5. When he (give, gives) me the book, I will lend it to you.

Certain verbs are used differently in sentences.

Singular Form	Plural Form
is	are
was	were
has	have
does	do

> *Examples:* There is (There's) the parade. (one parade)
> There are (There're) several parades. (more than one parade)
> Here is (Here's) the book for the report. (one book)
> Here are (Here're) the books for the report. (more than one book)

Directions: Underline the correct verb.

1. Billy (is, are) near home.

2. There (is, are) three cars in the driveway.

3. My socks (have, has) holes.

4. (Was, Were) the girls on time for the movie?

5. No two snowflakes (has, have) the same pattern.

Compound Subject-Verb Agreement

Compound subjects are plural if they are united by the word *and*. If two subjects are linked by the words *neither . . . nor* or by the words *either . . . or*, they use the singular verb form.

Examples

1. Lisa and Judy are going to the school dance.
   (Lisa is linked to Judy with the word *and*. The subject is plural.)

2. Neither Lisa nor Judy is going to the school dance.
   (*Neither* and *nor* mean that each girl is singular.)

3. Either Lisa or Judy is going to the school dance.
   (*Either* and *or* mean each girl is singular.)

Directions: Write the subject and the verb from each sentence under the proper heading.

Sentence	Subject	Verb
1. One of my feet hurts.	_____	_____
2. Neither the chicken nor the fish tasted good.	_____	_____
3. Jim and Steve play hockey.	_____	_____
4. The dog in the window of the pet store seems tired.	_____	_____
5. The people on the bus are going home.	_____	_____
6. You are my best friend.	_____	_____
7. Have you heard the news?	_____	_____
8. Everyone loves the new dresses.	_____	_____
9. Jane and Carla have new dresses.	_____	_____
10. All the television programs were good.	_____	_____
11. Someone took my coat by mistake.	_____	_____
12. English and science are my two best subjects.	_____	_____
13. No one knows the combination to the locker.	_____	_____
14. Either Lisa or I will call you later.	_____	_____
15. In from the rain ran Aunt Maggie and Uncle Fred.	_____	_____

Adjectives

Adjectives are used to give added meaning to a noun or pronoun.

A. An adjective can tell what kind.
   Example: The *large* bus passed us.
   Bus is the noun, and *large* describes what kind of bus.

B. An adjective can tell which one.
   Example: This bus is mine.
   Bus is the noun, and *this* describes which one.

C. An adjective can tell how many.
   Example: One bus came by.
   Bus is the noun, and *one* tells how many.

Directions: Underline the adjective or adjectives in each sentence. On the lines, write whether the adjective tells *what kind, which one,* or *how many.*

1. My favorite doll is on the dresser. _____

2. The tree in the front yard loses its leaves in autumn. _____

3. Eight boys went to the movies after lunch. _____

4. It is difficult to see on cloudy, rainy nights. _____

5. I put chocolate sauce on the ice cream. _____

6. I like well-baked, cheese-covered pizza. _____

7. Nine players are needed to complete the team. _____

8. The cute little Dalmatian puppies licked my face. _____

9. The boy in the front of the line wore a red hat. _____

10. We saw the flashing lights as the two ships passed. _____

11. The Empire State Building is a tourist attraction. _____

12. Children love to learn about long, winding rivers. _____

13. Many large and small countries belong to the U.N. _____

14. Five hot, tired, happy children finished the race. _____

15. Several balloons needed to be inflated for the parade. _____

Directions: Choose a word from the word box that will describe the noun.

• big	• hairy	• wet	• six	• the	• this

1. A (what kind?) dog came around the corner. (three words)   _____

2. He was (how many?) years old.   _____

3. He was carrying a (what kind?) boot in his mouth.   _____

4. He looked like (which one?) was the best thing he ever found.   _____

Demonstrative Adjectives

Demonstrative adjectives are words that point out specific things.

A. **Articles** are words that describe a noun. They point out that a noun is the next word in the sentence.

a and the

    Example: The dog ran to his owner.
                        (*The* is the article and is followed by the noun *dog*.)

B. **Singular demonstrative adjectives** are used with singular nouns and the word *kind*.

this that

Examples: This book is what I need for my report.
                 (*This* is the demonstrative adjective followed by the word *book*.)
                 This kind of apple is my favorite.
                 (*This* is the demonstrative adjective followed by the word *kind*.)

C. **Plural demonstrative adjectives** are used with plural nouns. They are also used with the word *kinds*.

these those

Examples: These toys belong to Neil.
                 (*These* is the demonstrative adjective and *toys* is the noun.)
                 Those kinds of balloons are on the left side of the truck.
                 (*Those* is the demonstrative adjective and *kinds* is the noun.)

Directions: Underline the correct word in each sentence.

1. Look at (this, these) flowers and tell me which to buy.

2. (Those, This) kinds of roses are the prettiest I've ever seen.

3. (This, These) ice cream is cool and creamy.

4. I think (this, these) kind of coat is the one I will buy.

5. I've never seen (this, these) fabric used before.

6. (This, These) songs were the same ones we played at my cousins' party.

7. Would you ever pick (that, those) colors?

8. Please place (those, them) books on the back shelf.

9. (The, A) girls are reading the story now.

10. Tom's newspaper covered (these, the) entire kitchen table.

11. (These, Them) trees lose their leaves in the fall.

12. When the knives become dull, we sharpen (these, them).

13. Don't let the baby go down (those, them) aisles in the store.

14. (Those, That) kinds of fruits are best in this recipe.

Degrees of Comparison

Degrees of comparison are ways in which adjectives show levels of quality, quantity, or intensity.

A. The **positive degree** is used to describe only one thing.
   Examples: This pie is sweet.
   This pie is delicious.
   (There is only one pie being described.)

B. The **comparative degree** is used to compare only two things. To form the comparative degree, *er* is added at the end of most adjectives. Sometimes the word *more* comes before the adjective.
   Examples: The cherry pie is sweeter than the apple pie.
   The cherry pie is more delicious than the apple pie.
   (There are two different kinds of pie that are compared.)

C. The **superlative degree** is used to compare three or more things. Usually *est* is added at the end of most adjectives. Sometimes the word *most* comes before the adjective.
   Examples: The peach pie was the sweetest of all.
   The peach pie was the most delicious of all.

D. A few adjectives form *irregular degrees of comparison,* such as *good, better,* and *best* or *many, more,* and *most.*

Directions: Pick the correct form of comparison in each of the following sentences.

1. The boy was (small, smaller, smallest) for his age.
2. That joke was even (funny, funnier, funniest) than the first one.
3. I liked the (big, bigger, biggest) of the two stuffed animals.
4. Do you want to be the (tall, taller, tallest) in your family?
5. That was (thrilling, more thrilling, the most thrilling) than the last movie I saw.
6. Doing that skating trick was the (difficult, more difficult, most difficult) thing I have ever done.
7. I know that I can do (good, better, best) than I did last time.
8. I counted the (few, fewer, fewest) marbles of all.

Directions: Fill in the correct form of the adjective on the chart below.

Positive	Comparative	Superlative
1. good	_____	best
2. _____	more happy	most happy
3. big	bigger	_____
4. lonely	_____	loneliest
5. enjoyable	_____	most enjoyable
6. many	more	_____
7. _____	nicer	nicest

Adverbs

Adverbs are words that modify or describe verbs, adjectives, or other adverbs. They answer the questions *how, when, where,* and *to what extent.* Many adverbs are formed by adding *ly* to adjectives: loud + *ly* = loudly. Other common adverbs include such words as *now, later, tomorrow, first, here, there, away, nearby, very, mostly, quite, ever, never, too, not, well, worse, worst, much, more, little, less, least.*

Directions: In each sentence below draw a line under each adverb. Then circle the word that it modifies or describes.

   Example: The bird (flew) swiftly across the sky.

1. Penicillin was discovered accidentally by Alexander Fleming.

2. This medicine is usually prescribed to treat illnesses caused by bacteria.

3. During the seventh century the Quakers were treated badly in England.

4. William Penn, the founder of Pennsylvania, was a very famous Quaker.

5. Porcupine quills are really slender bunches of hair that have grown together.

6. Poplar trees grow best in moist places.

7. Alexander Pope was one of the greatest English poets.

8. Young pony express riders rode swiftly from Missouri to California.

9. These riders always delivered the mail, rain or snow.

10. The promoters of the pony express were ruined financially when the telegraph connections were completed from coast to coast.

Directions: Draw a line under each adverb in the sentence. On the line to the right, write whether the adverb tells *how, when, where,* or *to what extent.*

11. The pagodas of India are elaborately designed houses of worship.   _____

12. Japanese pagodas are usually built of wood.   _____

13. The paint was applied thickly to the canvas.   _____

14. Often, parsley is used to decorate meat dishes.   _____

15. Please place the turkey platter here.   _____

Adverb Comparisons

Like adjectives, *adverbs* also have degrees of comparison. The *positive degree* is used when only one thing is being described. The *comparative degree* is used when two actions are being compared. The *superlative degree* is used when comparing three or more things.

The comparative and superlative are formed in three ways. Most one-syllable and a few two-syllable words add *er* and *est* to the positive form. Most adverbs that end in *ly* or have two or more syllables usually add *more* or *most, less* or *least.* A few adverbs change completely.

Positive	Comparative	Superlative
soon	sooner	soonest
fast	faster	fastest
early	earlier	earliest
quickly	more quickly	most quickly
carefully	more carefully	most carefully
swiftly	less swiftly	least swiftly
little	less	least
much	more	most
well	better	best
badly	worse	worst

Directions: In each sentence below, underline the adverb that is being used in the comparison. On the line identify the form by writing **P** for *positive,* **C** for *comparative,* or **S** for *superlative.*

_____ 1. The front tires are firmer than the rear tires.

_____ 2. Which type of fish swims the fastest?

_____ 3. Hurricanes usually form over warm, tropical waters.

_____ 4. In the eye of the hurricane, the winds are less severe.

_____ 5. Hurricanes develop most often in the summer or early fall.

Directions: In the sentences below underline the correct form of the adverb in parentheses.

6. The rain fell (steadily, more steadily, most steadily) for the entire day.

7. The Jets quarterback throws (far, farther, farthest) than the Giants quarterback.

8. Our basketball team ranks (high, higher, highest) than any other team in the league.

9. Which tennis player hits the ball the (hard, hardest, most hard)?

10. The New York Rangers hockey team plays the (skillfulliest, more skillfully, most skillfully) of all the American teams.

Reviewing Adjective and Adverb Usage

Knowing whether to use an adjective or an adverb can be very confusing since at times the words look very much alike. In addition, some words can be used as adjectives or as adverbs, depending upon their placement in a sentence. To know when to use an adjective or an adverb, decide which word is being modified.

An **adjective** *modifies a noun or pronoun.* It tells which one, what kind, or how many. An **adverb** *modifies a verb, adjective, or another adverb* (or sometimes an entire sentence). It tells *how, when, where,* or *to what extent.*

Directions: In the sentences below, identify the underlined words as adjectives or adverbs. Circle the word that is being modified.

_____ 1. The <u>patient</u> teacher explained the lesson again.

_____ 2. The conductor waited <u>patiently</u> to begin the concert.

_____ 3. The department store sale ended <u>today</u>.

_____ 4. In the restaurants, the customers ordered their <u>favorite</u> desserts.

_____ 5. The young artist paints <u>beautifully</u> in oils and watercolors.

Directions: In the sentences below, circle the correct modifiers in parentheses.

6. The first airplane flew (slow, slowly) and (steady, steadily) across the sky.

7. Today jets speed (smoothly, smooth) and (quick, quickly) through the air.

8. The sheep were (terrible, terribly) frightened during the (fierce, fiercely) hurricane.

9. The dog turned (sudden, suddenly) and growled (ferociously, ferocious) at the cat.

10. Harry Houdini became (famous, famously) for his (amazing, amazingly) escapes.

Directions: In the sentences below, underline the errors in the use of modifiers. Write the correct modifier on the line.

_____ 11. The colors in a rainbow look so beautifully.

_____ 12. Babe Ruth is sure remembered as an outstanding baseball player.

_____ 13. The audience listened attentive to the guest speaker.

_____ 14. The Boston Marathon was a real close race this year.

Reviewing Confusing Adverbs and Adjectives

The words *good* and *well*, *bad* and *badly* are used incorrectly many times. *Good* and *bad* are adjectives that tell what kind. They follow linking verbs. The words *well* and *badly* are adverbs that tell how something is done. They follow action words. *Well* is also an adjective when it modifies a noun or pronoun meaning "healthy."

Examples: The cake looks *good*. (adjective)
Joe skates *well*. (adverb)
Joan does not feel *well* today. (adjective)
I feel *bad* about the accident. (adjective)
Dan acted *badly* at the show. (adverb)

Directions: In the sentences below circle the correct word in parentheses.

1. James looked (good, well) in the Halloween costume.

2. My tennis instructor serves really (good, well).

3. Homeless children need food and clothing (bad, badly).

4. Everyone at the party had a (good, well) time.

5. The patient feels (good, well) today.

6. Characters in fairy tales are either (good, well) or evil.

Negatives are words that are used to say "not." The appearance of two negatives in one sentence is called a *double negative*. Double negatives should be avoided when speaking or writing. Examples of negatives include *no, no one, none, nobody, not, nowhere, never, nothing,* and contractions with *n't.*

- The lost puppy didn't have no food to eat.   *Incorrect*
- The lost puppy didn't have any food to eat.   *Correct*
- The lost puppy had no food to eat.   *Correct*

Directions: In the sentences below circle the correct word in parentheses.

7. The thieves searched the house for the jewelry, but couldn't find (any, none).

8. I have not (ever, never) traveled to Europe.

9. The owner of the pet store doesn't know (anything, nothing) about turtles.

10. Never go (anywhere, nowhere) without telling your parents.

11. Nobody has ever seen (no, any) UFOs in New York City.

12. The fire engines arrived, even though there wasn't (no, any) fire.

Conjunctions and Interjections

Conjunctions are words that are used to join parts of sentences or whole sentences.

Following are frequently used conjunctions:

    and   *for*   *or*   *but*   *nor*   *yet*   *so*

    Examples: Tina and Toni went to the store.
               (The word *and* connects two subjects.)
               Tina can talk on the phone. Tina can glance at the newspaper.
               Tina can talk on the phone and glance at the newspaper.
               (The word *and* connects the two sentences by joining the predicates with the word *and*.)

Directions: Use a conjunction to join each of the following sentences. Write the new sentence on the line below.

1. I enjoy going to the theater. I enjoy going ice skating.

    _____

2. I eat lunch with Mary in the school cafeteria. I eat lunch with Brian in school.

    _____

3. Debra can swim faster than Henry. Henry won the race.

    _____

4. I don't like to go mountain climbing. I don't enjoy building things.

    _____

Interjections are words that express surprise or strong emotions. If strong emotion is expressed, an exclamation point usually follows it, but mild emotion is usually followed be a comma. Some commonly used interjections are these:

    oh   *my*   *wow*   *hey*   *gosh*   *yeah*   *yes*

    Examples: Oh! This is an unexpected surprise.
               Yes, it was wonderful.

Directions: Underline each interjection and punctuate each sentence.

1. oh said Sylvia as she suddenly fell forward
2. ouch the hammer hit my finger
3. hey wait for me
4. oh no what did I do with my homework
5. well that might just work
6. ah I see what you mean
7. ssh be quiet so he doesn't hear you
8. ugh what an ugly shirt
9. wow I've never seen a bug like that before

Prepositions

Prepositions are words that relate a noun or pronoun to other words in a sentence. Some commonly used prepositions are these:

into	*over*	*beneath*	*above*	*around*	*under*	*alongside*	*by*
from	*onto*	*of*	*upon*	*between*	*through*	*during*	*in*
on	*for*	*among*	*across*	*toward*	*against*	*besides*	*about*

Directions: Underline the preposition in each of the following sentences.

1. The green car pulled alongside the tan truck.

2. Billy climbed into the upper bunk bed first.

3. We looked around the corner to see if they were coming.

4. Over the cloud flew the airplane.

5. Harry and Frank stood in front of the line.

6. We found the reddest apple among the bunch.

7. The little girl crossed the street against the crowd.

8. The dog looked beneath the couch.

9. To get to his house, you must drive through the Holland Tunnel.

10. We had to go across the George Washington Bridge.

A *prepositional phrase* is a group of words that begin with a preposition.

    Example: The tiger ran into the cage.

Into is the preposition that begins the phrase *into the cage*.

Directions: Match the sentence in column A with the correct prepositional phrase in column B to form a complete sentence.

Column A	Match	Column B
1. All the people handed their tickets	_____	A. against the wall.
2. She was laughing so loudly that people	_____	B. into the clouds.
3. We decided to take the train	_____	C. to the attendant at the entrance.
4. The booklet was buried	_____	D. under all the papers.
5. Did you receive a letter	_____	E. from Aunt Millie?
6. The plane rose	_____	F. during the movie.
7. The baby dropped the rattle	_____	G. onto the floor.
8. They told funny stories	_____	H. into the city.
9. We decided to move the couch	_____	I. across the way turned to look.
10. Everyone told him not to talk	_____	J. about our vacation.

Prepositions *(cont.)*

The *object* in a prepositional phrase is a noun or a pronoun. Sometimes other words may separate the preposition and the object of the preposition.

> *Example:* Tom works at the local supermarket.
>
> *At* is the preposition.
>
> *At the supermarket* is the prepositional phrase.
>
> *Supermarket* is the noun in the prepositional phrase, otherwise known as the object of the preposition.

Directions: In each of the following sentences, underline the prepositional phrase and circle the object of the preposition.

1. The children were running around the playground.

2. The house was located on the next block.

3. The little boy ate everything except the broccoli.

4. Out of the front door ran the barking dog.

5. The baseball was hit over the foul line.

6. Like me, he wanted to see that television show.

7. I haven't eaten since breakfast.

8. With a shout of hello, she entered the quiet room.

9. This letter from Aunt Rose arrived today.

10. Into the mailbox we placed the party invitations.

11. The red car was parked near the road.

12. Alongside the stable were the horses.

Prefixes, Suffixes, and Roots

A *prefix* is a syllable or syllables attached to the beginning of a word that changes the meaning of the word.

A *suffix* is a syllable or syllables attached to the end of a base word. A suffix changes a word's meaning or its part of speech.

A *root* is a word part that can combine with prefixes, suffixes, base words, or other roots to create new words.

Prefixes, suffixes, and roots have predetermined meanings.

Directions: Match the prefix to its meaning.

_____	1. bi	A.	ahead, in front of
_____	2. ex	B.	above, too much
_____	3. extra	C.	two, twice
_____	4. fore	D.	former
_____	5. over	E.	three
_____	6. post	F.	half, partly
_____	7. pre	G.	after
_____	8. re	H.	before
_____	9. semi	I.	again
_____	10. tri	J.	beyond, outside of

Directions: Use one of the prefixes meaning *not* to complete the words below. The following prefixes mean *not*: *dis, il, im, in, ir, mis, non, un.*

_____ cooperative	_____ logical	_____ regular
_____ approve	_____ correct	_____ understand
_____ proper	_____ sense	_____ balance

Directions: Circle the suffix in the following words. Underline the base word.

powerful	dangerous	foolish	countless
softness	humidity	artist	production
responsible	farmer	acceptance	applicant
government	Swedish	gently	tighten

Directions: Draw a line between each root or word part. Write the correct root next to its meaning.

automatic	geography	thermometer	telescope	photograph
microsurgery	telephone	periscope	kilowatt	autograph
geology	multimedia	photogenic	television	tripod

heat_____	see _____	far_____	study of _____
measure _____	self _____	hear _____	small_____
earth _____	light _____	many _____	thousand_____

Homophones

Homophones are words that sound the same but have different meanings and spellings. *Homographs* are words that are spelled alike but have different meanings and sometimes different pronunciations.

Directions: Circle the correct word in each sentence.

1. (Two, Too) uninvited guests came (to, too) the party.

2. The children (road, rode) in the bus down the bumpy (rode, road).

3. The (nights, knights) wore their armor for many (knights, nights).

4. Do you (know, no) how to slide into a base?

5. I could not (wear, where) my (new, knew) coat to play.

6. John (won, one) a Tony for his (role, roll) in the Broadway show.

7. The glistening (sun, son) was shining on the (pier, peer).

8. Do you order your (steak, stake) rare or well done?

9. The (steel, steal) bridge was swaying during the storm.

10. Michael Jordan has designed a new (pair, pear) of sneakers.

11. The (clothes, close) closet is packed with winter items.

12. Do you like to fly in a (plane, plain)?

13. The collie gave (birth, berth) to five puppies.

14. During the avalanche, the mountain climber's (toes, tows) became frostbitten.

15. Ten (guests, guessed) arrived at the party late.

Reviewing Capitalization

- **Capitalize proper nouns** (*people, places, and things*):
  Michelle Ohio River

- **Capitalize proper adjectives:**
  Islamic   French   Chinese   Norwegian   French   Spanish rice   Greek myths

- **Capitalize the pronoun *I*.**

- **Capitalize titles when abbreviated or used with names:**
  Dr.   Mrs.   Rev.   Gen.   President Kennedy   Queen Elizabeth

- **Capitalize months, days, holidays, and historical events:**
  January   Tuesday   Labor Day   World War II

- **Capitalize words referring to religions, their scriptures, or God:**
  Bible   Jehovah   Koran   Islam   Judaism   Christianity

- **Capitalize clubs, businesses, and organizations:**
  Boy Scouts of America   IBM   Chamber of Commerce

- **Capitalize abbreviations and parts of addresses:**
  Rd.   St.   Ave.   NY   NJ   Detroit

- **Capitalize the first word of every sentence:**
  The boat sailed around the world.

- **Capitalize the first word, the last word, and all other words except articles, conjunctions, and short prepositions in titles of any written work such as a book or magazine:**
  Number the Stars   *National Geographic*   *The Adventures of Huckleberry Finn*

- **Capitalize *B.C., A.M., P.M.***

Reviewing Capitalization *(cont.)*

Directions: In the following sentences use capital letters where necessary.

1. the eiffel tower is located in paris, france.

2. rhode island, delaware, connecticut, hawaii, and new jersey are the five smallest states by area in the u.s.

3. *the nutcracker,* a famous ballet, is performed during the christmas season.

4. edgar allan poe wrote the thrilling short story "the fall of the house of usher."

5. the flight is scheduled to depart from la guardia airport at 10:30 a.m. and arrive in san francisco at 5:30 p.m.

6. i am going to receive the magazine *car and driver* on the first tuesday of march.

7. the novel the *castle in the attic* is an adventure story based on the middle ages.

8. the statue of liberty, a gift to the united states from france, is visible from new york city.

9. did you see the thanksgiving day parade as it proceeded down fifth avenue?

10. the taj mahal, an indian tomb, is an example of the blending of hindu and muslim architecture.

Directions: Correct these titles and names.

11. dr. erica weiss _____

12. *sports illustrated* _____

13. mr. james frank _____

14. dallas, texas _____

15. park place _____

16. george washington bridge _____

17. 5:40 a.m. _____

18. *the island of the blue dolphins* _____

19. pres. ronald reagan _____

20. the civil war _____

Reviewing Punctuation

(Periods, Question Marks, and Exclamation Points)

- Periods are used at the ends of declarative sentences and most imperative ones.
    The bird flew out of the cage. Please leave a tip.

- Periods are used after an abbreviation or an initial.
    Apr.   Mt.   St.   Mr.   R. L. Stine   Capt. R. B. White

- Periods are used after a number in the main topic and after a letter subtopic of an outline
    I.   Largest cities of the world
        A.   New York
        B.   London
        C.   Paris

- Question marks are placed at the ends of interrogative sentences.
    What time did the train leave the tracks?

- Exclamation points are used at the end of exclamatory sentences and after a strong interjection.
    What a wonderful play that was! Wow! That game was exciting.

Directions: Add periods, question marks, and exclamation points where needed.

1. How do male humpbacks communicate to the female humpback whales
2. What an incredible landing the pilot made
3. Great Your performance on the test was nearly perfect
4. The New York Knicks played the Chicago Bulls in Madison Square Garden
5. The Super Bowl was broadcast at 6:00 P M on Jan 31, 1999
6. Which president was elected first, Franklin D Roosevelt or Rutherford B Hayes
7. Mrs. B B Johnson, Jr was chosen to lead the parade
8. Watch out A deer is crossing the highway
9. Oh, no The elephants are stampeding toward the audience
10. Wow My bedroom will be 20 ft long and 15 ft wide

Directions: Place periods and capital letters where needed.

11. mr james mulligan
12. mt rushmore
13. the year 456 b c
14. p o box 345
15. rev jesse jackson
16. j h thompson and co
17. i museums of new york
        a guggenheim
        b metropolitan museum of art
        c museum of natural history

Reviewing Punctuation *(cont.)*

(Commas, Apostrophes, and Quotation Marks)

- Commas separate three or more items in a series:
  A tiger, lion, and elephant were in the circus ring.

- Commas are placed before *and, but,* or *or* when they are used to combine two sentences:
  Do you want to rent a movie, or shall we go bowling?

- Commas are used to help the reader pause and understand the sentence better:
  After I left the baby started to cry.
  After I left, the baby started to cry.

- Commas are used after mild interjections:
  Well, I guess I missed the train.

- Commas are used to set off an appositive:
  Mr. Jones, the mailman, is new.

- Commas are used to set off the name of a person spoken to:
  Mary, may I borrow your book?
  Please take out your pencil, Johnny.
  I hope, Sue, that you have your keys.

- Commas are used to separate the city from the state or country and in dates:
  Have you ever been to Melbourne, Australia?
  Chicago, Illinois, is known as the Windy City.
  March 15, 1978, is Jordan's birthday.

- Commas are used after the greeting of a friendly letter and the closing of any letter:
  Dear Pam,   Sincerely,   Your pal,

- Commas are used to set off words in a direct quotation. Quotation marks are placed before and after the words of a direct quotation. Capitalize the first word of a quotation. Place the comma, question mark, or exclamation point inside the quotation marks if it belongs to the quotation itself.
  "How was the gift?" asked Heather.
  Julie answered, "It was perfect!"
  "Don't water the plants," said Joey.

- Apostrophes are used to show possession or in a contraction.
  Gary's   can't

Directions: Add commas, quotation marks, and apostrophes where needed.

1. Please give our guest a warm welcome said the host of the talk show.
2. Governor how will the new tax increase affect the local schools asked the reporter.
3. Be careful driving to work warned the meteorologist Freezing temperatures have caused black ice to form on the roads.
4. Mars Jupiter Venus and Saturn are planets in our solar system.
5. The babys tears wouldnt stop for hours.
6. The *Titanic* sank in the atlantic ocean on April 15 1912.

Flight

At the turn of the century, very few believed that flight was possible in a heavier-than-air machine. Two of the few who did believe were Wilbur and Orville Wright. Wilbur Wright was born in 1867 in Indiana, and Orville was born four years later in Ohio. As children the two were fascinated by mechanics and even earned small amounts of money by selling homemade mechanical toys. Both went to school, but neither received a high school diploma. When they grew up, Orville built a printing press and started a printing business, developing a weekly newspaper which Wilbur edited. Next, they tried their hands at renting and selling bicycles, and finally they began to manufacture the bikes themselves.

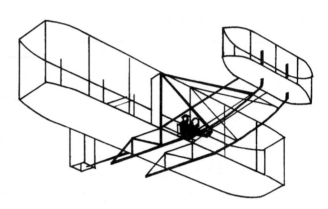

In 1886 the brothers read about the death of a pioneer glider named Otto Lilienthal, and his work sparked their interest. They started to read everything available on aeronautics and soon became as expert on the subject as any pioneer could be. The Wrights then contacted the National Weather Bureau to determine the best place to carry out their experiments with flight. The Bureau advised them to try a narrow strip of sandy land called Kill Devil Hill near Kittyhawk, North Carolina. In 1900, they tested a glider that could hold a person, and in 1901 they tried again with a larger glider. Neither glider could lift as they had hoped, although they did achieve some success in controlling balance.

The Wright brothers felt confident that flight was possible; therefore, they theorized that previous data concerning air pressure on curved surfaces must be inaccurate. They built their own wind tunnel and over 200 model wings in order to make their own pressure tables. Their tables became the first reliable ones ever made.

In 1902 they tried a third glider, using their new information. It vastly exceeded the success of all previous gliders, with some glides exceeding 600 feet (184 meters). This led the brothers to plan and build a power airplane. In 1903, at a cost just under one thousand dollars, the plane was complete. Its wings measured 40.5 feet (12 meters), and it weighed 750 pounds (340 kilograms) with the pilot. In September of 1903, they arrived in Kittyhawk, but a series of bad storms and defects delayed them. However, on December 17, 1903, they achieved flight.

Over the next few years, their experiments produced even longer and better flights. On October 5, 1905, their plane flew for 24.2 miles (39 kilometers) in just over 38 minutes. In 1908, they closed a contract with the United States Department of War for the first military airplane ever made.

The brothers went on to exhibit flight in France and the United States as well as to teach others to be pilots. Eventually, the inevitable happened: on September 17, 1890, Orville and his passenger, Lieutenant Thomas E. Selfridge, crashed due to a malfunction. Orville recovered, but Selfridge died. However, the work of the brothers continued until Wilbur died of typhoid fever in 1912. Orville carried on alone until his death in 1948. Today they are remembered as the fathers of modern flight.

Flight *(cont.)*

Vocabulary

Directions: Use the words from the word bank to complete the sentences correctly.

Word Bank			
• aerodynamic	• confident	• exceeded	• glider

1. Phyllis was _____ that she could finish all her school work in time to go to the party.

2. We watched as the _____ flew above us across the open field.

3. The car was built for racing, so the engineers chose an _____ design to cut back on wind resistance.

4. The amount of money that was raised for charity _____ our expectations.

Comprehension

Directions: Answer the following questions in complete sentences.

1. Why did most people believe that flight was not possible?

   _____

2. Name three accomplishments Orville Wright achieved prior to 1886.

   _____

   _____

   _____

3. Name three businesses in which both brothers were involved.

   _____

   _____

   _____

4. Why was their interest in flight sparked in 1886?

   _____

5. Where and when was their first glider tested?

   _____

6. Why did the Wright brothers build a wind tunnel?

   _____

Flight _(cont.)_

7. Using the information presented in the story "Flight," choose an accomplishment achieved by the Wright brothers for each year and record it in the proper space on the chart below.

Year	Accomplishments
1900	
1901	
1902	
1903	
1905	
1908	

Choices
A. A contract to build the first military airplanes is signed with the U.S. Department of War.
B. A second glider is successfully flown.
C. A 24.2-mile flight is achieved by an airplane.
D. A glider that holds a person is built and tried.
E. The first power airplane is introduced.
F. A glide exceeding 600 feet is made.

The Unsinkable Titanic

In April of 1912, approximately 2,200 passengers and crew members boarded the *Titanic*, a new luxury liner ready for its maiden voyage. The *Titanic* had the best of everything, and only the elite could afford passage. Some even paid more than $4,000 for the trip, while many of the crew did not even earn $1,000 in a year. The ship's promoters claimed that their vessel was unsinkable, primarily because its hull had 16 watertight compartments. Even if two compartments flooded, the ship would still float. Everyone had complete confidence in the boat.

A number of famous people were on board, including millionaire John Jacob Astor and his wife, as well as Isidor and Ida Straus, the wealthy department store owners. In general, the passengers had complete confidence in the ship because the best design and latest technology was at their fingertips.

Late on the night of April 14, the *Titanic* was sailing in the North Atlantic Ocean on its trip from Southampton, England, to New York City. The ship was traveling at a speed of 21 knots (nautical miles per hour), which was nearly top speed. Since there was danger of icebergs in the area, the ship's speed was far too fast. At 11:40 P.M., the *Titanic* rubbed alongside an iceberg for approximately ten seconds. That was enough. The hull of the ship was made of a type of steel that became brittle in the icy waters of the North Atlantic. Several small cracks appeared instantly, and seams were unriveted. Water started to pour inside, weakening the hull still further.

Six distress signals were sent out immediately. Another passenger ship, the *California*, was just 20 minutes away at the time; however, its radio operator was not on duty, so no one there heard the *Titanic*'s signal. Another ship, the *Carpathia*, was approximately four hours away, and it responded to the signal. However, when the *Carpathia* arrived at 4:00 A.M., it was too late for many of the passengers. The *Titanic* had long since sunk. Just after 2:00 A.M., water had flooded through the hull to the ship's bow, causing the entire vessel to split in two.

At first, the passengers aboard the ship were calm, expecting to reach lifeboats with ease and then be rescued by other ships. They did not know that the *Titanic's* lifeboats only had room for approximately 1,200 people, far fewer than the number of people on board. When the passengers and crew saw how dire the situation was, many stepped aside for younger passengers to board lifeboats safely. Among these heroes were the Astors and Strauses. Captain Edward J. Smith went down with his ship. In all, 705 people survived the wreck, most of them women and children. The remaining 1,517 died in the icy waters of the North Atlantic Ocean.

When the ship was first endangered, the band on board began to play a ragtime melody to encourage the passengers. As time passed and the situation grew grim, they continued to play, but this time it was an old English hymn calling for mercy and compassion from God.

In 1985, a team of scientists found the wreckage of the *Titanic* 12,500 feet (3,800 meters) beneath the sea. Although people had previously thought that a large gash was immediately ripped in the boat because of the iceberg, the scientists were able to prove that the steel composition of the hull was truly the fatal flaw as was the speed at which the boat was traveling.

The Unsinkable Titanic *(cont.)*

Vocabulary

Directions: Match the word in Column A with the correct definition in Column B.

Column A	Column B
_____ 1. elite	A. facing trouble
_____ 2. knots	B. came apart
_____ 3. unriveted	C. wealthy
_____ 4. dire	D. rip
_____ 5. endangered	E. the speed of a ship
_____ 6. gash	F. serious

Comprehension

Directions: Answer the following questions in complete sentences.

1. When was the voyage of the *Titanic*, and why was it such an exciting event?

   _____

2. How did the Titanic come to be known as a ship that could not sink?

   _____

3. Name two famous couples on the *Titanic*.

   _____

   _____

4. What were the planned departure and arrival points of the *Titanic*?

   _____

5. What problem did they face with the lifeboats?

   _____

The Unsinkable Titanic (cont.)

Directions: Fill in the cause or the effect on the chart below. The first one has been done for you.

Cause	Effect
1. The *Titanic* was traveling at a speed of 21 knots.	1. The collision couldn't be avoided.
2. The ship rubbed against an iceberg for ten seconds.	2.
3.	3. He couldn't hear the *Titanic*'s distress signal.
4. The *Carpathia* was four hours away.	4.
5. The vessel split in half.	5.
6. The band played ragtime music.	6.
7. The *Titanic* sank.	7.
8.	8. 1,517 passengers died.

Directions: Use the following chart to help you write a summary of the events aboard the *Titanic*.

Time	Event
11:40 P.M.	The ship rubs against an iceberg.
2:00 A.M.	The vessel splits in two.
4:00 A.M.	The *Carpathia* arrives.

Coming to America

Immigration was not new to the 1920s, but the complexion for the situation changed dramatically in the early part of the twentieth century. From its earliest years the United States of America had an open door policy toward immigrants, placing few restrictions on the number of people entering this country. It was not until 1882 that the first law was passed banning people from a specific country. The Chinese Exclusion Act forbade Chinese laborers because it was feared that they would work for lower pay. In 1907 a "gentleman's agreement" between the United States and Japan barred Japanese immigrants.

In the early 1900s there were two groups who sought to have the doors closed to certain ethnic members. American laborers feared that they would lose their jobs to new immigrants who were willing to work for lower wages. A second group believed that the newcomers were inferior. Still, it was not until 1917 that restrictions were in place, preventing 33 different categories of people from obtaining entry to the United States.

Immigration in the 1920s changed in another important way. Prior to 1880 newcomers originated mostly from countries in northern and western Europe. When the immigration population shifted to southern and eastern European countries, some Americans became alarmed at the customs and languages. World War I produced a temporary halt to the problem as very few people came to America during that period. Once the war ended, the wave of immigrants rose steadily, with over 600,000 people arriving in 1921. With the passage of a new law that same year, immigration was limited by a quota system. The National Origins Act of 1924 established severe quotas from southern and eastern European countries. For example, 100,000 Italians had arrived in one year in the early 1900s, but the new quota limited Italy to 5,082 people per year; Greece was allowed only 307 people per year, while Russia was permitted 2,784 per year. Not until the 1960s, when Lyndon Johnson became president, did those quota laws change.

Coming to America *(cont.)*

Directions: Complete each sentence correctly by choosing one of the words in the word bank.

<table>
<tr><td colspan="3" align="center">**Word Bank**</td></tr>
<tr><td>• immigrants</td><td>• gentleman's agreement</td><td>• ban</td></tr>
<tr><td>• quota</td><td>• restriction</td><td>• excluded</td></tr>
</table>

1. Even though Mr. Reed had no contract showing that he agreed to buy the horse from Mr. Eagan, they shook hands with each other, knowing they had reached a _____ .

2. The colonists in Boston agreed to _____ the purchase of tea from the British.

3. _____ coming from all countries saw the Statue of Liberty as their ship came into New York Harbor.

4. The merchant had a _____ on the amount of merchandise he could sell at one time.

5. When Tom was sick, he knew that he would be _____ from the class picnic and confined to bed.

6. The _____ stated that a person under 18 cannot drive in some states.

Directions: Answer the following questions in complete sentences.

1. What law was passed in 1882, and why was it enacted?

   _____

2. Name two reasons new immigrants were prevented from entering the United States.

   _____

   _____

3. From which areas were immigrants arriving prior to the 1880s and after the 1920s?

   _____

   _____

4. What did the National Origin Act of 1924 seek to do?

   _____

Coming to America *(cont.)*

5. Organize the countries according to their quotas of immigrants from greatest to least. Next to each country list their quota of immigrants. Research to see if you can find quotas for some countries not mentioned on page 11.

Country	Quota

Prefixes

Prefixes are added to the beginnings of many words. They change the meanings of the base words. Circle the prefixes of each word and then use them in a sentence of your own.

im—not　　**in**—not　　**pre**—before　　**re**—again　　**ex**—not

1. exclude _____

2. inferior _____

3. prevent _____

4. restrict _____

5. immigrant _____

6. incomplete _____

Farmers and the Dust Bowl

Farmers did not share in the prosperity of World War I, and things were worse after the recession of 1921. Federal support for agriculture ended, and many farmers who had expanded their production to meet wartime needs lost their land and stock. For those who survived, low crop prices meant low income. In the 1930s wheat prices dropped to below what it cost to grow the crop. Rather than sell at such prices, some farmers destroyed their own crops. A series of natural disasters made matters even worse and led to the greatest westward migration that the United States has ever seen.

Americans had long disregarded the warnings of conservationists. Farmers had misused the land, depleting fertile soil and then moving on to farm new land. In the Great Plains, farmers plowed up natural grasses to plant wheat. Agriculturalists who advised the use of contour plowing to prevent erosion and planting trees as windbreakers were ignored. When a seven-year drought struck, beginning in 1931, winds blew the topsoil into thick, dark clouds of dust that sometimes lasted for several days. To protect themselves from the dust storms, farmers hung damp sheets over the windows of their homes. Still, dust poured through the cracks of the farmhouse walls, leaving dust in their food, hair, eyes, mouths, and pockets. For many, there was nothing left to do but leave their farms and head west.

Over three million people eventually migrated from the Great Plains region to California, where there was the promise of jobs. In most cases, that was all it was—a promise. Conditions in California proved little better than the farms they had left. While there was not much dust to contend with, there were not nearly enough jobs. Californians resented these new people and labeled them "Okies," a synonym for dumb and lazy. Hatred against them was so great that some farmers destroyed their surplus food rather than share it with the starving Okie families.

Finally, the government stepped in and created some labor camps in the San Joaquin Valley, which provided relief and education for the migrants. Much was written about these people and their struggles. John Steinbeck's novel *The Grapes of Wrath* described conditions among the Okies in California. Dorothea Lange photographed and documented their misery, while Woody Guthrie sang songs about their predicament. It was a dark time in American history in more ways than one.

Farmers and the Dust Bowl *(cont.)*

Directions: Use the words in the word bank to complete the sentences.

Word Bank
• prosper   • agriculture   • conserve   • resent

1. Farmers study _____ so they can learn the best methods of growing crops.

2. John said, "I _____ the fact that you accepted the invitation to the party without asking me first."

3. We decided that we would _____ our food supply by eating only small amounts.

4. The students of the graduating class voted Tim the one most likely to achieve success and _____ in business.

Life worsened for the farmers after World War I. Match the effect that each of the following causes had on the farmers and agriculture.

Cause	Effect
_____ 1. End of federal support for agriculture	A. Westward migration begins.
_____ 2. Low crop prices	B. The topsoil of the land is blown away as clouds.
_____ 3. Natural disasters	C. Farmers lose their land and stock.
_____ 4. Farmers misuse of land	D. The soil is depleted.
_____ 5. Seven-year drought	E. Dust is found in food, hair, eyes, mouths, and pockets.

Directions: On the back of this page, answer the questions in full sentences.

1. Name two ways in which the farmers misused the land.

2. What is the meaning of the label *Okie,* and who are Okies?

3. How did the people in California show their resentment of the three million migrants?

4. What did the government do to help the migrant workers?

5. How did the following people make others aware of the problems and conditions faced by the Okies?

   A. John Steinbeck   B. Dorothea Lange   C. Woody Guthrie

Three First Ladies

During the 1970s there were three first ladies: Pat Nixon, Betty Ford, and Rosalyn Carter. Each had a distinctive personality and brought a different flair to the White House. Read the short biographies that follow and complete the activities on page 17.

Pat Nixon: When Pat Nixon became first lady, she was the mother of two teenage daughters, Tricia and Julie. Continuing in the tradition of Jackie Kennedy, Mrs. Nixon proceeded with the renovation of the White House to make it a museum of American heritage. In addition, she supported the cause of volunteerism and urged Americans to get involved with their communities. Her greatest political success was as a goodwill ambassador on trips to Africa. Pat Nixon died in 1993 and is buried beside her husband in Yorba Linda, California, at the Richard Nixon Library and Birthplace.

Betty Ford: Betty Ford is most remembered for her candor about her personal life. When she spoke publicly about her battle with breast cancer, she raised public awareness of the disease and served as an inspiration to others who faced cancer. As first lady, Betty Ford also supported the Equal Rights Amendment and valued both the traditional role of women and the role of women in the workplace. After leaving the White House, Mrs. Ford publicly described her struggle with addiction to alcohol and pain medication, and she founded the Betty Ford Clinic for substance abuse in Rancho Mirage, California.

Rosalyn Carter: When Jimmy Carter was president, his wife Rosalyn served as his most trusted advisor and represented him officially during a trip to Central and South American countries. She sometimes sat in on cabinet meetings where she quietly took notes. These acts aroused much criticism, but there were also those who admired her. Rosalyn's own agenda included supporting mental health reform, actively supporting legislation to reform Social Security, and urging approval of the Equal Rights Amendment. A woman of action, Rosalyn believed firmly in the necessity of women pursuing careers outside the home.

Three First Ladies *(cont.)*

Directions: Each of the women in the article accomplished many things while her husband was the president of the United States. Under each heading, list four things each woman accomplished.

I. **Pat Nixon**

A. _____

B. _____

C. _____

D. _____

II. **Betty Ford**

A. _____

B. _____

C. _____

D. _____

III. **Rosalyn Carter**

A. _____

B. _____

C. _____

D. _____

Directions: Use the information in your outline to help you answer the questions.

1. Which woman wanted to carry on the tradition set by a former first lady?_____

2. Which woman received great criticism for being involved in White House meetings?_____

3. Name one cause that each woman championed while her husband was in office.

A. Pat Nixon   _____

B. Betty Ford   _____

C. Rosalyn Carter   _____

The Technological Home and Office

The average American home of the eighties differed quite a bit from the same home in the seventies, and technology was the reason. Suddenly it seemed there were new technologies to handle a variety of tasks. Answering machines took phone messages, videocassette recorders (VCRs) taped television shows when people were not home to watch them, cable television broadened the spectrum of television viewing options, compact discs (CDs) enhanced sound for the listener of recorded music, and personal computers rapidly became an exciting new source of entertainment and productivity. Perhaps most significant and influential in the technologic advances of the decade were the VCR and the personal computer.

VCRs: VCRs brought about a revolution in the entertainment industry. Previously, people's choice of films was limited to what could be seen in theaters or the occasional few movies screened on network television. Children of the middle decades can recall special television events when popular movies such as *The Wizard of Oz* were broadcast annually. With the advent of VCRs, people could buy or rent videotapes of movies and watch them whenever they chose. They could also record any movie or show from television to watch at their leisure. Some even began watching a show on one channel while taping one on another. With the dawn of the VCR came a new line of stores that sold and rented videos. This became one of the fastest growing industries of the 1980s.

Initially developed in the late fifties and early sixties, VCR technology grew from the need of television studios for a reliable method of recording programs for viewing in different time zones, or for repeat usage. These early systems were far too complex and expensive for home use, however. In 1975 Sony corporation introduced its Betamax, based on the system used by stations and networks. Matsushita Electrical Industrial Corporation quickly released a competing system called Video Home System, or VHS. When the VHS system was adopted by the leading American television manufacturer, popularity of the Betamax waned. The VCR industry boomed throughout the eighties.

PCs: The personal computer also took off in popularity through the decade. Although in 1979 only 325,000 Americans had personal computers in their homes, by 1984 the number of owners had climbed to fifteen million.

The first home computers were used primarily for entertainment with such games as Space Invaders and Pac Man. Advances in microchip technology and the availability of affordable peripherals like modems and user-friendly software led to growing awareness of the computer's usefulness, particularly to students. By 1985, students had become the largest users of personal computers.

While the price of both VCRs and personal computers has dropped over time, VCRs are usually more affordable for the average family, while personal computers, still relatively expensive, are often out of reach. However, most schools have computers so that students are exposed to them before entering into the business world where they are a necessity.

The Technological Home and Office *(cont.)*

Directions: Column one contains the abbreviation of an invention of the 1980s. Write the full name for that invention in column two. In column three list the major achievement or contribution it made.

Invention	Full name	Contribution
VCR		
CD		
PC		

Directions: Answer the questions in complete sentences.

1. Name three ways that VCRs changed the entertainment industry.

    A. _____

    B. _____

    C. _____

    D. _____

2. How were VCRs first used?

    _____

3. Name the role each company played in popularizing the VCR.

    A. Sony Corporation _____

    _____

    B. Matsushita Electrical Industrial Corporation _____

    _____

4. What scientific advances contributed to the popularity of PC home use?

    _____

    _____

The Technological Home and Office *(cont.)*

Directions: The Venn diagram below compares the VCR to the personal computer by showing how each is different and alike. Insert the information in the correct area of the diagram.

Information
1. It is more affordable.
2. It is expensive.
3. Its prices became lower.
4. It advanced because of microchip technology.
5. It is used by schools.
6. It uses a modem and software.
7. It helped form a new line of business.
8. It was the fastest growing industry in the 1980s.
9. It was used in the entertainment industry.
10. It is used for home entertainment.

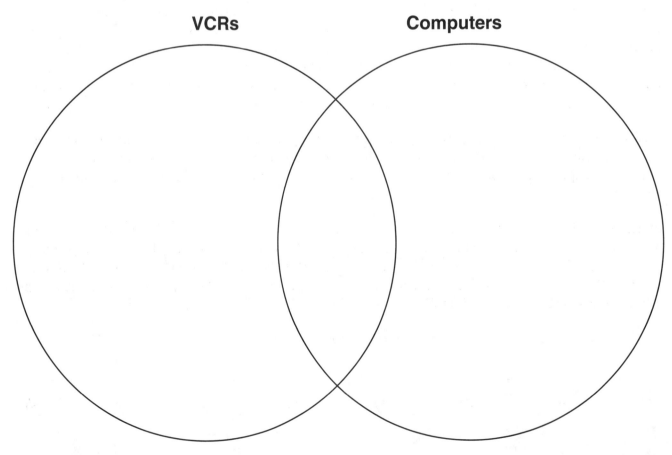

VCRs   **Computers**

Norman Rockwell

For 47 years Norman Rockwell painted covers for the *Saturday Evening Post.* His inviting paintings provided an intimate glimpse into the everyday lives of Americans during the first half of the century and have come to be regarded as classic Americana.

Norman Rockwell was born on February 2, 1894, in New York. When he was nine, the family moved to Mamaroneck. To gain acceptance, the resourceful Rockwell drew pictures to entertain his classmates. He left high school to study at the National Academy of Design and earned money by drawing greeting cards. At age 16, he studied at the Art Students League and began illustrating books and magazines. By the time he was 18, Rockwell was the art director for *Boys' Life* magazine.

Rockwell achieved fame after the five illustrations he sold to the editor of *Saturday Evening Post* were used as covers on the magazine. In all, Norman Rockwell provided 318 covers for the *Post* through his 47-year association with them.

When World War I broke out, Rockwell tried to enlist in the navy, but he was rejected for being underweight. Undeterred, he ate a diet of bananas and donuts until he gained the necessary ten pounds. After acceptance into the service, Rockwell was assigned to the navy yard in Charleston, South Carolina, where he painted for the navy. He also continued to work for the *Saturday Evening Post* and other magazines. After the war, he returned to New York, where he built a studio for himself. By that time he was enjoying both fame and fortune from his paintings.

The process used by Norman Rockwell to create a painting was long and detailed. First, he sketched the scene. Next, he made individual drawings of each element in the scene. Full-size charcoal drawings were the next step, followed by color sketches. Only then was he ready to begin actual painting.

In the late 1930s Rockwell moved to Arlington, Virginia. Fire destroyed his studio in 1943, along with many of his drawings and paintings. Although he was saddened by the loss, Rockwell began painting more directly from life rather than relying on a model. Although he ceased working for the *Saturday Evening Post* in 1963, he continued to work for other magazines. His latter years were spent traveling to foreign countries. Norman Rockwell died in 1978.

◆   ◆   ◆   ◆   ◆   ◆   ◆   ◆

Norman Rockwell *(cont.)*

Directions: The following events of Norman Rockwell's life are not in the correct order. Sequence them by number to show which happened first and last.

A. _____ His studio was destroyed by fire.

B. _____ He drew greeting cards.

C. _____ He moved to Mamaroneck.

D. _____ He illustrated books and magazines.

E. _____ He traveled to foreign countries.

F. _____ He drew for the *Saturday Evening Post*.

G. _____ He started drawing pictures to entertain people.

H. _____ He served in the navy.

I. _____ He became the art director for *Boy's Life Magazine*.

J. _____ He moved to New York and built an art studio.

Directions: Norman Rockwell followed a particular procedure when painting. Using the steps listed below, put them in the outline in correct order.

Steps

- He made full-size charcoal drawings.
- He sketched a picture.
- He painted the picture.
- He made individual drawings of each element in each scene.
- He made color sketches.

A. _____

B. _____

C. _____

D. _____

E. _____

Directions: Using the correctly ordered outline, write a paragraph explaining the steps that Norman Rockwell used to produce a finished painting. Be sure to include transition words such as *first, next, then, after, before,* and *finally* to make the paragraph flow smoothly.

An Extraordinary Bus Ride

She has been called the mother of the civil rights movement, but Rosa McCauley Parks does not consider herself to be extraordinary. Born on February 4, 1915, in Tuskegee, Alabama, McCauley had a normal childhood. She grew up on a farm and attended an all-black school in her neighborhood. Her high school education was cut short by her mother's death, but she finished her schooling after her marriage to Raymond Parks. In 1943 she joined the NAACP (National Association for the Advancement of Colored People) and worked with the Voters' League, registering African Americans to vote. Then came the fateful day.

Rosa McCauley Parks

The bus ride on December 1, 1955, began as usual. After completing her job as a seamstress for a Montgomery department store, Parks boarded the bus to go home. As was required, she took a seat in the back of the bus. When all the seats filled up, Parks was asked to vacate hers for a white man who was just getting on the bus. (At that time in Montgomery the law required blacks to sit at the back of the bus and to give up their seats for white people when all other seats were filled.) On this day, however, Parks refused to move. The bus driver stopped the bus and called for policemen who whisked her away to jail. NAACP leader Edgar Daniel Nixon posted her bail and determined that Rosa Parks would be the last African American arrested for such an action.

Along with other black leaders, including Dr. Martin Luther King, Jr., Nixon declared a one-day boycott of all city buses. Leaflets announcing the boycott were distributed throughout the city, and on the appointed day the results were dramatic. Not one African American rode on any buses there. Because it was such a success, the boycott was extended indefinitely.

For their actions blacks were harassed on the street, hundreds of their leaders were arrested, and many lost their jobs. Still, the boycott continued with African Americans turning to alternative methods of transportation, including walking, carpooling, riding bicycles, and even riding mules. The boycott ended when, after 381 days, the U.S. Supreme Court ruled in favor of Rosa Parks and declared Alabama bus segregation laws unconstitutional. It had cost the bus company $750,000 in lost revenues, but the gains in human dignity were priceless.

◆   ◆   ◆   ◆   ◆   ◆   ◆   ◆   ◆

An Extraordinary Bus Ride *(cont.)*

Directions: Choose the word that best completes each sentence.

1. John's mother felt that her grandmother's vase was _____ and could never be replaced.

    a. clay   b. new   c. priceless

2. The colonists decided to protest the tax on tea by _____ its purchase.

    a. delaying   b. boycotting   c. revolting

3. The new laws, having no time limit, will go on _____ unless a change is enacted.

    a. indefinitely   b. limited   c. repeal

4. When the fire broke out, the people had to _____ the burning building.

    a. support   b. vacate   c. uphold

5. The boys' and girls' locker rooms are _____ .

    a. revamped   b. abandoned   c. segregated

6. We had to plan an _____ activity in case it rained and our picnic was canceled.

    a. alternative   b. cooperative   c. coordinating

Directions: Complete each sentence by adding correct information.

1. Rosa Parks is called the _____ .

2. Rosa was born and educated in _____ .

3. She joined the _____ and worked with the _____ .

4. Rosa worked as a _____ in a department store.

5. Refusing to _____ caused her to be arrested.

6. _____ and _____ declared a boycott of city buses.

7. Three results of the boycott were

    A. _____

    B. _____

    C. _____

An Extraordinary Bus Ride *(cont.)*

8. Four alternative methods of transportation used during the boycott were the following:

_____

_____

_____

_____

9. The boycott lasted _____ days.

10. The United States Supreme Court ruled Alabama bus segregation laws were _____ .

Directions: Write a paragraph explaining how you as a bystander would have felt while watching the events unfold as Rosa Parks was told to give up her seat on the bus.

_____

_____

_____

_____

_____

_____

_____

_____

_____

_____

_____

_____

The Black Pearl

Pelé, born Edson Arantes do Nascimento, was only 17 when he played in his first World Cup of soccer in 1958. Some 60,000 people had jammed into the 50,000-seat arena in hopes that they would see Sweden win its first world title. The Swedish coach thought his team could win if they scored first. Brazil had a tendency to become disorganized when they trailed in a game. What happened at that game, however, stunned everyone—the spectators, coaches, and players. Pelé inspired his teammates with his enthusiastic and energetic pace. It was his magnificent moves on the field, though, that really wowed the crowd. He displayed such control of his body and such athleticism that even the Swedish fans began to chant his name. After their win, the Brazilian team returned home as national heroes, and Pelé was nicknamed "The Black Pearl."

Pelé

Pelé was born on October 23, 1940, in a small town in Minas Gerais state. His father, a soccer player, was pleased with his firstborn and predicted that the boy would grow up to become a great soccer player. As a young child Pelé ran and played with the other students in his neighborhood. They had to use grapefruits or socks filled with rags because there was not enough money for a real soccer ball. Bored with school, he quit in the fourth grade and became a cobbler's apprentice. His free time was spent playing soccer. When he was 12, he was chosen to play in a junior league where he learned the strategies and tactics of professional soccer. By the time he was 14, he was invited to join a professional team. It meant leaving home and moving to Santos near Brazil's largest city, São Paulo. Often he would be homesick, but he kept busy attending school between games and practicing with the team. Soon, people began coming out to the games just to watch this remarkable new player. Then, at age 17 he found himself on the Brazilian World Cup team.

Before the team left for Stockholm, Pelé injured his knee. He was fearful that it would not heal correctly and he would be unable to continue his professional career. Though in pain, he put on an unforgettable performance at the World Cup and led his team to victory. He went on to play until he retired from the Santos team in 1974. For three years after that, he played for a team in the newly formed North American Soccer League.

Pelé remains a public figure in his native Brazil. He starred in some movies and recorded a hit song. His future plans may include something in the political arena. Whatever his goal, he remains the most popular soccer player in the history of the game.

The Black Pearl *(cont.)*

Directions: Some of the following sentences are true, and some are false. Place a check mark before each sentence that is true. If a sentence is false, change it to make it correct.

_____ 1. Pelé played World Cup soccer when he was 17 years of age.

_____ 2. People thought Brazil would win first place at the competition.

_____ 3. Pelé was able to exhibit great control, and the Brazilian fans chanted his name.

_____ 4. The Swedish team named him "The Black Pearl."

_____ 5. Pelé's family could not afford to buy him a soccer ball with which to practice.

_____ 6. He quit school in the fourth grade.

_____ 7. He was 12 years old when he joined a professional soccer team.

_____ 8. He suffered an injury to his head but still played in the World Cup.

Directions: Facts are pieces of information that can be proven. People's opinions reflect their personal thoughts and cannot be verified. Label each sentence as a fact or an opinion.

_____ 1. Pelé was the best player to ever live.

_____ 2. He played for the North American Soccer League for three years.

_____ 3. He was very popular with all the people in Brazil.

_____ 4. Pelé recorded a hit song and appeared in movies.

_____ 5. He will take on a government job.

_____ 6. His real name is Edson Arantes do Nascimento.

Henry Ingersoll Bowditch

Henry Ingersoll Bowditch was born on August 9, 1808, in Salem, Massachusetts. His father was a famous mathematician named Nathaniel Bowditch, and his mother was Mary. Bowditch went to private school when he was young. When his family moved to Boston in 1823, he attended Public Latin School. Bowditch went on to study at Harvard College where he graduated in 1828. He was not sure what he wanted to do with his life, so he decided to enter Harvard Medical School. In 1832, Bowditch graduated with a degree in medicine. During his internship at Massachusetts General Hospital, Bowditch discovered that he really enjoyed the field of medicine.

Bowditch traveled to Europe in order to study medicine in France. While in Paris, he had the opportunity to work with some of the finest French physicians. They taught him to make close observations and use inductive reasoning. They inspired him to be deeply committed to the study of medicine. After spending a year in France, Bowditch went to study medicine in England. However, he did not feel that the English were as advanced in the field of medicine as the French. As a result, he returned to France for one more year of study.

In 1834, Bowditch went home to Boston where he started a medical practice. He was extremely opposed to slavery and joined the work of the abolitionists. He helped many slaves escape to the North and spoke out against fugitive slave laws. In 1861, the Civil War was being fought, and Bowditch volunteered to be a doctor for Union soldiers who were fighting in Virginia. He worked hard to convince the Senate to institute an army ambulance corps so that wounded soldiers could be taken off the battlefield.

Bowditch also struggled to improve public health in the 1860s by making people more aware of how tuberculosis was being spread. He helped to create many health boards that were used to monitor public health. He personally served on many of these boards. In 1879, he became the president of the American Medical Association. Until his death on January 14, 1892, Bowditch spoke out about many public health issues and encouraged women to pursue careers in medicine.

◆   ◆   ◆   ◆   ◆   ◆   ◆   ◆

Henry Ingersoll Bowditch *(cont.)*

Directions: Use information that you found in "Henry Ingersoll Bowditch" to complete this outline.

I. Early Life

    A. Date of birth   _____

    B. Place of birth   _____

II. Education (schools attended)

    A. _____

    B. _____

    C. _____

    D. _____

III. Places of study

    A. _____

    B. _____

    C. _____

IV. Employment

    A. Pre-Civil War

        1. _____

        2. _____

    B. Civil War Era

        1. _____

        2. _____

V. Accomplishments

    A. _____

    B. _____

    C. _____

    D. _____

    E. _____

    F. _____

Evaluation: What do you think was Henry Ingersoll Bowditch's greatest accomplishment? Give at least two reasons to support your answer.

"The Road Not Taken"

Two roads diverged in a yellow wood,
And sorry I could not travel both
And be one traveler, long I stood
And looked down one as far as I could
To where it bent in the undergrowth;

Then took the other, as just as fair,
And having perhaps the better claim,
Because it was grassy and wanted wear;
Though as for that, the passing there
Had worn them really about the same,

And both that morning equally lay
In leaves no step had trodden black.
Oh, I kept the first for another day!
Yet knowing how way leads on to way,
I doubted if I should ever come back.

I shall be telling this with a sigh
Somewhere ages and ages hence:
Two roads diverged in a wood, and I—
I took the one less traveled by,
And that has made all the difference.

—Robert Frost

"The Road Not Taken" *(cont.)*

Directions: Using the poem "The Road Not Taken," answer the questions in complete sentences.

1. How many stanzas does this poem contain?_____

2. How many lines does each stanza contain? _____

In each of the four stanzas, Frost uses end-line rhyme.

> *Example:* **Stanza 1**,
> *Line 1* ends with *wood*.
> This rhymes with line 3, which ends with *stood* and line 4, which ends with *could*.
> *Line 2* ends with *both*.
> This rhymes with line 5, which ends with under*growth*.

Directions: Read each stanza and list the final word in each line. Check to see if this pattern is repeated.

Stanza #2

Line 1 ends with _____ .

This rhymes with line ____ , which ends with _____ and line ____ , which ends with _____ .

Line 2 ends with _____ .

This rhymes with line ____ , which ends with _____ .

Stanza #3

Line 1 ends with _____ .

This rhymes with line ____ , which ends with _____ and line ____ , which ends with _____ .

Line 2 ends with _____ .

This rhymes with line ____ , which ends with _____ .

Stanza #4

Line 1 ends with _____ .

This rhymes with line ____ , which ends with _____ and line ____ , which ends with _____ .

Line 2 ends with _____ .

This rhymes with line ____ , which ends with _____ .

"The Road Not Taken" *(cont.)*

In all stanzas of "The Road Not Taken," Frost rhymes the ending word in line one with the ending word in line _____ and line _____ . In addition, he rhymes the ending word in line 2 with the ending word in line _____ .

Frost also uses rhythm. This is achieved by using the same number of accented syllables in each line.

1. How many syllables per line are used most often?_____

2. What is the setting of this poem? _____

3. Who is the main character in the poem?_____

4. What problem does the character face? _____

_____

_____

_____

_____

5. What does the character decide to do? _____

_____

_____

_____

_____

_____

6. How does the character feel about his decision? _____

_____

_____

_____

_____

"The Road Not Taken" *(cont.)*

1. In the last stanza of the poem, the traveler chooses the road that fewer people traveled. Why is this a courageous decision?

   _____

   _____

   _____

2. Besides courage, what other characteristics are possessed by this traveler? List three of them below.

   _____

   _____

   _____

3. Why do you think most travelers chose the well-worn path rather than the one "less traveled by"?

   _____

   _____

   _____

4. What lessons about life do you think Robert Frost wants the reader to learn?

   _____

   _____

   _____

Activity: What important decision have you recently made? Write a paragraph about how that decision "has made all the difference" in your life.

_____

_____

_____

_____

_____

_____

"The Courage That My Mother Had"

The courage that my mother had
Went with her, and is with her still:
Rock from New England quarried;
Now granite in a granite hill.

The golden brooch my mother wore
She left behind for me to wear;
I have no thing I treasure more:
Yet, it is something I could spare.

Oh, if instead she'd left to me
The thing she took into the grave!
That courage like a rock, which she
Has no more need of, and I have.

—Edna St. Vincent Millay

496

"The Courage That My Mother Had" (cont.)

Directions: Match the words in column one with the correct definitions in column two.

Column One	Column Two
1. granite	A. a type of rock or stone
2. quarried	B. bravery
3. brooch	C. to receive from a previous generation
4. courage	D. a decorative pin
5. inherit	E. to dig or blast stone

A *metaphor* is a comparison of two things without the use of the words *like* or *as*.
> *Example:* The cloud is fluffy white cotton candy.

A *simile* is a comparison of two things using the words *like* or *as*.
> *Example:* The cloud is like fluffy white candy.

Directions: Answer these questions in complete sentences.

1. In stanza one, the poet compares her mother to a *rock*.

    A. Is this a *simile* or a *metaphor*? How do you know?

    metaphor   no words

    B. Why is this a good choice?

    Because that's what it says

2. In stanza three, Edna St. Vincent Millay again compares her mother to a rock. Is this a metaphor or a simile, and how do you know?

    Simile uses like.

3. Who is the storyteller or speaker?

    The Daughter (Edna St. Vincent Millay

"The Courage That My Mother Had" *(cont.)*

4. What does the author inherit from her mother?

   A Brooch

5. How does she feel about this object?

   She knows she dosent need it but she keeps it Because her mother gave it to her.

6. What does the speaker mean by the line "Yet, it is something I could spare"?

   She dose not need it 4 anything.

7. What does the speaker wish she had inherited from her mother and why?

   She wish she would have her mothers courage, she needs it.

8. What qualities do you feel your parents have passed down to you? Explain in the space below.

   My temper. My parents Both have tempers like most parents and same with me.

Math Terminology

Complete each sentence below with the proper term from the vocabulary listed in the word bank.

Word Bank

• addend	• difference	• discount	• dividend
• denominator	• edge	• estimate	• even number
• divisor	• factors	• fraction	• integers
• exponent	• mean	• median	• mixed number
• mass	• multiple	• numerator	• odd number
• mode	• prime number	• product	• quotient
• range	• sum	• variable	• volume
• average	• capacity	• congruent	

1. The segment formed when two faces of a space figure meet is called the _____ .

2. In division the number that divides the dividend is called the _____ .

3. In division the _____ is the answer.

4. In multiplication the _____ is the answer.

5. The _____ is the answer in addition.

6. The _____ is the answer in subtraction.

7. In division the number being divided is called the _____ .

8. The _____ are the numbers being added together in an addition problem.

9. Any number that can be divided by 2 without having a remainder is considered an _____ number.

10. An _____ number is any number that cannot be divided by 2 without a remainder.

11. A _____ is a number that compares part of an object or a set with the whole object or set.

12. The top number in a fraction is called the _____ ; the bottom number of any fraction is called the _____ .

13. An answer that is approximately exact is an _____ .

Reviewing Math Terminology

14. The numbers being multiplied together to obtain a product are the _____ .

15. A _____ number is a whole number and a fraction ($2^3/_4$).

16. If a number has only two factors, itself and 1, it is called a _____ number.

17. Any number greater than zero is a _____ number, while any number less than zero is a _____ number.

18. The _____ is the quotient found by dividing the sum of a set of data by the number of items of data.

19. The middle number in a set of data after the data is arranged in order from the least to the greatest is the _____ .

20. A _____ is the difference between the greatest number and the least number..

21. The amount of fluid a container can hold is its _____ measured in milliliters/liters or cups/quarts/gallons.

22. The _____ of an object is the amount of matter in it as determined by its weight in grams/kilograms or ounces/pounds.

23. When buying an object on sale, the _____ is the decrease in the price of the item.

24. The _____ is the number that appears most often in a set of data.

25. The _____ is the amount of space an object contains measured in cubic units.

26. A _____ is a letter that takes the place of a number. *Ex:* $5 + n = 9$, n=4.

27. Two objects are _____ when they have the same size and shape.

28. The _____ tells the number of times a factor is used.

29. Whole numbers and their opposites are called _____ ; any positive number, any negative number, and zero.

30. The numeral 16 is a _____ of 4 because it is the product of a given number and any whole number.

Mathematical Properties

In order to add, subtract, multiply, and divide, it is important to know the basic principles associated with these procedures.

A. **Commutative Property of Addition:** Changing the order of the addends does not change the sum.

B. **Associative Property of Addition:** Changing the grouping of the addends does not change the sum. To know what to do first, look at the parentheses.

C. **Opposites Property of Addition and Subtraction:** Addition and subtraction are opposite operations. One undoes the other.

D. **Zero Property of Addition:** The sum of any number and zero is the number.

Mathematical Properties *(cont.)*

E. **Zero Properties of Subtraction:** The difference between any number and zero is that number. The difference between any number and itself is zero.

F. **Commutative Property of Multiplication:** Changing the order of factors does not change the product.

G. **Associative Property of Multiplication:** Changing the grouping of factors does not change the product.

H. **Zero Property of Multiplication:** The product of zero and any number is zero.

I. **Property of One in Multiplication:** The product of one and any number is that number.

J. **Distributive Property of Multiplication:** When two or more numbers are being multiplied by the same factor, you can multiply and then add or add and then multiply.

K. **Opposites Property of Multiplication and Division:** Multiplying by a number is the opposite of dividing by that number.

Mathematical Properties *(cont.)*

Match the Mathematical Properties (A–K) on pages 183 and 184 to the associated equations:

_____   1. $9 - 0 = 9, 9 - 9 = 0$

_____   2. $4 + 2 = 4, 6 - 4 = 2$

_____   3. $5 + 0 = 5, 0 + 5 = 5$

_____   4. $(3 + 2) + 4 = 9$ and $3 + (2 + 4) = 9$, so $(3 + 2) + 4 = 3 + (2 + 4)$

_____   5. $5 + 3 = 8, 3 + 5 = 8$

_____   6. $7 \times 1 = 7, 1 \times 7 = 7$

_____   7. $3 \times 0 = 0, 0 \times 3 = 0$

_____   8. $(3 \times 2) \times 5 = 3 \times (2 \times 5)$

_____   9. $3 \times (2 + 3) = (3 \times 2) + (3 \times 3)$

_____   10. $3 \times 5 = 15$, so $15 \div 3 = 5$

_____   11. $7 \times 4 = 4 \times 7$

Practice: Use one of the properties to complete the equations.

12. $7 + 8 = 8 +$ _____

13. $3 \times 8 = 8 \times$ _____

14. $6 \times 8 = 8 \times$ _____

15. _____ $\times$ _____ $= 0$

16. $(4 + 8) + 5 = 4 + ($ _____ $+ 5)$

17. $0 + 6 =$ _____ , so _____ $-$ _____ $= 0$

18. $(6 \times 4) \times 3 = 6 \times ($ _____ $\times 3)$

19. $2 \times ($ _____ $\times 4) = (2 \times 3) \times 4$

20. _____ $\times (3 + 5) = (7 \times 3) + (7 \times 5)$

21. _____ $\times ($ _____ $+$ _____ $) = (8 \times 4) + (8 \times 6)$

22. $4 \times ($ _____ $+$ _____ $) = (4 \times 5) + (4 \times 9)$

23. $n \times 5 = 40$ $n =$ _____

24. $7 \times n = 56$ $n =$ _____

25. $72 - n = 8$ $n =$ _____

Estimation

Estimate by rounding to the place value indicated.

1. 56
   tens _____

2. 3,653
   hundreds _____

3. 457,830
   thousands _____

4. $2.96
   dollar_____

5. $17.75
   10 cents_____

6. $351.72
   10 cents_____

7. 36,245
   hundreds

   _____

8. 463,781
   ten thousands

   _____

9. $57.68
   dollar

   _____

The number has been rounded to the place value indicated. Write the least whole number that rounds to the given number.

10. 75,000
    thousand_____

11. 20,000
    ten thousand_____

12. 53,000,000
    million _____

13. 900,000
    hundred thousand_____

Write the greatest whole number that rounds to the given number.

14. 36,000
    thousand_____

15. 80,000
    ten thousand_____

16. 37,000,000
    million _____

17. 600,000
    hundred thousand_____

Applying Estimation:

18. A restaurant chain earned $73,853,361 last year after paying expenses. The owners expect to earn approximately the same amount next year, rounded to the nearest hundred thousand dollars. What is their projected profit?

    _____

Addition and Subtraction

Calculate the difference or the sum. Use the inverse operation (addition or subtraction) to check your answer.

1. $\begin{array}{r} 748 \\ -\ 359 \\ \hline \end{array}$ + _____

2. $\begin{array}{r} 456 \\ +\ 789 \\ \hline \end{array}$ − _____

3. $\begin{array}{r} 8,675 \\ +\ 3,489 \\ \hline \end{array}$ − _____

4. $\begin{array}{r} 8,974 \\ -\ 6,975 \\ \hline \end{array}$ + _____

5. $\begin{array}{r} 15,908 \\ -\ 13,989 \\ \hline \end{array}$ + _____

6. $\begin{array}{r} 36,371 \\ -\ 16,565 \\ \hline \end{array}$ + _____

Round to estimate the sum or difference, using the adjusted front-end method.

Reminder: Adjusted front-end estimation means to estimate to the value on the left.

7. $\begin{array}{r} 39,735 \\ +\ 91,306 \\ \hline \end{array}$

8. $\begin{array}{r} 77,431 \\ -\ 16,356 \\ \hline \end{array}$

9. $\begin{array}{r} 35,251 \\ +\ 43,300 \\ \hline \end{array}$

10. $\begin{array}{r} 73,086 \\ -\ 29,731 \\ \hline \end{array}$

11. $\begin{array}{r} 88,880 \\ +\ 25,365 \\ \hline \end{array}$

12. $\begin{array}{r} 3456 \\ +\ 5730 \\ \hline \end{array}$

13. $\begin{array}{r} 5561 \\ -\ 2453 \\ \hline \end{array}$

14. $\begin{array}{r} 4783 \\ +\ 2936 \\ \hline \end{array}$

15. $\begin{array}{r} 6482 \\ -\ 3509 \\ \hline \end{array}$

Problem Solving: Estimation in Addition and Subtraction

Solve the following word problems involving estimation, rounding, and actual computation in addition and subtraction.

1. George collected 365 coins last year. This year he has collected an additional 256 different coins. About how many coins has he collected altogether in these two years? Exactly how many were collected?

   Estimated Answer   _____

   Actual Answer   _____

2. The Browns and the Beimals bought new cars. The Browns paid $27,328, and the Beimals paid $32,751. Approximately what is the difference between the buying prices of the two cars rounded to the nearest thousand? How much more did the Beimals actually pay?

   Estimated Difference   _____

   Actual Difference   _____

3. The local Boy Scout troop is planning a family picnic. They ordered 156 hot dogs and 275 hamburgers. If each person eats one item, approximately how many people does the troop plan to feed? (Use front end-adjustment.) Exactly how many people will be attending?

   Estimated Attendance   _____

   Actual Attendance   _____

4. Juan hiked 404 miles during August and biked 824 miles during July. About how many miles has he covered during the summer? Calculate the actual mileage.

   Estimated Mileage   _____

   Actual Mileage   _____

5. Mrs. Ballin owns a candy shop. Last year her costs were $66,350. She sold $115,849 worth of candy. Approximately what was her profit, rounded to the nearest thousand? What was her precise profit?

   Approximate Profit   _____

   Exact Profit   _____

Estimating Decimals

Estimate the sum or difference using the adjusted front-end estimation. Then calculate the actual sum or difference.

1. $\begin{array}{r} 2.7 \\ + 6.93 \\ \hline \end{array}$ estimate _____

2. $\begin{array}{r} 4.75 \\ - 1.76 \\ \hline \end{array}$ estimate _____

3. $\begin{array}{r} 9.57 \\ + 0.44 \\ \hline \end{array}$ estimate _____

4. $\begin{array}{r} 0.58 \\ - 0.435 \\ \hline \end{array}$ estimate _____

5. $\begin{array}{r} 6.77 \\ + 2.8 \\ \hline \end{array}$ estimate _____

6. $\begin{array}{r} 15.3 \\ - 7.5 \\ \hline \end{array}$ estimate _____

7. $\begin{array}{r} 19.2 \\ + 36.5 \\ \hline \end{array}$ estimate _____

8. $\begin{array}{r} 4.2 \\ - 0.723 \\ \hline \end{array}$ estimate _____

9. $\begin{array}{r} 27.3 \\ - 22.9 \\ \hline \end{array}$ estimate _____

Estimate to compare the sum or difference. Use > for greater than and < for lesser than.

10. $16.3 + 2.33$ ◯ 18

11. $26.75 - 12.09$ ◯ 19

Tell whether the estimate is an overestimate or underestimate

12. $7.3 + 9.6 \approx 20$

13. $10.7 + 9.9 \approx 30$

On Your Own!

14. Cindy needs to cut ribbon for gift wrapping. She needs ribbons 2.6 meters, 1.5 meters, 0.75 meters, and 1.8 meters long. Her roll of ribbon has 5 meters. Will she have enough ribbon to wrap the gifts?

_____

_____

_____

_____

Adding and Subtracting Decimals

Place the decimal point in the sum.

1. 7.5 + 0.33 + 12.654 _____

2. 6.053 + 2.271 + 12.6 _____

Find the sum.

3. 5.6 + 4.7 _____

4. 22.75 + 16.1 _____

5. $66.21 + $6.93 _____

6. 12.306 + 0.19 _____

7.
```
    3.82
   14.254
 +  6.75
 _____
```

8.
```
    4.3
   31.72
 + 5.246
 _____
```

9.
```
   0.1437
  50.22
 + 7.34
 _____
```

10.
```
    6.7
   52.43
 + 1.625
 _____
```

11. $0.55 + $37.81 + $55.00 = _____

12. 60.1 + 352.33 + 5,075 + 0.88 = _____

Place the decimal point in the difference.

13. 6.75 – 3.25 = _____

14. 36.005 – 0.35 = _____

Find the difference.

15. 10.6 – 4.35 = _____

16. 245.8 – 83.19 = _____

17. 77.112 – 6.03 = _____

18. 8.045 – 3.72 = _____

19.
```
   60.44
 – 2.755
 _____
```

20.
```
    5.6
 – 0.89
 _____
```

21.
```
   72.8
 – 0.654
 _____
```

22.
```
   67.03
 – 0.0058
 _____
```

23. $37.82 – $8.46 =

24. 456.08 – 93.95 = _____

Problem Solving: Adding and Subtracting Decimals

1. The monthly rainfall during the spring was 3.4 inches, 8.6 inches, and 10.2 inches over three months. What was the total rainfall?

     _____

2. Sheila is redecorating the guest room. She needs 8.25 yards for the curtains and 16.25 yards for the bedspread and to recover the chair. How many yards must be bought to assure Sheila that she will have enough material?

     _____

3. The tennis player served the tennis ball at a top speed of 111.35 miles per hour. His opponent serves at a top speed of 106.85 miles per hour. What is the difference between the two speeds?

     _____

4. Deacon and Gary had lunch together at a restaurant. Deacon's entree cost $13.75, while Gary's entree was $12.55. Both men had dessert for $1.95 each. How much was the total bill?

     _____

5. Mr. James has 3 deposits of $1,242.30, $653.21, and $125.89 to make in his checking account. How much is his total deposit?

     _____

6. Mr. Lee has a balance of $2,563.37 in his checking account. He needs to write two checks: one for $833.25 and the other for $475.66. How much will be left in his checking account?

     _____

7. Stacey scored a 5.75 in the technical merit category in the ice skating championship. In the artistic interpretation category, she scored a 5.9. Meredith outscored Stacey by 0.32. What was Meredith's overall score?

     _____

8. When John went shopping, he bought sneakers for $65.75, a pair of shorts for $18.50, and a T-shirt for $12.95. How much money did he have left for lunch if he started out with $100.00?

     _____

9. Heather wants to buy a new video game that costs $74.99. She only has $33.50. How much more does she need?

     _____

Factors

- *Factors* are numbers that can be equally divided with no remainder.

- A *prime number* has itself and one as a factor.

- A *composite number* has more than two factors.

Example: Find the factors of 15.

15
/\
1 x 15

or

15
/\
3 x 5

The factors of 15 are 1, 3, 5.

15 is a composite number because it has more than two factors.

Directions: Factor each number and then identify it as being a prime or a composite number.

1. Factor 6

3 x 2

or

6
/\
6 x 1

The factors of 6 are 1 2 3 6 .

6 is a (prime, composite) number.

2. Factor 8

4 x 2

or

8
/\
8 x 1

The factors of 8 are 1 2 4 8 .

8 is a (prime, composite) number.

3. Factor 7

/\
1 x 7

The factors of 7 are 1 7 .

7 is a (prime, composite) number.

4. Factor 18

/\
9 x 2

or

18
/\
18 x 1

or

18
/\
6 x 3

The factors of 18 are 1 2 3 6 9 18 .

18 is a (prime, composite) number.

Factors *(cont.)*

Factors can be written in exponent form.

Example: Find the factors of 20 and write them in exponent form.

20

2 x 10

5 x 2

The factors of 20 are

2 x 2 x 5 =

2^2 x 5

Directions: Find the factors of each number and then write the factors in exponent form.

1. 18 _____

2. 16 _____

3. 20 _____

4. 24 _____

5. 9 _____

6. 32 _____

7. 75 _____

8. 12 _____

9. 36 _____

The *greatest common factor* (GCF) is the largest factor that a set of numbers has in common.

Example: Find the GCF of 6 and 12.

    A. Find the factors of both numbers.
        6 = 1, 2, 3
        12 = 1, 2, 3, 4, 6

    B. Find the common factors.
        2 and 3 are factors of 6 and 12.

    C. The GCF of 6 and 12 is 3 (excluding 6 itself).

Directions: Find the GCF for each set of numbers.

10. 4 _____

    12 _____

11. 10 _____

    30 _____

12. 20 _____

    30 _____

13. 12 _____

    18 _____

14. 15 _____

    50 _____

15. 18 _____

    20 _____

Multiples

Any whole number can be multiplied by another. When we do this, the resulting number is a *multiple*.

Directions: Fill in the chart with the missing multiples. To find the multiples of 4, multiply by 4.

4 x	1	2	3	4	5	6	7	8	9	10
multiple		8								40

Find the multiples of 2.

2 x	1	2	3	4	5	6	7	8	9	10
multiple										

As we look across the chart, we can see that (excluding the number itself and 1) 8, 12, 16, and 20 appear as multiples of both 2 and 4. These are called *common multiples*.

The least common multiple (excluding itself and 1) is the lowest common number that both numbers have in common. For 2 and 4, the least common multiple (LCM) is 8.

Exercise: Find the multiples of 3 and 5.

3 multiples   0 __ __ __ __ __ __ __ 24

5 multiples   0 __ __ __ __ __ __ 35 __

Circle the least common multiple of 3 and 5.

What are the first two LCM for the following numbers?

a. 3 and 6 _____   b. 6 and 9 _____   c. 8 and 10 _____

d. 10 and 20 _____   e. 3 and 8 _____   f. 4 and 7 _____

g. Tom and Karen are planning a party. They want to buy bags of blue and yellow balloons. The blue balloons have 4 in a package and the yellow balloons have 5 in each package. In order to have an equal number of blue and yellow balloons, what is the least number of packages of each color they will have to buy?

Multiplication Practice

Estimate the product and compare. Use > or <.

1. 47 x 23 ◯ 2000   2. 9 x 58 ◯ 700   3. 196 x 36 ◯ 3000

Use mental math to choose the best estimate.

4. 653 x 345 =   a. 100,000   b. 210,000   c. 400,000

5. 2,860 x 9 =   a. 7,000   b. 27,000   c. 18,000

6. 6,957 x 520 =   a. 3,500,000   b. 350,000   c. 35,000

Estimate the product.

7.	78 x 8	8.	4,630 x 5	9.	247 x 7	10.	419 x 6

Find the product in the following multiplication problems with two- and three-digit factors.

11.	71 x 38	12.	89 x 56	13.	436 x 84	14.	2,306 x 275

15.	436 x 805	16.	2,657 x 838	17.	82,467 x 247	18.	367,478 x 658

19. 735,669 x 302 = _____   20. 23,509 x 1,017 = _____

Multiplying Decimals

Place the decimal point in the product by estimating first.

1. 7.6 x 8.3 = _____

2. 4.65 x 6.8 = _____

3. 0.84 x 5.3 = _____

4. 0.45 x 0.93 = _____

Estimate the product. Then calculate the exact product.

5.   26.73
     x 6.8
     _____

6.   78
     x 2.9
     _____

7.   6.245
     x 0.7
     _____

8.   65.8
     x 337
     _____

Calculate the product. Round money problems to the nearest cent.

9.   7.356
     x 6.8
     _____

10. $17.93
     x 0.6
     _____

11. $683.25
     x 0.27
     _____

12. $43.78
     x 0.5
     _____

13.   0.035
     x 8
     _____

14.   25.89
     x 30.5
     _____

15.   0.0057
     x 778
     _____

16.   7.206
     x 18
     _____

17. $365.27 x 2.8 = _____

18. 6,983 x 6.217 = _____

19. 15.3 x 1,000 = _____

20. 536 x 100 = _____

21. 0.25 x 10 = _____

22. 0.884 x 100 = _____

23. 928.75 x 10 = _____

24. 8.6 x 1000 = _____

Problem Solving: Multiplication

Solve the following word problems involving multiplication.

1. Turkey costs $7.99 a pound. How much will 3.125 pounds cost, rounded to the nearest cent?

2. Sheets of foam board are 0.50 cm thick. How thick is a pile of two dozen foam boards?

3. The ferry makes 8 round trips across the river each day. A one-way excursion is 3.5 miles. How many miles are traveled in a week?

4. Mrs. Ruby drove 152 miles. Her husband drove the next 273 miles. The next day they drove twice as far. How many miles were traveled in the two-day trip?

5. A plane travels a distance of 1,637 miles in three hours. How many miles will the plane travel in 12 hours?

6. Andrew earns $6.50 per hour working the night shift at McDonald's. Last week he worked 39.75 hours How much did he earn?

7. Sherry went shopping at the neighborhood drugstore. She bought three bottles of nail polish at $2.19 each, two new lipsticks at $4.66 each, and four shampoos at $3.25 each. How much did she spend in the drugstore?

8. Mrs. Miller bought 16 rolls of film for her photography class. There were 36 exposures on each roll of film. All the pictures were developed except for two rolls. How many pictures were developed? Each print cost $0.28 to develop. How much did Mrs. Miller spend on developing?

Estimation in Division

Estimate to find the best quotient. Circle the answer.

1. $6\overline{)487}$ a. 60   b. 70   c. 80   d. 50

2. $5\overline{)14,482}$ a. 300   b. 30   c. 2,500   d. 3,000

3. $4,627 \div 23$ a. 100   b. 2,000   c. 200   d. 3,000

4. $8\overline{)688}$ a. 100   b. 10   c. 80   d. 800

Write the best estimated quotient.

5. $7\overline{)65}$ 6. $6\overline{)358}$ 7. $5\overline{)3889}$

Divide to find the quotient.

8. $4\overline{)316}$ 9. $6\overline{)2,586}$ 10. $7\overline{)5,103}$

11. $9\overline{)73,463}$ 12. $8\overline{)46,065}$ 13. $3\overline{)14,053}$

14. $16,084 \div 4 =$ 15. $37,398 \div 7 =$ 16. $5\overline{)26,009}$

Division with Decimals

Find the quotient.

1. $6.6 \div 3.3 =$ _____

2. $8.8 \div 11 =$ _____

3. $8.4 \div 2.1 =$ _____

4. $19.8 \div 9.9 =$ _____

5. $18.6 \div 6.2 =$ _____

6. $14.8 \div 3.7 =$ _____

7. $0.34 \overline{)266.56}$

8. $0.134 \overline{)3.39824}$

9. $6.5 \overline{)300.3}$

10. $2.6 \overline{)9.1}$

11. $0.035 \overline{)2.5249}$

12. $0.12 \overline{)2.832}$

13. $2.36 \overline{)107.852}$

14. $0.57 \overline{)0.3249}$

15. $27 \overline{)0.96768}$

Divide. Then round the quotient to the place value shown.

16. $\$3.76 \div 5 =$ _____
   (cents)

17. $643.2 \div 2.8 =$ _____
   (hundredths)

18. $97 \div 13 =$ _____
   (tenths)

More Division Practice

Estimate the quotient.

1. $41\overline{)248}$ 2. $32\overline{)155}$ 3. $17\overline{)3,605}$

_____   _____   _____

4. $15,689 \div 31 =$ 5. $1,856 \div 29 =$ 6. $57,352 \div 82 =$

_____   _____   _____

Divide to find the quotient.

7. $75\overline{)66,389}$ 8. $66\overline{)135,472}$ 9. $84\overline{)589}$

10. $7\overline{)8,400}$ 11. $34\overline{)5,900}$ 12. $33\overline{)2,860}$

13. $5\overline{)18}$ 14. $6\overline{)25.62}$ 15. $28\overline{)165.088}$

16. $6.540 \div 30 =$ 17. $15.15 \div 25 =$ 18. $32.550 \div 70 =$

Division Word Problems

Solve each of the word problems.

1. An SST travels at an average rate of 1,200 miles per hour. About how many miles does it travel in one minute?

   _____

2. Ms. Gray is baking cookies for the school fair. She plans on baking 450 cookies. Each tray of cookies holds about 16 cookies. About how many trays will she need to prepare?

   _____

3. A school in Detroit receives a delivery of 1,185 magazines each month in packages of 30. About how many classes are getting class sets of this magazine?

   _____

   If there are five grades in the school, how many classes are on each grade level?

   _____

4. There are 4,556 chickens on the farm. If 34 chickens are kept in each room in the coop, how many rooms are needed?

   _____

5. Jackie counted 2,100 pennies. If she places 50 pennies in each roll, how many rolls will she have?

   _____

6. Samantha earns $318.75 a week in salary. She worked 37.5 hours last week. How much does she earn an hour as a bookkeeper?

   _____

7. Jimmy jogs y miles each day, regardless of the weather. How many miles does Jimmy jog each year? Use $y = 6$ for the expression.

   _____

8. Christina receives d dollars a week for school lunches from her mother. Christina attended school all five days last week. If she spends the same amount each day, how much is the school lunch? Estimate the expression for $12.75.

   _____

Range, Mean, Median, and Mode

Tom picked these five numbers: 92, 36, 40, 52, 40. He knew that the difference between the greatest number and the least number is called the **range.**

Example: The range between 92 and 36 is
$$92 - 36 = 56$$

Tom knew that he had five numbers and their sum was equal to 260. If he divided the sum by the total numbers he had, he could find the **mean.**

Example: $$\frac{36 + 40 + 52 + 40 + 92}{5} = \frac{260}{5} = 52$$

When Tom looked at the numbers after he listed them in order from least to greatest, he was able to find the **median.** The median is the number in the middle of the sequence (or the mean of the two middle numbers if there are an even number of items in the sequence).

Example: 36   40   ⟨40⟩   52   92

The **mode** is the number that appears most often.

Example: 36   ⟨40⟩   52   ⟨40⟩   92

The number 40 appears twice, so it is the mode.

Directions: Find the *range, mean, median* and *mode* for each set of numbers.

1. 25, 73, 12, 25, 35

   A. Order: ____   ____   ____   ____   ____

   B. Range: ____ – ____ = ____

   C. Mean: $\dfrac{\text{____} + \text{____} + \text{____} + \text{____} + \text{____}}{5}$ = $\dfrac{\text{____}}{5}$ = ____

   D. Median: _____

   E. Mode: _____

2. 100, 23, 49, 88, 30, 23, 51

   A. Order: ____   ____   ____   ____   ____   ____   ____

   B. Range: _____

   C. Mean: _____

   D. Median: _____

   E. Mode: _____

Range, Mean, Median, and Mode *(cont.)*

3. 18, 36, 24, 18

    A. Order: _____

    B. Range: _____

    C. Mean: _____

    D. Median: _____

    E. Mode: _____

4. 22, 70, 22, 84, 36, 42

    A. Order: _____

    B. Range: _____

    C. Mean: _____

    D. Median: _____

    E. Mode: _____

5. 170, 200, 305

    A. Order: _____

    B. Range: _____

    C. Mean: _____

    D. Median: _____

    E. Mode: _____

6. 45, 66, 89, 69, 77, 22, 66

    A. Order: _____

    B. Range: _____

    C. Mean: _____

    D. Median: _____

    E. Mode: _____

Solving Equations

Use the values below to solve the expression 4.8 x a = _____ .

1. a = 25 _____

2. a = 55 _____

3. a = 362 _____

4. a = 13.8 _____

Use the values below to solve the expression $\dfrac{x}{6}$ = _____ .

5. x = 54 _____

6. x = 222 _____

7. x = 4659 _____

8. x = 93 _____

Evaluate the expressions.

9. 26 b, when b = 7

10. $\dfrac{s}{5}$, when s = 155

11. 74 m, when m = 6

12. 5.3 s, when s = 2.6

13. $\dfrac{n}{4.6}$, when n = 35.88

14. $\dfrac{y}{1.8}$, when y = 6.3

Tell how to solve each equation (multiply or divide). Then solve the problem.

Reminder: The inverse of multiplication is division.
The inverse of division is multiplication.

Example: 2 x = 10 divide by 2
$\dfrac{c}{3}$ = 15 multiply by 3

15. 45a = 135

16. 35t = 1,050

17. $\dfrac{m}{16}$ = 100

_____

_____

_____

18. $\dfrac{s}{215}$ = 1

19. 81f = 729

20. 15p = 360

_____

_____

_____

Fractions

A *fraction* represents a part of a whole. It compares part of an object or set with the whole object or set. The *numerator* is the top number in the fraction. The *denominator*, or the bottom number, represents into how many parts the whole item is divided. The line separating the numerator and the denominator actually means "divide by."

Write the fraction stated in words.

1. three-sevenths _____

2. six-eighths _____

3. three-fourths _____

4. seven-tenths _____

5. eight-twelfths _____

6. fifty-two hundredths _____

Equivalent fractions are those that are equal to one another. The terms of the fraction, the numerator and the denominator, can be multiplied by the same number (other than zero) to write an equivalent fraction.

Example: $\dfrac{3}{5} = \dfrac{3 \times 2}{5 \times 2} = \dfrac{6}{10}$

What is the equivalent fraction?

7. $\dfrac{1}{2} = \dfrac{1 \times 4}{2 \times 4} = $ _____

8. $\dfrac{1}{3} = \dfrac{1 \times 3}{3 \times 3} = $ _____

9. $\dfrac{6}{10} = \dfrac{6 \times 3}{10 \times 3} = $ _____

Complete the following, using mental math.

10. $\dfrac{1}{2} = \dfrac{5}{}$

11. $\dfrac{3}{7} = \dfrac{15}{}$

12. $\dfrac{7}{12} = \dfrac{}{36}$

13. $\dfrac{2}{9} = \dfrac{}{27}$

14. $\dfrac{2}{3} = \dfrac{16}{}$

15. $\dfrac{4}{6} = \dfrac{2}{}$

16. $\dfrac{8}{20} = \dfrac{}{100}$

17. $\dfrac{5}{21} = \dfrac{}{105}$

You can write an equivalent fraction that is lower than the original fraction. To write a fraction in lowest terms, divide both terms (the numerator and denominator) by their greatest common factor (GCF). This is called "reducing the fraction."

Reduce the fraction to its lowest terms.

18. $\dfrac{7}{21} = $

19. $\dfrac{10}{25} = $

20. $\dfrac{12}{36} = $

21. $\dfrac{8}{12} = $

22. $\dfrac{8}{28} = $

23. $\dfrac{25}{100} = $

24. $\dfrac{90}{100} = $

25. $\dfrac{174}{1,000} = $

Fractions and Decimals

A *mixed number* is a fraction greater than 1, written as a whole number and a fraction. A fraction written with the numerator larger than the denominator is called an *improper fraction*. Improper fractions should be changed into proper fractions or mixed fractions. To change an improper fraction into a mixed fraction, divide the numerator by the denominator.

Example: $\dfrac{16}{5} = 3\dfrac{1}{5}$ $5\overline{)\begin{array}{l} 3\ r1 \\ 16 \\ -15 \\ \hline 1 \end{array}}$ or $3\dfrac{1\ \text{(remainder)}}{5\ \text{(divisor)}}$

Write the fraction as a mixed number or a whole number.

1. $\dfrac{25}{6}$ 2. $\dfrac{13}{4}$ 3. $\dfrac{40}{5}$ 4. $\dfrac{38}{7}$ 5. $\dfrac{27}{9}$

Write the mixed number as a fraction.

6. $3\dfrac{2}{7}$ 7. $5\dfrac{3}{5}$ 8. $7\dfrac{2}{9}$ 9. $4\dfrac{3}{8}$ 10. $2\dfrac{9}{10}$

Write the quotient as a mixed number. Write the fraction in lowest terms.

11. $5\overline{)11}$ 12. $8\overline{)38}$ 13. $5\overline{)48}$ 14. $8\overline{)74}$

Mixed numbers may be written as decimals. To write a mixed number as a decimal, first write the fraction as a decimal by dividing the numerator by the denominator. Then add the whole number and the decimal.

Example: $2\dfrac{3}{5}$ $\dfrac{3}{5} = 5\overline{)\begin{array}{l} 0.6 \\ 3.0 \end{array}}$ $2 + 0.6 = 2.6$

Write the fraction or the mixed number as a decimal.

15. $\dfrac{2}{8}$ $8\overline{)2.0}$ 16. $\dfrac{3}{4}$ $4\overline{)3.0}$ 17. $6\dfrac{4}{20}$ $20\overline{)4.00}$

18. $\dfrac{1}{2}$ 19. $\dfrac{2}{8}$ 20. $\dfrac{15}{25}$ 21. $3\dfrac{6}{10}$

Comparing and Ordering Fractions

Comparing fractions and ordering them from least to greatest is simple when the denominator is the same.

Example: $\dfrac{2}{7} < \dfrac{5}{7}$ because $2 < 5$

In order to compare fractions with different denominators, find the least common multiple (LCM) of the denominators. That is the least common denominator (LCD).

Example: Compare the fractions $\dfrac{2}{4}$ and $\dfrac{3}{4}$ (think 3 x 4 = 12).

$$\dfrac{2}{3} = \dfrac{8}{12} \qquad \dfrac{3}{4} = \dfrac{9}{12} \qquad \dfrac{8}{12} < \dfrac{9}{12} \quad \text{so} \quad \dfrac{2}{3} < \dfrac{3}{4}$$

Example: Order the fractions $\dfrac{5}{9}$, $\dfrac{2}{3}$, $\dfrac{3}{4}$ (think 36 9, 3, & 4).

$$\dfrac{5}{9} = \dfrac{20}{36} \qquad \dfrac{2}{3} = \dfrac{24}{36} \qquad \dfrac{3}{4} = \dfrac{27}{36} \quad \text{so} \quad \dfrac{5}{9} < \dfrac{2}{3} < \dfrac{3}{4}$$

Write < or > to compare the fractions.

1. $\dfrac{4}{9} \bigcirc \dfrac{3}{9}$ 2. $\dfrac{2}{3} \bigcirc \dfrac{5}{9}$ 3. $\dfrac{3}{7} \bigcirc \dfrac{15}{21}$ 4. $\dfrac{3}{5} \bigcirc \dfrac{2}{3}$

Arrange the fractions in order from least to greatest.

5. $\dfrac{2}{8}$, $\dfrac{3}{6}$, $\dfrac{5}{12}$ _____ , _____ , _____

6. $\dfrac{3}{15}$, $\dfrac{2}{3}$, $\dfrac{7}{10}$ _____ , _____ , _____

7. $\dfrac{7}{18}$, $\dfrac{2}{9}$, $\dfrac{4}{6}$ _____ , _____ , _____

8. $\dfrac{10}{25}$, $\dfrac{3}{5}$, $\dfrac{16}{50}$ _____ , _____ , _____

9. $\dfrac{2}{4}$, $\dfrac{5}{16}$, $\dfrac{5}{8}$ _____ , _____ , _____

Adding and Subtracting Fractions

To add fractions with the same denominator, add the numerators and write the sum over the same denominator. To subtract fractions with the same denominator, subtract the numerators and write the difference over the same denominator. Always write the sum or difference in lowest terms.

1. $\dfrac{5}{6} - \dfrac{3}{6}$

2. $\dfrac{4}{7} + \dfrac{2}{7}$

3. $\dfrac{7}{12} - \dfrac{4}{12}$

4. $\dfrac{5}{16} + \dfrac{3}{16}$

To add or subtract fractions with different denominators, first write equivalent fractions with a common denominator. Then add or subtract. Write the sum or difference in lowest terms.

5. $\dfrac{3}{5} + \dfrac{2}{8}$

6. $\dfrac{3}{5} + \dfrac{5}{7}$

7. $\dfrac{7}{9} - \dfrac{1}{2}$

8. $\dfrac{4}{5} - \dfrac{3}{4}$

To add or subtract mixed numbers, determine if the fractions have to be changed to equivalent fractions. First change the fractions to equivalent fractions and then proceed with the addition or subtraction.

Sometimes the mixed number will have to be renamed. Change the whole number to a fraction equal to one and add it to the fraction portion, resulting in an improper fraction.

Proceed with the addition or subtraction. Write the sum or difference in lowest terms.

Add or subtract. Then write the answer in lowest terms.

9. $\dfrac{7}{10}$
$-\dfrac{5}{10}$
_____

10. $\dfrac{3}{8}$
$+\dfrac{5}{12}$
_____

11. $\dfrac{3}{4}$
$-\dfrac{1}{5}$
_____

12. $\dfrac{5}{16}$
$+\dfrac{3}{8}$
_____

13. $4\,^3/_4 + 5\,^5/_6 \ = \ $ _____

14. $9\,^7/_8 - 6\,^2/_4 \ = \ $ _____

15. $5\,^2/_3 - 2\,^4/_9 \ = \ $ _____

Multiplying and Dividing Fractions

To multiply a fraction and a whole number, first multiply the numerator of the fraction by the whole number. Then write the product above the denominator.

Example: $4 \times \frac{1}{2} = 4 \times 1 = 4$, then $\frac{4}{2}$ which $= 2$

To multiply fractions, multiply the numerators and then multiply the denominators.

Example: $\frac{1}{2} \times \frac{3}{4} = \frac{1}{2} \times \frac{3}{4} = \frac{3}{8}$

To multiply mixed numbers as fractions, first write the mixed numbers as fractions. Simplify if possible. Then multiply.

Example: $4 \frac{1}{2} \times 6 \frac{3}{4} = \frac{9}{2} \times \frac{27}{4} = \frac{243}{8} = 30 \frac{3}{8}$

Example: $5 \frac{1}{3} \times 3 \frac{1}{4} = \frac{\overset{4}{\cancel{16}}}{3} \times \frac{13}{\underset{1}{\cancel{4}}} = \frac{4 \times 13}{3 \times 1} = \frac{52}{3} = 17 \frac{1}{3}$

To divide a whole number by a fraction, first convert the fraction into its reciprocal (its reverse), and then multiply.

Example: $6 \div \frac{1}{2} = \frac{6}{1} \times \frac{2}{1} = 12$

To divide a fraction by a whole number, first write the reciprocal of the whole number divisor and then multiply.

Example: $\frac{3}{4} \div 3 = \frac{3}{4} \times \frac{1}{3} = \frac{3}{12} = \frac{1}{4}$

To divide a fraction by a fraction, multiply the fraction by the reciprocal of the divisor.

Example: $\frac{3}{4} \div \frac{1}{2} = \frac{3}{4} \times \frac{2}{1} = \frac{6}{4} = 1 \frac{2}{4} = 1 \frac{1}{2}$

To divide mixed numbers, first write the mixed numbers as fractions. Then multiply by the reciprocal of the divisor.

Example: $5 \frac{1}{2} \div 2 \frac{1}{4} = \frac{11}{2} \div \frac{9}{4} = \frac{11}{\underset{1}{\cancel{2}}} \times \frac{\overset{2}{\cancel{4}}}{9} = \frac{11 \times 2}{1 \times 9} = \frac{22}{9} = 2 \frac{4}{9}$

Practice Multiplying and Dividing Fractions and Mixed Numbers

Multiply and reduce to lowest terms.

1. $5 \times \dfrac{6}{8}$

2. $\dfrac{4}{10} \times 34$

3. $\dfrac{6}{12} \times \dfrac{8}{9}$

4. $\dfrac{5}{11} \times \dfrac{4}{7}$

5. $\dfrac{15}{6} \times \dfrac{3}{8}$

6. $8 \times 3\dfrac{1}{5}$

7. $3\dfrac{3}{7} \times \dfrac{7}{8}$

8. $4\dfrac{1}{4} \times 6\dfrac{2}{5}$

9. $\dfrac{3}{15} \times 60$

10. $\dfrac{13}{15} \times \dfrac{3}{36}$

11. $5\dfrac{5}{7} \times 2\dfrac{3}{5}$

12. $4\dfrac{1}{4} \times 2\dfrac{7}{9}$

Divide and reduce to lowest terms.

13. $4 \div \dfrac{7}{10}$

14. $16 \div \dfrac{3}{8}$

15. $\dfrac{1}{3} \div 5$

16. $\dfrac{4}{9} \div 18$

17. $\dfrac{5}{8} \div \dfrac{3}{5}$

18. $\dfrac{3}{10} \div \dfrac{16}{20}$

19. $4\dfrac{5}{6} \div \dfrac{8}{7}$

20. $2\dfrac{2}{7} \div 3\dfrac{4}{7}$

21. $3\dfrac{1}{12} \div 9\dfrac{2}{3}$

22. $\dfrac{9}{11} \div 36$

23. $5\dfrac{4}{5} \div 6\dfrac{2}{5}$

24. $28 \div \dfrac{1}{2}$

25. Mary made cupcakes. She gave half of them to Joan. Joan shared the cupcakes equally with two friends. How many cupcakes did Mary make if Joan and her friends each got 12 cupcakes?

26. Jerry found three dozen fireflies one summer evening. He gave half of them to his friend Joe, one fourth of them to his friend Larry, and one third of his share to his sister. How many fireflies did he have left?

Customary Measurement

Liquid Measures

Ounces		Cups		Pints		Quarts		Gallons
8	=	1						
16	=	2						
32	=	4	=	1				
64	=	8	=	2	=	1		
128	=	16	=	8	=	4	=	1

Exercises: Change each unit of measurement into an equivalent measurement.

1. 3 gallons = _____ quarts

   = _____ pints

   = _____ cups

   = _____ ounces

2. 4 quarts = _____ pints

   = _____ cups

   = _____ ounces

3. 10 ounces = _____ cups and _____ ounces

4. 250 ounces = _____ cups and _____ ounces

5. 5 pints = _____ cups and _____ ounces

Dry Measures

Ounces		Pounds		Tons
16	=	1		
		2000	=	1

Exercise: Change each unit of measurement into the equivalent measurement.

6. 12,000 pounds = _____ tons

7. 7,500 pounds = _____ tons

8. 80 ounces = _____ pounds

9. 4.5 pounds = _____ ounces

10. Mary bought three pounds of turkey at the deli counter. How many ounces of turkey did she buy?

11. An apple orchard harvested 2.5 tons of apples last year. How many pounds of apples were harvested?

12. A cheesecake recipe called for two quarts of heavy cream and 2 cups of sour cream. How many pints of heavy cream and sour cream were needed to make this cake?

Customary Measurement *(cont.)*

Linear Measures

Inches		Feet		Yards
12	=	1		
36	=	3	=	1

To change a measurement of feet into a measurement of inches, multiply by 12.

Example: How many inches are equal to 4 feet?
4 feet x 12 inches = 48 inches

Exercise: Change the following measurements into inches.

1. 7 feet = _____ inches

2. 12 feet = _____ inches

3. 9 feet = _____ inches

4. 24 feet = _____ inches

To change a measurement of inches into feet, divide by twelve.

Example: How many feet are equal to 60 inches?
$$\frac{60 \text{ inches}}{12 \text{ inches}} = 5 \text{ feet}$$

Exercise: Change the following measurements into feet.

5. 48 inches = _____ feet

6. 9,816 inches = _____ feet

7. 7,200 inches = _____ feet

8. 24 inches = _____ feet

To change a measurement of yards to feet, multiply by three.

Example: How many feet are equal to 7 yards?
7 yards x 3 feet = 21 feet

Exercise: Change the yards to feet.

9. 15 yards = _____ feet

10. 3 yards = _____ feet

11. 6 yards = _____ feet

12. 9 yards = _____ feet

To change feet to yards, divide by three.

Example: $\dfrac{66 \text{ feet}}{3 \text{ feet}} = 22 \text{ yards}$

Exercise: Change the feet to yards.

13. 366 feet = _____ yards

14. 27 feet = _____ yards

15. 915 feet = _____ yards

16. 1,536 feet = _____ yards

Customary Measurement *(cont.)*

Time

Seconds		Minutes		Hours
60	=	1		
3600	=	60	=	1

To find the total number of hours and minutes in an addition problem, you must regroup the sum of the problem. Your answer should contain 59 minutes or less.

Example:

2 hours 24 minutes
+ 7 hours 45 minutes

9 hours 69 minutes

69 minutes is more than 1 hour. It is equal to 1 hour 9 minutes.

9 hours + 1 hour + 9 minutes = 10 hours 9 minutes

Solve the following problems. Remember to regroup.

1.   9 hours 15 minutes
    + 4 hours 50 minutes

2.   14 hours 25 minutes
    + 12 hours 42 minutes

3.   6 hours 59 minutes
    + 5 hours 3 minutes

4.   7 hours 37 minutes
    + 6 hours 32 minutes

To find the difference, regroup before subtracting.

Example:

$\overset{4}{\cancel{5}}$ hours $\overset{74}{\cancel{14}}$ minutes
– 3 hours 22 minutes

1 hour 52 minutes

5 hours can be regrouped to 4 hours 60 minutes. When we add the existing 14 minutes to the 60, the problem can be solved.

Exercise: Regroup to find the difference.

5.   8 hours 12 minutes
    – 6 hours 8 minutes

6.   12 hours 34 minutes
    – 5 hours 57 minutes

7.   15 hours 11 minutes
    – 13 hours 45 minutes

8.   2 hours 29 minutes
    – 1 hour 30 minutes

Distance–Time–Rate

Most of *Tuck Everlasting* is set in the 1880s, a time when people usually depended on horses for transportation. The epilogue takes place in 1950, and although the Tucks continue to use their horse-drawn buggy, cars are predominant. Solve the following problems (round to the nearest hundredth). Then compare the speeds of both methods of transportation.

1. It was 20 miles from Treegap to the Tuck's house. The man in the yellow suit and the constable had a 3- or 4-hour ride ahead of them on horseback. Fill in the chart below to tell the speed of the horse for each time listed. (Remember that the rate is calculated by dividing the distance by the time.)

Distance	Time	Rate (m.p.h.)
20 mi.	3 hrs.	
20 mi.	3.25 hrs.	
20 mi.	3.50 hrs.	
20 mi.	3.75 hrs.	
20 mi.	4 hrs.	

2. Today we usually travel by car to go 20 miles. If you were moving at an average speed of 45 miles per hour, how long would it take you to get to the Tuck's house from Treegap?_____

   At 60 miles per hour? _____

3a. Using a map of North America, estimate the distance from your home to Washington, D.C. How long would it take you to get there by car going 50 m.p.h.? by horse going 5 m.p.h.?

Distance to Washington, D.C. = _____

Time by car = _____

Time by horse = _____

3b. Using a map of North America, estimate the distance from your home to Disneyland, located in Anaheim, California. How long would it take you to get there by car going 50 m.p.h.? by horse going 5 m.p.h.?

Distance to Disneyland = _____

Time by car = _____

Time by horse = _____

3c. Using a map of North America, estimate the distance from your home to Vancouver, Canada. How long would it take you to get there by car going 50 m.p.h.? by horse going 5 m.p.h.?

Distance to Vancouver = _____

Time by car = _____

Time by horse = _____

Metric Measurement

Metric Measurement Tips:

• A *meter* (m) is about the length from your fingertips to the end of your opposite shoulder if your arms are extended outward from your shoulder.

• One *centimeter* (cm) is about the distance across the nail of your pinky.

• A *millimeter* (mm) is about the thickness of a dime.

• A *kilometer* (km) is the distance a person can walk in about 10–12 minutes.

Circle the best estimate.

1. length of a workbook	a. 35 m	b. 35 mm	c. 35 cm	d. 2 km
2. length of a bus	a. km	b. m	c. cm	d. ml
3. length of a new pencil	a. 20 kg	b. 20 mm	c. 20 cm	d. 20 m
4. distance on plane from NY to CA	a. km	b. kg	c. m	d. L
5. width of your hand	a. 12 cm	b. 1.2 cm	c. 120 m	d. 12 mm

Choose the most appropriate measurement: mm, cm, m, km

6. height of a tree ___m___

7. diameter of Mars ___km___

8. length of a turtle ___cm___

9. width of a paper clip ___cm___

10. diameter of a penny ___mm___

11. height of a vase ___cm___

12. perimeter of a room ___m___

13. Nile River ___km___

Match the best estimate for each picture below. Remember that the width of your pinky is 1 cm.

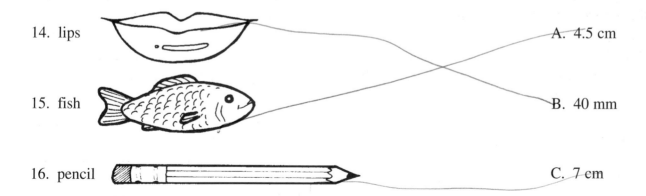

14. lips   A. 4.5 cm

15. fish   B. 40 mm

16. pencil   C. 7 cm

Measurement Practice

10 mm = 1 cm	1 cm = 10 mm
100 cm = 1 m	1 m = 100 cm
1000 mm = 1 m	1 m = 1000 mm
1000 m = 1 km	1 km = 1000 m
1 L = 1000 mL	1 kL = 1000 L
1 kg = 1000 g	1 g = 1000 mg

Complete the conversions.

1. 10 mm = _____ cm

2. 50 cm = _____ mm

3. 30 mm = _____ cm

4. 10 cm = _____ mm

5. 50 mm = _____ cm

6. 90 cm = _____ mm

7. 65 mm = _____ cm

8. 33 cm = _____ mm

9. 100 cm = _____ m

10. 1,000 m = _____ km

11. 600 cm = _____ m

12. 5,000 m = _____ km

13. 800 cm = _____ m

14. 7,000 m = _____ km

15. 753 cm = _____ m

16. 8,350 m = _____ km

17. 4 m = _____ cm

18. 3 km = _____ m

19. 7 m = _____ cm

20. 6 km = _____ m

21. 9 m = _____ cm

22. 10 km = _____ m

23. 6.8 m = _____ cm

24. 15.5 km = _____ m

Complete the equations.

25. 4 mL = _____ L

26. 7 mm = _____ m

27. 650 mm = _____ cm

28. 70 mm = _____ m

29. 650 mm = _____ m

30. 4 mL = _____ L

31. 650 cm = _____ m

32. 4 L = _____ mL

33. 4 g = _____ kg

34. 7.5 L = _____ mL

35. 4 kg = _____ g

36. 6,500 L = _____ kL

37. 225 g = _____ kg

38. 3.5 kL = _____ L

39. 225 kg = _____ g

40. 57 g = _____ kg

Problem Solving: Measurement and Decimals

1. A fisherman uses a fishing pole that is about 350 cm long. How many millimeters is the fishing pole? How many meters is this pole?

   _____

2. Which race is longer: a 5 kilometer (km) walk, a 700 meter (m) walk, or a 6,500 meter (m) walk?

   _____

3. The football was thrown 1,350 meters in the first half of the Super Bowl. At the end of the second half, the football had traveled a total of 2.875 kilometers in the air. During which half did the football travel farther?

   _____

4. The mass of a golf ball is about 75 grams (g). What is the mass of 18 new golf balls? How many kilograms is this?

   _____

5. Sean has a set of checkers whose total mass is 36 grams. There are 24 checkers in the set. What is the mass of each checker?

   _____

6. A vase has a capacity of 240 mL. A 650 mL pitcher is used to fill it. How much water is left in the pitcher?

   _____

7. Each science book is 2 centimeters thick. There are 30 books stacked on the shelf. How high is the stack in meters?

   _____

8. Kristen poured 175 mL of milk into a 3 L pitcher. How much more milk must be added to fill the pitcher?

   _____

9. Jan is 1,600 cm tall, Christina is 1,250 cm tall, and Cindy is 1,500 cm tall. What is the average height of the girls? What is the average height in meters?

   _____

Geometric Terms

Match each definition in column A with the correct picture in column B.

Column A		Column B
	Column A	**Column B**

	Column A		Column B
_____	1. A *point* is a particular location.	A.	←•————•→
_____	2. A *line* contains a set of points. It has arrows on the ends to indicate that it extends outward in the same direction.	B.	
_____	3. A *line segment* is part of a line marked by points.	C.	
_____	4. A *ray* is part of a line with one end point.	D.	
_____	5. *Intersecting lines* cross each other. In doing so, the lines create *angles*.	E.	
_____	6. *Perpendicular lines* are lines that intersect, forming right angles.	F.	X Y
_____	7. *Parallel lines* are lines that run in the same direction but never intersect.	G.	
_____	8. A *plane* is a flat figure that continues out in all directions.	H.	●

Angles

- *Angles* are formed when two or more rays intersect. The point of intersection is called the *vertex*.

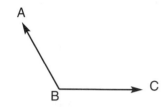

Ray BA intersects with ray BC at point B.
Point B is the vertex of angle ABC.

- Any angle that measures less than 90° is called an *acute angle*.

- A *right angle* measures 90°.
  Angle DEF measures 90°.
  Point E is the vertex.

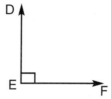

- Any angle that measures less than 180° but measures more than 90° is an *obtuse angle*.

Using a protractor, measure the following angles and label them as *acute*, *right*, or *obtuse* angles.

1.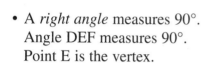

   _____

2.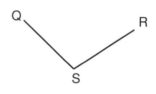

   _____

3.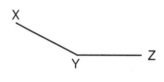

   _____

Draw angles that measure the following degrees:

4. 50°   5. 78°   6. 125°   7. 60°   8. 30°

Use the following diagram to answer these questions.

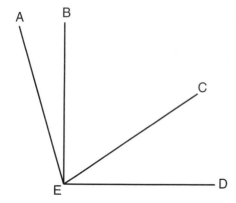

9. The right angle is _____ .

10. One acute angle is _____ .

11. A second acute angle is _____ .

12. A third acute angle is _____ .

13. The obtuse angle is _____ .

14. The vertex is _____ .

Triangles

- A *right triangle* has one angle that measures 90°.

- An *isosceles triangle* has two equal angles and two sides of equal length.

- An *equilateral triangle* has three equal angles and three sides of equal length.

- A *scalene triangle* has no equal angles and no sides of equal length.

- The sum of all three angles in any triangle is equal to 180°.

Directions: Label each triangle as *right, isosceles, equilateral,* or *scalene.*

1. 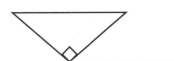 _____   2.  _____   3. _____

4. _____

5. a triangle with sides of 9 in., 9 in., 9 in.

6. a triangle with sides of 4 cm, 8 cm, 8 cm _____

7. a triangle with angles of 95°, 55°, 30° _____

8. a triangle with angles of 110°, 35°, 35° _____

Find the measurement of the third angle for each unfinished triangle below.

9. 110°, 60° _____   12. 90°, 43° _____

10. 45°, 58° _____   13. 45°, 66° _____

11. 75°, 35° _____   14. 120°, 30° _____

Perimeter

Perimeter is the distance around the outside edges of a figure. It can be found by adding the lengths of all the sides of a figure together.

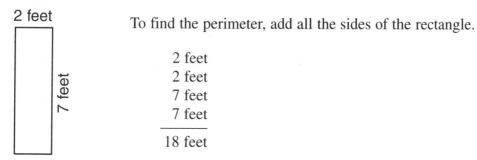

To find the perimeter, add all the sides of the rectangle.

2 feet
2 feet
7 feet
7 feet
_____
18 feet

Exercises: Find the perimeter of each of the following figures.

1.

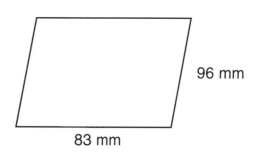

1.24 cm   1.24 cm

2.9 cm

2.

96 mm

83 mm

3.

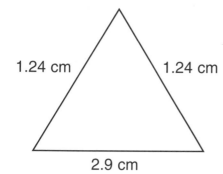

6.4 m

5.3 m   3 m

4.5 m   5 m

4.

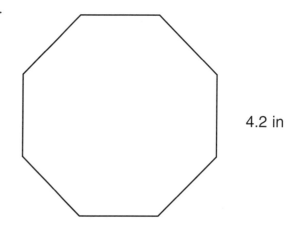

4.2 in

5. Jane skates around a rectangular ice rink three times each day. The length of the rink is 12.4 meters, and the width is 8.6 meters. What is the total distance she skates in a day?

6. Mr. Beecher purchased fencing to go around the outside edge of his property. How much fencing does he need to buy if the length of his yard is 30 feet and the width is 75 feet?

7. Mrs. Curtis needs to frame a picture that is 11 inches by 8 inches. How many inches of wood does she need?

Finding the Area of a Rectangle

The *area* of an object is the number of square units that fit inside the figure. For a rectangle, area is measured by multiplying the length by the width.

L x W = A
L = 3 cm, W = 5 cm
3 x 5 = 15 sq cm
A = 15 sq cm

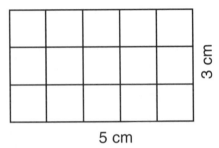

3 cm

5 cm

Exercise: Find the area of the following figures:

1.

5.2 meters

7.3 meters

2.

12 in.

2 in

3.

3.7 cm

4.

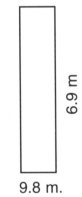

6.9 m

9.8 m.

5. a rectangle with a length of 9.2 meters and a width of 11 meters _____

6. a square with a length of 4 cm _____

7. a rectangle with a length of 1.3 cm and a width of 0.5 cm _____

8. a rectangle with a length of 2.4 cm and a width of 4.7 cm _____

9. a square with a length of 30 meters _____

10. a rectangle with a length of 8.1 inches and a width of 8 inches_____

Finding the Area of a Parallelogram

The area of a parallelogram can be found by multiplying the base by the height. This will tell how many square units are needed to fill the figure.

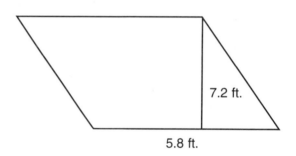

Area = base x height

A = b x h

Example: A parallelogram has a base of 15 centimeters and a height of 6 centimeters. What is the area?

A = b x h

A = 15 x 6

A = 90 square centimeters

Directions: Find the area of the following parallelograms.

1.

4.6 in.

10 in.

_____

2.

7.2 ft.

5.8 ft.

_____

3.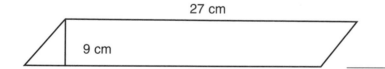

27 cm

9 cm

_____

4. Bill is building a greenhouse with four windows. Each window has a base of 4 feet and a height of 6 feet. What is the area of the piece of plastic that he will need to cover the four windows?

_____

5. Philip and Margie selected carpeting for their den. The length of the room is 8 feet 5 inches and the width is 9 feet. What is the area that will be covered by the rug?_____

6. Tim made a parallelogram with an area of 15 square centimeters. If the height was 3 cm, what was the base?

_____

Circles

Directions: Match the following definitions in column A with the correct pictures in column B.

Column A	Column B

Column A

1. The *center* of the circle is the *midpoint*. All lines drawn from the center to the outer edge are of equal distance.

2. The *diameter* is a line segment that begins on one edge of the circle and passes through the center point, ending on the other edge of the circle.

3. The *radius* is a line starting from the center point and ending on the outer edge. It is equal to one-half the diameter.

4. A *chord* is any line beginning at one edge of the circle and ending on the other edge. It need not pass through the center.

Directions: Identify each segment of the circle.

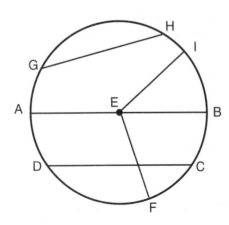

Column B

_____ A.

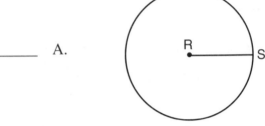

_____ B.

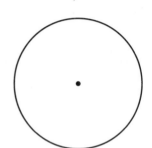

_____ C.

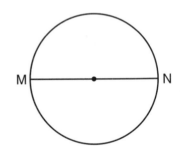

_____ D.

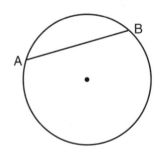

1. The diameter is _____ .

2. The center point is _____ .

3. Four radii are _____ .

4. Two chords are _____ .

Finding the Circumference of a Circle

The distance around the outer edge of a circle is the *circumference*. To find the circumference, you can use this formula:

$$C = \pi \text{ x diameter}$$

Pi (π) is equal to 3.14 or, if used as a fraction, $\dfrac{22}{7}$.

Example: Find the circumference of a circle with a diameter of 6 centimeters.
$C = \pi$ x diameter
$C = 3.14$ x 6 cm
$C = 18.84$ centimeters

Exercise: Find the circumference of each circle.

1.

 8 mm diameter

2.

 1.5 cm diameter

3.

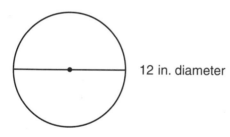 12 in. diameter

4.

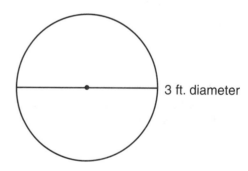 3 ft. diameter

If a circle has a radius given, then use the following formula:

$$C = 2 \pi \text{ x radius}$$

Example: 3 cm = radius
$C = 2 \pi$ x radius
$C = 2 \pi$ x 3
$C = 2(3.14)$ x 3
$C = 6.28$ x 3
$C = 18.84$ cm

Exercises: Find the circumference of the following circles.

5. a circle with a radius of 2 mm_____

6. a circle with a radius of 10 in._____

7. a circle with a diameter of 26 centimeters _____

8. a circle with a radius of 13 mm_____

543 © Teacher Created Materials, Inc.

Finding the Area of a Circle

The *area of a circle* is the amount of space within that circle. Area is computed by squaring the length of the radius of a circle and multiplying that number by pi. Remember that the radius is equal to one half the length of the diameter.

The formula we use is this:

$$A = \pi r^2$$

Example: Find the area of a circle with a radius of 6 inches.

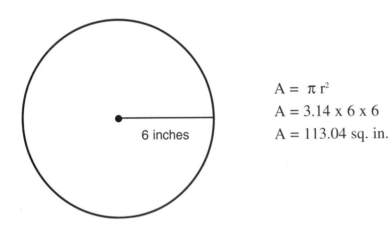

6 inches

$A = \pi r^2$
$A = 3.14 \times 6 \times 6$
$A = 113.04$ sq. in.

Exercises

1. Find the area of a circle with a radius of 8 centimeters._____

2. Find the area of a circle with a diameter of 8 inches._____

3. Find the area of a circle with a radius of 5 millimeters._____

4. Find the area of a circle with a radius of 4.2 centimeters. _____

5. Find the area of a circle with a diameter of 6 meters. _____

6. Find the area of a circle with a diameter of 10.4 feet. _____

7. Tom bought a plate with a diameter of 18 inches. What is the area of the entire plate?

8. Phyllis dug a circle in her garden. A smaller circle with a diameter of 5 feet had a tree planted in the center. The larger circle that went around the circle with the tree had a diameter of 22 feet. Phyllis wanted to plant flowers between the outer edge of the small circle and large circle. What is the difference in the area between the two circles?

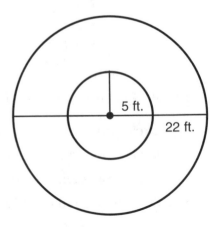

5 ft.

22 ft.

Volume of a Rectangular Prism

The amount of space that an object occupies is its *volume*. To find the volume of a rectangular prism, you can use this formula:

Volume = length x width x height

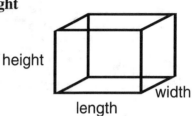

height
width
length

Example: Find the volume of the rectangular prism.

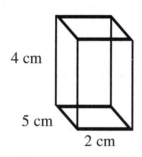

4 cm
5 cm
2 cm

V = L x W x H
V = 5 x 2 x 4
V = 40 cm³

A *cube* is a special rectangle. Since all its sides are equal in length, we can use this formula:

V = S³

3 cm

V = S³
S = Side
S = 3 cm
V = 3 x 3 x 3
V = 9 cm³

Exercises

What is the volume of each object?

1.

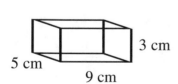

3 cm
5 cm
9 cm

2.

4 cm

3.

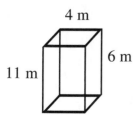

4 m
6 m
11 m

4. What is the volume of a box with a length of 1.7 in, a width of 2.3 in, and a height of 6.2 in.?

Volume of a Cylinder

Many objects are *cylinders*, such as cans, jars, and hat boxes. The volume of a cylinder can be found by multiplying the area of the base of the cylinder by the height. The base of the cylinder is a circle, so we can use the formula for the area of a circle, $\pi \times r^2$. Volume is expressed in *cubic units*.

π is equal to 3.14.

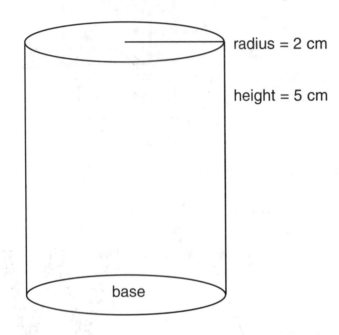

radius = 2 cm

height = 5 cm

base

V = area of base x height

V = (3.14×2^2) x 5

V = 62.8 cubic centimeters

Exercises: Find the volume of the cylinders with the following measurements.

1. R = 7 cm, h = 10 cm _____

2. R = 3 cm, h = 8 cm _____

3. R = 5 in., h = 9 in. _____

4. R = 2 m, h = 4 m _____

5. R = 12 cm, h = 2 cm _____

6. R = 8 cm, h = 4 cm _____

7. R = 11 cm, h = 11 cm _____

Symmetry

If a figure can be cut or folded in half so that each half exactly matches the other half, the two figures are called *figures of symmetry*. The line that divides each figure exactly in half is called the *line of symmetry*. Some figures may have more than one line of symmetry.

Examples:

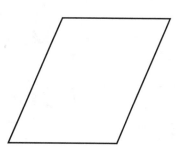

Draw the lines of symmetry for each figure.

1.

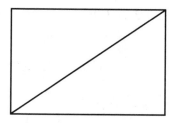

2.

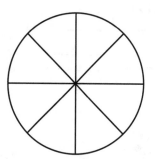

3.

W

4.

I

5.

S

6.

U

7.

B

8.

9.

Reflections, Translations, and Rotations

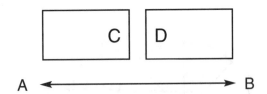

You can slide a figure along a straight line. If figure C slides along line AB, it will fit on figure D. This is called *translation*.

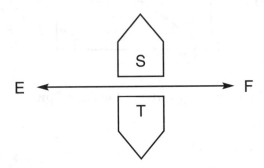

If you flip figure S over line EF, it will fit over figure T. This is called *reflection*.

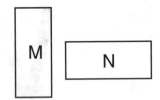

If figure M is turned, we say it is *rotated*.

Label each figure as a *reflection*, *translation*, or *rotation*.

1.

2.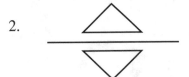

3.

4.

5.

6.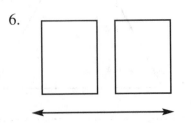

7.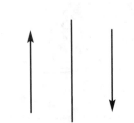

8.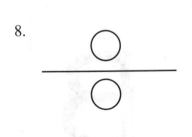

Similar and Congruent Figures

Two figures which have the same shape but are not the same size are called *similar* figures.

Example:

Two figures that have the same shape and the same size are *congruent* figures.

Example:

Exercises: Label each set of figures as *congruent* or *similar.*

1.

2.

3.

Pick the figure that is congruent to the first one shown.

4. 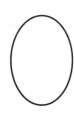				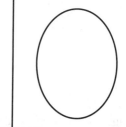
	figure A	figure B	figure C	figure D
5. 				

Probability

What is the probability of landing on the number 9 after the wheel stops spinning?

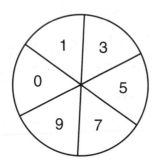

There is only one 9 on the wheel.

There are six spaces on which a spinner can stop.

The probability of the spinner landing on the number 9 is one chance out of six, or $P = \frac{1}{6}$ or 1 out of 6.

Directions: Find the probability for each question.

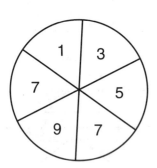

1. What is the probability of spinning a 7?

   A. There is/are _____ number 7.

   B. $P = \frac{\square}{\square}$ or _____ out of _____ .

2. What is the probability of landing on the number 3?

   A. There is/are _____ number 3.

   B. There are _____ numbers on the spinner.

   C. $P = \frac{\square}{\square}$ or _____ out of _____ .

3. What is the probability of *not* landing on 5?

   A. There are _____ numbers that are not 5.

   B. There are _____ numbers on the spinner.

   C. $P = \frac{\square}{\square}$ or _____ out of _____ chances.

Ben puts 2 black (B) marbles, 7 red (R) marbles, and 1 clear (C) marble in a bag. He then shakes the bag to mix all the marbles together. The marbles are the same size, weight, and texture.

4. What is the probability of choosing a clear marble? _____

5. What is the probability of choosing a red marble? _____

6. What is the probability of choosing a black marble? _____

7. What is the probability of choosing a clear or black marble? _____

8. What is the probability of choosing a yellow marble? _____

Combinations

Melinda has two blouses and four skirts. How many different outfits can she make by combining her blouses and skirts in different ways?

Blouses	Skirts	Combinations
pink	white	pink and white
pink	yellow	pink and yellow
pink	black	pink and black
pink	brown	pink and brown
blue	white	blue and white
blue	yellow	blue and yellow
blue	black	blue and black
blue	brown	blue and brown

Melinda had two blouses and four skirts that she was able to combine in eight different ways. If we multiply the number of blouses by the number of skirts, we have the number of combinations.

2 blouses x 4 skirts = 8 combinations

Combinations *(cont.)*

Directions: Find the number of combinations.

1. A restaurant offers an omelet for breakfast. It can be made by using eggs with a choice of ham or bacon or cheese as a filling. How many different omelet choices are on the menu?

Egg   Filling   Combination

eggs ⟨ _____   _____

_____   _____

_____   _____

_____ egg x _____ fillings = _____ combinations or choices.

2. Mark has a pair of boots and a pair of sneakers. He has one pair of white socks, one pair of black socks, and one pair of brown socks. How many combinations can Mark form?

_____ shoes x _____ pairs of socks = _____ combinations.

3. Karen wants to buy an ice-cream sundae with vanilla ice cream. She has a choice of strawberry, hot fudge, or caramel sauce. Her sundae can be topped with chocolate sprinkles or nuts. How many combinations are there from which to choose?

vanilla ice cream x _____ sauces x _____ toppings = _____ choices

4. Ben had five television sets in his home. Each set can be tuned to seven channels. How many combinations can Ben tape at one time?

_____ televisions x _____ channels = _____ combinations

5. The school cafeteria offers three sandwiches, four vegetables, and five juice drinks daily. How many combinations are available to the students each day?

_____ sandwiches x _____ vegetables x _____ drinks = _____ choices.

Measuring Temperature

Temperature is the degree of heat or cold. It is measured with a thermometer, an instrument which usually contains mercury or alcohol in a narrow tube. The liquid goes up by expanding when the heat rises, and the liquid drops by contracting when the temperature outside the tube goes down.

A thermometer is like a ruler, a scale for measuring the temperature in degrees. In the metric system, the *Celsius scale* is generally used. *Centigrade* is another term for Celsius. The zero degree (0°) marks the freezing point of water, and 100 degrees (100°) marks the boiling point of water. The Celsius scale is named for the Swedish astronomer *Anders Celsius* (1701–1744), who invented it in 1742.

Another thermometer, named for *Gabriel Fahrenheit* (1686–1736), the German physicist who introduced it, is marked off according to a scale for measuring temperature in which 32 degrees (32°) marks the freezing point of water. The boiling point of water is marked at 212 degrees (212°).

A third type of thermometer, the *Kelvin thermometer,* is based on a scaled for measuring temperature on which 273 degrees (273°) marks the freezing point of water, 373 degrees (373°) marks the boiling point, and 0 degrees (0°) marks absolute zero. It is named for *Lord Kelvin* (1824–1907), a British physicist.

Answer the following questions about thermometers.

1. Name the three different types of thermometers.

   _____   _____   _____

2. Thermometers are like _____ .

3. The unit of measurement on a thermometer is a _____ .

4. Thermometers measure the degree of _____ or _____ .

5. What is inside the glass tube of a thermometer? _____

6. What is the basic principle upon which thermometers are based?_____

   _____

7. Which thermometer was invented first? _____ second?_____

8. All three thermometers are based upon the freezing and boiling point of _____ .

9. 0° C = _____ ° F = _____ on the Kelvin scale.

10. 100° C = _____ ° F = _____ on the Kelvin scale.

Reading a Celsius/Fahrenheit Thermometer

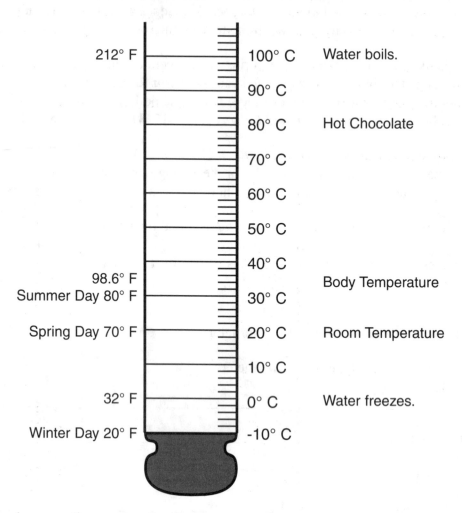

212° F — 100° C   Water boils.

90° C

80° C   Hot Chocolate

70° C

60° C

50° C

40° C

98.6° F   Body Temperature
Summer Day 80° F — 30° C

Spring Day 70° F — 20° C   Room Temperature

10° C

32° F — 0° C   Water freezes.

Winter Day 20° F — -10° C

Answer the following questions using the thermometer above.

1. At which temperatures would water be ready to make spaghetti? _____

2. At which temperatures could ice cubes start to form? _____

3. Which temperatures are good for building snowmen? _____

4. At which temperatures would you set your thermostat at home so you would be comfortable in the winter? _____

5. What is the temperature of hot chocolate when it is served? _____

6. At which temperature would you most likely be wearing a jacket while riding your bike? _____

7. At which temperatures would you most likely be going to the neighborhood pool or beach? _____

8. What is your temperature when you are healthy? _____

Reading a Thermometer

The markings on a thermometer indicate *degrees*. All markings above zero are *positive*. All markings below zero are *negative* and are read as below zero. A minus sign is placed to the left of the number read when it is below zero. No sign is placed to the left of the degree indicated when it is above zero.

Always count down if the portion of the thermometer being observed is below zero. Some thermometers are scaled by twos, while others are marked by ones. Therefore, when reading the thermometer, first determine how it is scaled. Then determine if the mercury or alcohol has leveled off at a point above or below zero.

Record the temperatures shown.

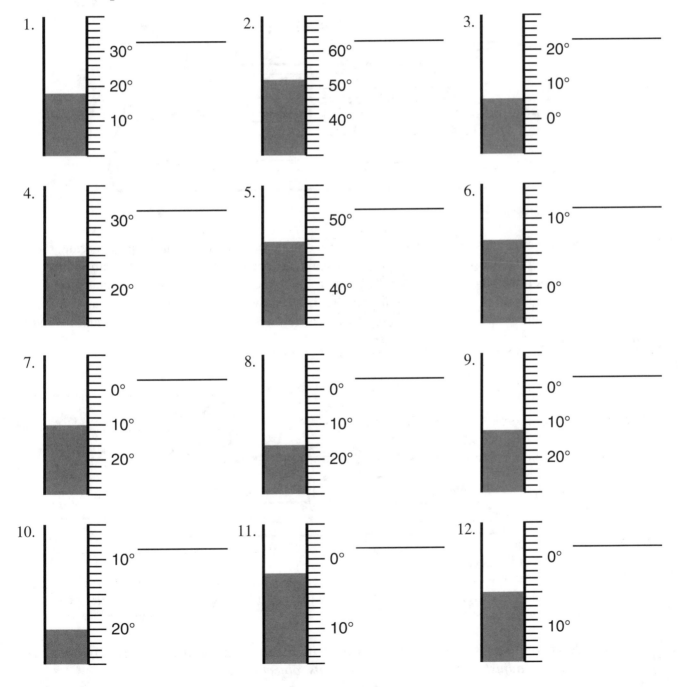

Measuring Mass

The *mass of* an object is the amount of matter a body contains, giving it the ability to stay still or continue to move. The mass of an object is always the same. Its weight, however, varies depending upon the force of gravity.

The mass of an object can be measured by finding its weight on a triple-beam balance scale. This scale uses three beams to register weight in grams or kilograms. The riders are moved on each beam to the appropriate notch—e.g., 100, 20, 30, 5.6, 3, etc. When the pointer is in the center of the scale, the mass of the object on the pan can be determined.

Calculate the total weight or mass by adding the number of grams indicated by the riders.

Example:

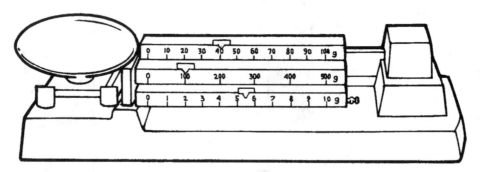

The mass of the object is 145.5 grams.

The mass of an object can also be measured by using a double-pan balance scale. On this scale, the object being observed is placed on one pan after the scale has been zero-adjusted. Standard gram weights are placed on the other pan. When the pointer is in the center of the scale, the pans are determined to be balanced. Compute the total number of gram weights in the pan. The mass of the object equals the total number of gram weights. To balance the scale, add or subtract standard weights until the pans are even.

Example:

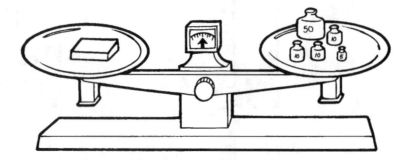

The mass of the object is 85 grams.

• Label the diagram of the triple-beam balance scale with the following terms: *pan, riders, beams, pointer scale, object mass.*

• Label the diagram of the double-pan balance scale with the following terms: *left pan, right pan, pointer, scale, zero adjustment knob, standard weights, object mass.*

Practice Measuring Mass

Find the gram weights indicated on the triple-beam balance scale.

1. _____ g

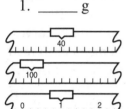

2. _____ g

3. _____ g

4. _____ g

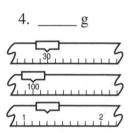

5. _____ g

6. _____ g

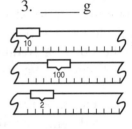

Calculate the mass of the objects on the double-pan balance scale.

7. _____ g

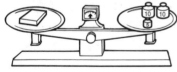

8. _____ g

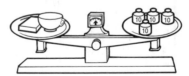

9. _____ g

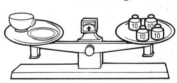

10. _____ g

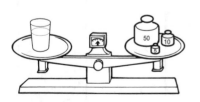

11. _____ g

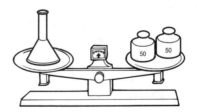

12. _____ g

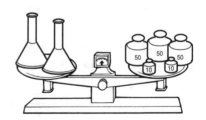

Reading a Graduated Cylinder

A *graduated cylinder* is an instrument used to measure small amounts of a liquid. The scientist uses this cylinder to measure liquid volume. There are many sizes of graduated cylinders. Some measure 1,000 milliliters (mL) or 1 liter (L). Some measure 500 milliliters (mL). Some measure only 10 milliliters (mL). The lines on the graduated cylinder are called *graduations*. The liquid usually curves up the side of a graduated cylinder. To achieve an accurate reading, it is important to remember to read the measurement at the lowest point or the bottom of the curve. This low point is called the *meniscus*.

Sometimes scientists need to find the volume of small, irregularly-shaped solid objects. They use the graduated cylinder and the *water displacement method* to calculate the volume. The graduated cylinder is filled to a specific height and recorded. The object is then placed inside the graduated cylinder. The water will rise above the object. Then a second reading of the cylinder is recorded. The first reading is subtracted from the second or higher reading. The difference is the volume of the solid object in milliliters or cubic centimeters.

Read the following volumes in the graduated cylinders.

1. mL   2. mL   3. mL   4. mL

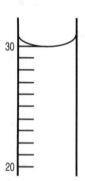
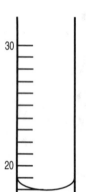
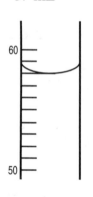
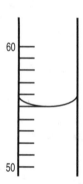

Calculate the volume of the marbles, using the water displacement method.

5. What is the volume of the water in the graduated cylinder?

_____

6. What is the volume of the water in the graduated cylinder after five marbles were placed in it?

_____

7. What is the volume of the five marbles?

_____

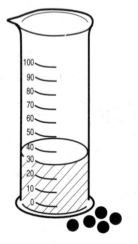
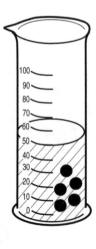

Metric Math

Metric measures that will help you:

- 10 millimeters = 1 centimeter
  (about the width of a dime)

- 100 centimeters = 1 meter
  (about the height of a desk)

- 1,000 meters = 1 kilometer
  (about the distance you can walk in 10 to 12 minutes)

Abbreviations that will help you:

mm = millimeters   cm = centimeters   m = meters   km = kilometers

Practice

1. 20 mm = ___2___ cm

2. 4 cm = ___40___ mm

3. 200 cm = ___2___ m

4. 8 m = ___800___ cm

5. 5,000 meters = ___5___ km

6. 7 km = ___7000___ meters

Carly
6/21/0)

How would you measure the following?

7. the length of a pen   (a) cm   (b) meters   (c) km

8. the width of a paper clip   (a) mm   (b) cm   (c) km

9. the height of an adult   (a) cm   (b) m   (c) mm

10. the length of a river   (a) mm   (b) cm   (c) km

Measure each line segment to the nearest millimeter.

11. _____   12. _____

13.   _____   14. _____

Measure each object to the nearest centimeter.

15.    16.

17.    18.

Answer Key

Answer Key

Page 4

1. My cousin spent the night at my house.
2. John said I could look at his snake.
3. Jim entered the bicycle race.
4. What a race it was!
5. Did he wear a helmet?
6. Who won the race?

Page 5

1. .
2. ?
3. !
4. ?
5. .
6. ! or .
7. !
8. .
9. ?
10. ?

Page 6

1. The cat chased the bird, or, The bird chased the cat.
2. I wrote a letter to my friend.
3. The family solved the puzzle together.
4. The baker baked a cake.
5. A penguin jumped into the sea.
6. The frog leaped over the log.

Page 7

Person: Adam, Dr. Roberts, farmer, mother, scientist, zookeeper
Place: attic, London, museum, room, Russia, state
Thing: comb, door, football, hoe, motor, rainbow
(Accept attic, museum, room, and state as things, also.)

Page 8

1. sand; thing
2. truck; thing
3. sister; person
4. dentist; person
5. school; place
6. tire; thing
7. house; place

Page 9

1. canes
2. brushes
3. ducks
4. bears
5. foxes
6. dresses
7. glasses
8. bags
9. buckets
10. sleds

Page 10

1. puppies
2. ladies
3. babies
4. candies
5. ponies
6. funnies
7. kitties
8. daddies
9. jellies
10. rubies

Page 11

1. Grandmother Davis
2. Mister Hayes
3. Captain Jack
4. Cousin Jimmy
5. Doctor Morton
6. Coach Russell

Page 12

Sunday
Monday
Tuesday
Wednesday
Thursday
Friday
Saturday

Page 13

1. January
2. February
3. March
4. April
5. May
6. June
7. July
8. August
9. September
10. October
11. November
12. December

Page 14

The colored hearts made the letter H. Two holidays that begin with this letter are Hanukkah and Halloween.

Page 15

1. Pacific Ocean
2. Grand Canyon
3. Mt. Rushmore
4. Amazon River
5. San Diego Zoo
6. Hyde Park
7. Sahara Desert
8. Lake Louise
9. Disneyland
10. North Pole
11. Rocky Mountains
12. Niagara Falls

Page 16

1. twinkles
2. watched
3. chased
4. set
5. swim
6. sings
7. eat
8. threw

Page 17

1. plays
2. wins
3. matches
4. dance
5. barks
6. eats
7. likes
8. shines
9. watches
10. walks

Page 18

1. B
2. C

Page 19

1. He gets up at dawn.
2. He goes for a swim.
3. At ten o'clock he gets out of the water to eat.
4. He takes a nap.
5. He swims.
6. He plays.
7. At six o'clock, he eats again.
8. He swims and plays.
9. When it becomes dark, he goes to bed for the night.

Page 20

1. C
2. A

Page 21

1. They cleaned their rooms.
2. They washed the family's car.
1. They visited the wolf den.
2. They saw alligators.
3. They met their mother.

Page 22

1. delivers
2. wash
3. cough
4. drove
5. snore
6. ate

Answer Key *(cont.)*

7. wrote
8. knock
9. laughed
10. cries

Page 23

1. Stacie is playing baseball or softball.
2. This is Stacie's first home run. She does not hit them often.
3. The team rushes to meet Stacie at the plate.

Page 24

1. Buttons is a cat.
2. Kenny, does not like the rain. He is disappointed.
3. Buttons wants to play with Kenny and that cheers him up.

Page 25

1. There are four and twenty (24) blackbirds.
2. The birds begin to sing.
3. The king is counting his money.
4. The queen is in the parlor.
5. A blackbird pecks off the maid's nose.

Page 26

1. The crooked man walked a mile.
2. He found a crooked sixpence.
3. He bought a crooked cat.
4. It caught a crooked mouse.
5. Some answers may vary, but the best answer is that they are all crooked.

Page 27

1. King Cole is a merry old soul.
2. King Cole calls for his bowl.
3. There are three fiddlers.
4. The fiddlers have very fine fiddles.
5. List any two of the following pairs: Cole/soul; he/three; Cole/bowl; soul/bowl; rare/compare.

Page 28

1. The story is about Amy and Melanie.
2. They try washing dogs and babysitting.
3. They open their stand on a Saturday morning in June.
4. A glass of lemonade costs one quarter.
5. Yes, they can go to the movies.

Page 29

1. 6
2. 14
3. 12
4. 7
5. 8
6. 11
7. 10
8. 8

Page 30

1. 12
2. 10
3. 11
4. 8
5. 6
6. 7
7. 9

Page 31

a. 42
b. 35
c. 61
d. 29
e. 20
g. 37
i. 51
l. 53
m. 92
n. 84
o. 67
r. 31
s. 66
t. 25
u. 39
w. 48
y. 72

Message: Congratulations! You are adding two-digit numbers.

Page 33

Sunday: 32
Monday: 30
Tuesday: 36
Wednesday: 34
Thursday: 31
Friday: 33
Saturday: 38

Page 34

i = 31
r = 72
e = 100
t = 61
g = 73
o = 60
m = 91

p = 54
u = 81
Message: TIME TO REGROUP

Page 35

1. 119
2. 81
3. 41
4. 101
5. 90
6. 31
7. 71
8. 102
9. 93
10. 72
11. 81
12. 83

smallest sum: 31

Page 37

1. $81 - 3 = 78$
2. $80 - 6 = 74$
3. $80 - 3 = 77$
4. $30 - 8 = 22$
5. $35 - 7 = 28$
6. $60 - 9 = 51$
7. $37 - 8 = 29$
8. $97 - 8 = 89$
9. $31 - 6 = 25$

elephant—orange
ostrich—green
cheetah—blue
bee—brown
dog—red
horse—pink
snail—purple
giraffe—yellow
turtle—black

Page 38

27, 69, 18
39, 17, 55
53, 21, 77

Page 39

1. 13
2. 4
3. 18
4. 57
5. 16
6. 37

Number 5 took the cookies.

Answer Key *(cont.)*

Page 40
a. $60 - 48 = 12$
b. $72 - 13 = 59$
c. $32 - 23 = 9$
d. $40 - 32 = 8$
e. $61 - 15 = 46$
f. $58 - 29 = 29$
g. $83 - 38 = 45$
h. $74 - 46 = 28$
i. $22 - 18 = 4$
j. $94 - 28 = 66$

Page 42
1. dancer, air
2. boy, television
3. Mr. Smith, class
4. baby, mother
5. sisters, store
6. school, stories
7. teenagers, skateboards, park
8. dentist, patient
9. dog, fight, cat
10. presents, cake, candles, party

Page 43
1. I live in the green (house) on Elm Street.
2. My (dog,) Max, and I went for a (walk.)
3. There are three Ryans in my (class.)
4. My (family) is planning a (trip) to the Grand Canyon.
5. "Mom, where is my yellow (shirt)?" Jenny asked her (mother.)
6. Where is Primrose Park?
7. The only (vegetable) I like is (broccoli.)
8. Our neighbor's (cat) is named Sylvester.
9. My (teacher) is Mrs. Simms.
10. Ricky, Sam, and Tim are going to play (football) in the (park.)

Page 44
1. cats
2. dogs
3. houses
4. gates
5. churches
6. monkeys
7. trees
8. classes
9. doors
10. chairs
11. lunches
12. boxes
13. bushes
14. glasses
15. trucks
16. brushes

Page 45
1. pennies
2. ponies
3. berries
4. families
5. factories
6. candies
7. parties
8. cherries
9. babies
10. fillies
11. jellies
12. lilies
13. ladies
14. patties
15. flies
16. stories

Page 46
1. women
2. teeth
3. men
4. children
5. feet
6. mice
7. oxen
8. wives
9. geese
10. loaves

Page 47
1. baby's
2. Mary's
3. boys'
4. tree's
5. Ken's
6. dogs'
7. children's
8. kitten's
9. woman's
10. pan's

Page 48
1. seems
2. is
3. is
4. looks
5. are
6. are
7. were
8. are
9. are
10. is

Page 49
1. walked
2. climbed
3. jumped
4. played
5. combed
6. roared
7. smiled
8. folded
9. closed
10. painted
11. color
12. scribble
13. turn
14. cook
15. wash
16. share
17. stack
18. type
19. laugh
20. deliver

Page 50
run—ran; see—saw; eat—ate; come—came; make—made; build—built; sleep—slept; give—gave; take—took; bring—brought; sing—sang

Page 51
1. hops, singular
2. shines, singular
3. were, plural
4. roar, plural
5. rides, singular
6. is, singular
7. have, plural
8. are, plural
9. dances, singular
10. are, plural

Page 52
1. read
2. fly
3. swims
4. chases
5. climbs
6. run
7. hike
8. count
9. plays
10. watch

Page 53
1. were
2. was
3. was
4. were
5. was
6. were
7. do
8. do
9. do
10. does
11. does
12. does

Page 54
Answers will vary.

Page 55
1. striped
2. loose
3. Many
4. funny
5. large
6–10: Answers will vary.

Page 56
1. he
2. she
3. they
4. They
5. her
6. it
7. She
8. He
9. her
10. them
11. them
12. he
13. they
14. it
15. him

Page 57
1. they
2. she
3. he
4. they
5. she
6. she
7. he
8. she

Page 58
1. We
2. us
3. I
4. me
5. us
6. I
7. I
8. we
9. me
10. us

Page 59
1. watched
2. shore
3. eat
4. bucket
5. slept
6. asked
7. decorate
8. small
9. big
10. quiet

Page 60
1. busy, active
2. nibble, chew
3. flavorful, tasty
4. joyful, happy
5. fall, trip
6. huge, enormous
7. worried, anxious
8. mad, angry
9. talk, chat
10. rush, hurry

Answer Key *(cont.)*

Page 61
1. happy—sad
2. brave—afraid
3. right—wrong
4. fast—slow
5. big—little
6. rude—polite
7. old—young
8. strong—weak
9. crowded—empty
10. smile—frown
11. close—far
12. loud—quiet
13. ask—answer
14. wild—tame
15. beautiful—ugly
16. hard—easy

Page 62
1. low
2. empty
3. down
4. Few
5. white
6. difficult
7. Everybody
8. No one
9. calm
10. bad

Page 63
1. pail
2. Two
3. hear
4. wear
5. sew
6. high
7. wood
8. bee
9. blew
10. knew

Page 64
1. aunt
2. tear
3. dew
4. pearl
5. night
6. banned
7. sheer
8. role
9. guest
10. wee
11. doe
12. chilly
13. break
14. fir

Page 65
one, night, road, two, him, knew, where, some, not, too, to, him, their, way, to, in, ate, no

Page 66
1. When I went to the store, I saw my teacher, Mrs. Roe, buying strawberries.
2. My family will go to Disneyland in July.
3. I am reading *Old Yeller* this week.
4. My sister, Sarah, says her favorite subject is Spanish.
5. On Wednesday, we will celebrate Groundhog Day.
6. My brother said that Mom was a cheerleader at Roosevelt High School.
7. In August, we're going to visit Aunt Margaret in San Francisco, California.
8. Benjie, my little brother, had a birthday, and we sang, "Happy Birthday to You."
9. My friend, Rosa, speaks Spanish, and I speak English.
10. My neighbor, Julia, is going to be an exchange student in Paris, France, next August.

Page 67
names (people and pets): Alexander, Mr. Peterson, Sandy, Spot, Fluffy
places: Rocky Mountains, Colorado River, Plum Street, Russia, South America
days: Monday, Thursday, Saturday
months: November, August, March, February
holidays: Christmas, Thanksgiving, Mardi Gras

Page 68
1. The
2. Freddy Wilson's, Peepers, Mrs. Woolsey's
3. As, I, I
4. In, Robin Hood, Lieutenant Bronksy
5. The, Thursday, November, Thanksgiving
6. I, Halloween, Saturday
7. Aunt Susan, Yellowstone National Park
8. Connie, Maple Street, Bismarck, North Dakota
9. Brazil, Argentina, Peru, South America
10. The, Mediterranean Sea, Atlantic Ocean, Spain
11. The, Love, Esther
12. Davis Medical Center, January
13. One, African, Islam
14. Italians, Germans, Caucasian
15. Last, Tuesday, Ruben, Spotty, Tulip Street, Central Park

Page 69
she'll—she will; it's—it is; won't—will not; you'll—you will; you're—you are; isn't—is not; we're—we are; I'll—I will; they'll—they will; weren't—were not; I'm—I am; he's—he is; can't—can not; aren't—are not; they're—they are

Page 70
1. won't
2. He'll
3. It's
4. Where's
5. didn't
6. Let's
7. can't
8. I'd

Page 71
1. .
2. ?
3. !
4. ?
5. .
6. . or !
7. !
8. .
9. ?
10. ?
11. ?
12. .
13. ?
14. !
15. .

Page 72
1. No, Mary does not like marshmallows.
2. Well, maybe Bernard will try the s'mores.
3. Bobby, would you like to try a s'more?
4. Alice wants a hot dog, potato chips, and a pickle.
5. We played baseball, basketball, and volleyball.
6. Harry, would you like to dance?

Page 73
1. Jack, my brother, does not like to go to the dentist.
2. I like my dentist, Dr. Lee.
3. Dr. Payce, the dentist in the next office, is also a good dentist.
4. On March 2, 1999, Dr. Lee took David and me camping.
5. My first visit to Dr. Lee was on February 27, 1994.
6. By June 30, 2012, I will have become a dentist myself.
7. I was born in Brooklyn, New York and so was Dr. Lee.
8. He visits Chicago, Illinois, every summer.
9. David wishes they would go to Orlando, Florida, each year instead.

Page 74
1. You wear your blue jeans, and I'll wear my black jeans.
2. Your white T-shirt fits better, but your red T-shirt is more colorful.
3. Do you want yellow patches on your jeans, or do you want pink patches?
4. Jill's T-shirt looks great, and Amy's jeans are terrific.
5. I have three pairs of blue jeans, but I want another pair of green jeans.

Answer Key *(cont.)*

6. You need to wash your old jeans, and you should iron your new jeans.
7. This white T-shirt is mine, but that white T-shirt is yours.
8. Let's all wear our blue jeans today, and let's wear our red jeans tomorrow.

Page 75
1. Yes, I would love to go to the movie.
2. We have potato chips, cheese, and chili.
3. Grandma, could we please spend the night?
4. This red car belongs to my mom, and this blue car belongs to my dad.
5. John, may I borrow your football?
6. We saw swans, ducks, and an ostrich.
7. Invite Casey, Jackie, and Toby to go with us.
8. No, we can't go to the zoo today.
9. My sister likes hot dogs, and I like pizza.
10. Aunt Irene, my mom's sister, liked the book, but I liked the movie.

Page 76
1. Tasha's birthday is March 4, 1981.
2. Dennis, my best friend, lives in San Francisco, California, but he is moving to Oakland.
3. Our teacher, Mr. Hill, took us on a field trip to Boston, Massachusetts.
4. July 16, 1973, is my parents' anniversary.
5. The Davis family is moving to Orlando, Florida, on July 13, 2001.
6. My friend, Mrs. Allen, is a nurse.
7. The airplane will land in Paris, France, after taking off from London, England.
8. He visits Chicago, Illinois, every summer, but this year he will go to Montreal, Canada.

Page 77
1. dog's food
2. bird's cage
3. Kenny's bike
4. Mr. Stout's store
5. Janie's radio

6. Don's book
7. coach's baseball
8. student's desk
9. class' closet
10. Mrs. Davis' pencil

Page 78
1. "Yes, Ryan," Mom answered, "Matt can come over after lunch."
2. "Thanks, Mom," Ryan answered.
3. no quotation marks
4. Mom said, "While you play basketball, I'll bake cookies."
5. no quotation marks
6. no quotation marks

Page 79
1. Bobby yelled, "Mom, where are my blue jeans?"
2. "A plane is flying overhead," said Jim's dad.
3. Mindy said, "Look at the turtles."
4. "Watch out!" yelled Sara. "The dog will get out!"
5. no changes
6. "Grandma," cried Joey, "will you tie my shoe?"
7. The boys yelled, "Come out and play!"
8. Mother said, "Change the channel, boys."
9. no changes
10. "Can you ride a bicycle?" asked Joseph.

Page 80
Have you ever been on a farm? Mrs. Young took her third grade class to Mr. Frank's farm on Tuesday, morning. They saw cows, chickens, and horses. Mr. Frank wanted to know if any students would like to ride a horse. Leslie screamed, "I do!" Also, John and Carl wanted to ride. Mrs. Young's class will never forget the special day on the farm.

Page 81
1. I'm going swimming after school!
2. Chris opens the door.
3. Will we go to the store tomorrow?
4. My iguana ate my homework.
5. Juanita helps me.
6. Can you come with me?
7. Maria dances every day.
8. I have a cat.
9. That bicycle looks brand new!
10. Do you like candy?

Page 82
Sentences will vary.

Page 83
1. I have many things in my room.
2. There is a box of clothes under the bed.
3. A rug is in front of the closet.
4. Sentence will vary.
5. I can see trees from my window.
6. Sentence will vary.
7. Sentence will vary.

Page 84
1. It is windy today. I should fly my kite.
2. I like to read. *James and the Giant Peach* is my favorite book.
3. Where are you going? When will you be home?
4. The boy ran home after school. Then he did his homework.
5. The clown danced in the parade. He gave balloons to all the children.
6. My sister really enjoys camping. I do, too.
7. The puppies cried for their mother. They were hungry.
8. I don't feel like going to bed. I want to stay up to watch my show!
9. Who is there? What do you want?
10. They wanted to climb the tree. The branches were too high to reach.

Page 85
1. The monkeys danced to the peddler's music.
2. My sister cried for my mother. She wouldn't stop.
3. My favorite game to play is Chinese checkers.
4. The students wondered what the teacher had planned for the day.
5. They were late to the party. Everyone was worried about them.
6. The birds were singing in the trees. The flowers looked colorful in the sun.
7. He knew that it would be an exciting day the moment he saw the pony.

Answer Key *(cont.)*

Page 86
There are many answer possibilities:
e.g., honeymoon, playground,
headlight, moonlight, railroad,
sailboat, rattlesnake, rainbow,
plywood, takeover, salesperson

Page 87
1. out	6. fire	11. light
2. step	7. ball	12. side
3. head	8. down	13. out
4. side	9. store	14. back
5. pot	10. ball	15. where

Page 88
1. regular	6. loyal	11. joy
2. spell	7. known	12. form
3. pride	8. arrange	13. cycle
4. use	9. maid	14. stop
5. possible	10. plane	15. royal

Page 89
1. dance	4. collect	7. teach
2. bank	5. dream	8. visit
3. skate	6. build	9. act

Page 90
Answers will vary.

Page 91
	Prefix	Root	Definition
1.	re	read	to read again
2.	un	prepare	not prepared
3.	pre	school	schooling before regular school
4.	mis	spell	spelled incorrectly
5.	under	water	watered less than enough
6.	over	joy	exceedingly filled with joy
7.	mis	judge	judged wrongly
8.	over	eat	to eat more than enough

Page 92
1. *suffix:* ness; kind-ness
2. *suffix:* ful; care-ful
3. *suffix:* ful; help-ful
4. *suffix:* less; seed-less
5. *suffix:* ly; clear-ly
6. *suffix:* ful; health-ful

Page 93
1. *suffix:* ous; joyous
2. *suffix:* less; careless
3. *suffix:* less; thankless
4. *suffix:* ous; famous
5. *suffix:* ous; mountainous
6. *suffix:* less; thoughtless

Page 94
1. C	3. A	5. E
2. D	4. B	

Page 95
Barn owls are fully grown by about 12 weeks of age.

Page 96–98
Answers will vary

Page 99
1. S	5. M	9. S
2. S	6. S	10. S
3. M	7. S	
4. S	8. M	

Page 100
1. 336	3. 175
2. 412	4. 439

Page 101
1. 2 hundreds, 6 tens, 3 ones
2. 5 hundreds, 2 tens, 6 ones
3. 3 hundreds, 4 tens, 0 ones
4. 4 hundreds, 5 tens, 8 ones
5. 6 hundreds, 0 tens, 1 ones

Page 102
1. 194	4. 422	7. 272
2. 362	5. 503	8. 486
3. 98	6. 501	

Page 103
1. 50	7. 20	13. 300
2. 60	8. 400	14. 600
3. 90	9. 600	15. 200
4. 20	10. 200	16. 260
5. 70	11. 900	
6. 10	12. 800	

Page 104
a. 45	e. 69	i. 98
b. 90	f. 71	j. 161
c. 78	g. 142	
d. 74	h. 136	

Page 105
32 + 13 = 45	16 + 24 = 40
27 + 12 = 39	34 + 14 = 48
26 + 13 = 39	15 + 28 = 43

Page 106
a. 12 + 14 + 22 = 48
b. 28 + 32 + 46 = 106
c. 27 + 23 + 52 = 102
d. 14 + 33 + 21 = 68

Page 107
a. 77	i. 93	q. 74
b. 132	j. 57	r. 102
c. 46	k. 125	s. 147
d. 82	l. 137	t. 74
e. 73	m. 142	u. 51
f. 142	n. 53	v. 93
g. 89	o. 74	w. 55
h. 72	p. 66	x. 109

Page 108
a. 24	e. 25	i. 62
b. 64	f. 33	j. 37
c. 30	g. 6	
d. 2	h. 10	

Page 109
a. 12	e. 46	i. 12
b. 59	f. 29	j. 66
c. 9	g. 7	
d. 13	h. 33	

Page 110
a. 93 − 68 = 25   c. 53 − 28 = 25
b. 43 − 40 = 3   d. 83 − 62 = 21

Page 111
a. 21	i. 9	q. 46
b. 62	j. 7	r. 70
c. 14	k. 19	s. 47
d. 30	l. 7	t. 16
e. 7	m. 6	u. 17
f. 30	n. 23	v. 55
g. 2	o. 16	w. 0
h. 28	p. 47	x. 1

Page 112
a. 10	i. 65	q. 51
b. 52	j. 78	r. 46
c. 36	k. 29	s. 25
d. 23	l. 12	t. 47
e. 6	m. 12	u. 7
f. 30	n. 12	v. 28
g. 60	o. 4	w. 12
h. 64	p. 23	x. 43

Answer Key *(cont.)*

Page 113

0 x 0 = 0	2 x 12 = 24	1 x 0 = 0	3 x 12 = 36	2 x 0 = 0	4 x 12 = 48
0 x 1 = 0	3 x 0 = 0	1 x 1 = 1	4 x 0 = 0	2 x 1 = 2	5 x 0 = 0
0 x 2 = 0	3 x 1 = 3	1 x 2 = 2	4 x 1 = 4	2 x 2 = 4	5 x 1 = 5
0 x 3 = 0	3 x 2 = 6	1 x 3 = 3	4 x 2 = 8	2 x 3 = 6	5 x 2 = 10
0 x 4 = 0	3 x 3 = 9	1 x 4 = 4	4 x 3 = 12	2 x 4 = 8	5 x 3 = 15
0 x 5 = 0	3 x 4 = 12	1 x 5 = 5	4 x 4 = 16	2 x 5 = 10	5 x 4 = 20
0 x 6 = 0	3 x 5 = 15	1 x 6 = 6	4 x 5 = 20	2 x 6 = 12	5 x 5 = 25
0 x 7 = 0	3 x 6 = 18	1 x 7 = 7	4 x 6 = 24	2 x 7 = 14	5 x 6 = 30
0 x 8 = 0	3 x 7 = 21	1 x 8 = 8	4 x 7 = 28	2 x 8 = 16	5 x 7 = 35
0 x 9 = 0	3 x 8 = 24	1 x 9 = 9	4 x 8 = 32	2 x 9 = 18	5 x 8 = 40
0 x 10 = 0	3 x 9 = 27	1 x 10 = 10	4 x 9 = 36	2 x 10 = 20	5 x 9 = 45
0 x 11 = 0	3 x 10 = 30	1 x 11 = 11	4 x 10 = 40	2 x 11 = 22	5 x 10 = 50
0 x 12 = 0	3 x 11 = 33	1 x 12 = 12	4 x 11 = 44		

Page 114

5 x 11 = 55	7 x 4 = 28	8 x 10 = 80	10 x 3 = 30	11 x 9 = 99
5 x 12 = 60	7 x 5 = 35	8 x 11 = 88	10 x 4 = 40	11 x 10 = 110
6 x 0 = 0	7 x 6 = 42	8 x 12 = 96	10 x 5 = 50	11 x 11 = 121
6 x 1 = 6	7 x 7 = 49	9 x 0 = 0	10 x 6 = 60	11 x 12 = 132
6 x 2 = 12	7 x 8 = 56	9 x 1 = 9	10 x 7 = 70	12 x 0 = 0
6 x 3 = 18	7 x 9 = 63	9 x 2 = 18	10 x 8 = 80	12 x 1 = 12
6 x 4 = 24	7 x 10 = 70	9 x 3 = 27	10 x 9 = 90	12 x 2 = 24
6 x 5 = 30	7 x 11 = 77	9 x 4 = 36	10 x 10 = 100	12 x 3 = 36
6 x 6 = 36	7 x 12 = 84	9 x 5 = 45	10 x 11 = 110	12 x 4 = 48
6 x 7 = 42	8 x 0 = 0	9 x 6 = 54	10 x 12 = 120	12 x 5 = 60
6 x 8 = 48	8 x 1 = 8	9 x 7 = 63	11 x 0 = 0	12 x 6 = 72
6 x 9 = 54	8 x 2 = 16	9 x 8 = 72	11 x 1 = 11	12 x 7 = 84
6 x 10 = 60	8 x 3 = 24	9 x 9 = 81	11 x 2 = 22	12 x 8 = 96
6 x 11 = 66	8 x 4 = 32	9 x 10 = 90	11 x 3 = 33	12 x 9 = 108
6 x 12 = 72	8 x 5 = 40	9 x 11 = 99	11 x 4 = 44	12 x 10 = 120
7 x 0 = 0	8 x 6 = 48	9 x 12 = 108	11 x 5 = 55	12 x 11 = 132
7 x 1 = 7	8 x 7 = 56	10 x 0 = 0	11 x 6 = 66	12 x 12 = 144
7 x 2 = 14	8 x 8 = 64	10 x 1 = 10	11 x 7 = 77	
7 x 3 = 21	8 x 9 = 72	10 x 2 = 20	11 x 8 = 88	

Page 115

6 x 6 = 36	9 x 5 = 45	6 x 7 = 42	8 x 0 = 0
3 x 1 = 3	4 x 7 = 28	7 x 3 = 21	8 x 9 = 72
9 x 6 = 54	6 x 8 = 48	8 x 1 = 8	9 x 7 = 63
9 x 9 = 81	8 x 4 = 32	0 x 3 = 0	1 x 9 = 9
3 x 2 = 6	4 x 8 = 32	0 x 4 = 0	3 x 3 = 9
4 x 9 = 36	0 x 5 = 0	7 x 2 = 14	8 x 8 = 64
3 x 4 = 12	0 x 6 = 0	3 x 5 = 15	0 x 7 = 0
2 x 0 = 0	3 x 6 = 18	0 x 8 = 0	0 x 0 = 0
1 x 6 = 6	4 x 5 = 20	0 x 1 = 0	1 x 7 = 7
2 x 9 = 18	4 x 2 = 8	5 x 8 = 40	1 x 4 = 4
4 x 3 = 12	5 x 9 = 45	1 x 5 = 5	4 x 6 = 24
5 x 0 = 0	0 x 9 = 0	8 x 5 = 40	5 x 7 = 35

Answer Key *(cont.)*

Page 116

2 x 2 = 4	3 x 8 = 24	5 x 1 = 5	10 x 0 = 10
2 x 3 = 6	11 x 5 = 55	7 x 4 = 28	10 x 8 = 80
10 x 3 = 30	11 x 9 = 99	5 x 12 = 60	7 x 5 = 35
11 x 8 = 88	10 x 4 = 40	11 x 10 = 110	6 x 0 = 6
7 x 6 = 42	12 x 8 = 96	10 x 5 = 50	11 x 11 = 121
6 x 1 = 6	7 x 7 = 49	9 x 0 = 0	10 x 6 = 60
11 x 12 = 132	6 x 2 = 12	7 x 8 = 56	9 x 1 = 9
10 x 7 = 70	12 x 0 = 12	6 x 3 = 18	7 x 9 = 63
9 x 2 = 18	10 x 8 = 80	12 x 1 = 12	6 x 4 = 24
10 x 7 = 70	9 x 3 = 27	10 x 9 = 90	12 x 2 = 24

Page 117

96 x 6 = 576	90 x 3 = 270	47 x 9 = 423	25 x 1 = 25	16 x 6 = 96
40 x 8 = 320	82 x 5 = 410	60 x 2 = 120	71 x 7 = 497	32 x 4 = 128
68 x 8 = 544	33 x 1 = 33	20 x 6 = 120	24 x 9 = 216	41 x 4 = 164
46 x 2 = 92	49 x 7 = 343	38 x 4 = 152	24 x 3 = 72	27 x 3 = 81
56 x 7 = 392	84 x 2 = 168	70 x 9 = 630	58 x 7 = 406	50 x 1 = 50
21 x 2 = 42	77 x 6 = 462	79 x 4 = 316	86 x 3 = 258	13 x 2 = 26
22 x 6 = 132	74 x 1 = 74	26 x 9 = 234	14 x 7 = 98	48 x 3 = 144
42 x 4 = 168	88 x 5 = 440	69 x 8 = 552	43 x 3 = 129	19 x 2 = 38

Page 118

0 ÷ 0 = 0	6 ÷ 1 = 6	24 ÷ 2 = 12	24 ÷ 4 = 6
1 ÷ 0 = 0	7 ÷ 1 = 7	3 ÷ 3 = 1	28 ÷ 4 = 7
2 ÷ 0 = 0	8 ÷ 1 = 8	6 ÷ 3 = 2	32 ÷ 4 = 8
3 ÷ 0 = 0	9 ÷ 1 = 9	9 ÷ 3 = 3	36 ÷ 4 = 9
4 ÷ 0 = 0	10 ÷ 1 = 10	12 ÷ 3 = 4	40 ÷ 4 = 10
5 ÷ 0 = 0	11 ÷ 1 = 11	15 ÷ 3 = 5	44 ÷ 4 = 11
6 ÷ 0 = 0	12 ÷ 1 = 12	18 ÷ 3 = 6	48 ÷ 4 = 12
7 ÷ 0 = 0	2 ÷ 2 = 1	21 ÷ 3 = 7	5 ÷ 5 = 1
8 ÷ 0 = 0	4 ÷ 2 = 2	24 ÷ 3 = 8	10 ÷ 5 = 2
9 ÷ 0 = 0	6 ÷ 2 = 3	27 ÷ 3 = 9	15 ÷ 5 = 3
10 ÷ 0 = 0	8 ÷ 2 = 4	30 ÷ 3 = 10	20 ÷ 5 = 4
11 ÷ 0 = 0	10 ÷ 2 = 5	33 ÷ 3 = 11	25 ÷ 5 = 5
12 ÷ 0 = 0	12 ÷ 2 = 6	36 ÷ 3 = 12	30 ÷ 5 = 6
1 ÷ 1 = 1	14 ÷ 2 = 7	4 ÷ 4 = 1	35 ÷ 5 = 7
2 ÷ 1 = 2	16 ÷ 2 = 8	8 ÷ 4 = 2	40 ÷ 5 = 8
3 ÷ 1 = 3	18 ÷ 2 = 9	12 ÷ 4 = 3	45 ÷ 5 = 9
4 ÷ 1 = 4	20 ÷ 2 = 10	16 ÷ 4 = 4	50 ÷ 5 = 10
5 ÷ 1 = 5	22 ÷ 2 = 11	20 ÷ 4 = 5	55 ÷ 5 = 11

Page 119

60 ÷ 5 = 12	42 ÷ 7 = 6	96 ÷ 8 = 12	60 ÷ 10 = 6	132 ÷ 11 = 12
6 ÷ 6 = 1	49 ÷ 7 = 7	9 ÷ 9 = 1	70 ÷ 10 = 7	12 ÷ 12 = 1
12 ÷ 6 = 2	56 ÷ 7 = 8	18 ÷ 9 = 2	80 ÷ 10 = 8	24 ÷ 12 = 2
18 ÷ 6 = 3	63 ÷ 7 = 9	27 ÷ 9 = 3	90 ÷ 10 = 9	36 ÷ 12 = 3
24 ÷ 6 = 4	70 ÷ 7 = 10	36 ÷ 9 = 4	100 ÷ 10 = 10	48 ÷ 12 = 4
30 ÷ 6 = 5	77 ÷ 7 = 11	45 ÷ 9 = 5	110 ÷ 10 = 11	60 ÷ 12 = 5
36 ÷ 6 = 6	84 ÷ 7 = 12	54 ÷ 9 = 6	120 ÷ 10 = 12	72 ÷ 12 = 6
42 ÷ 6 = 7	8 ÷ 8 = 1	63 ÷ 9 = 7	11 ÷ 11 = 1	84 ÷ 12 = 7
48 ÷ 6 = 8	16 ÷ 8 = 2	72 ÷ 9 = 8	22 ÷ 11 = 2	96 ÷ 12 = 8
54 ÷ 6 = 9	24 ÷ 8 = 3	81 ÷ 9 = 9	33 ÷ 11 = 3	108 ÷ 12 = 9
60 ÷ 6 = 10	32 ÷ 8 = 4	90 ÷ 9 = 10	44 ÷ 11 = 4	120 ÷ 12 = 10
66 ÷ 6 = 11	40 ÷ 8 = 5	99 ÷ 9 = 11	55 ÷ 11 = 5	132 ÷ 12 = 11
72 ÷ 6 = 12	48 ÷ 8 = 6	108 ÷ 9 = 12	66 ÷ 11 = 6	144 ÷ 12 = 12
7 ÷ 7 = 1	56 ÷ 8 = 7	10 ÷ 10 = 1	77 ÷ 11 = 7	
14 ÷ 7 = 2	64 ÷ 8 = 8	20 ÷ 10 = 2	88 ÷ 11 = 8	
21 ÷ 7 = 3	72 ÷ 8 = 9	30 ÷ 10 = 3	99 ÷ 11 = 9	
28 ÷ 7 = 4	80 ÷ 8 = 10	40 ÷ 10 = 4	110 ÷ 11 = 10	
35 ÷ 7 = 5	88 ÷ 8 = 11	50 ÷ 10 = 5	121 ÷ 11 = 11	

Answer Key (cont.)

Page 120
1. 3:45
2. 6:05
3. 5:55
4. 4:25
5. 2:10
6. 4:15
7. 1:30
8. 12:45
9. 7:20
10. 8:35
11. 10:50
12. 6:00
13. 2:35
14. 1:00
15. 11:50

Page 121
1. P.M.
2. A.M.
3. P.M.
4. P.M.
5. A.M.
6. A.M.
7. P.M.
8. P.M.
9. P.M.
10. A.M.
11. A.M.
12. P.M.
13. P.M.
14. A.M.
15. P.M.
16. P.M.
17. A.M.
18. P.M.
19. P.M.
20. A.M.
21. A.M.
22. P.M.
23. P.M.
24. A.M.

Page 123
1. parties
2. companies
3. armies
4. countries
5. spies
6. puppies
7. liberties
8. flies
9. berries
10. factories
11. flurries
12. families
13. stories
14. victories
15. babies
16. ladies
17. monoplies
18. bodies

Page 124
1. dishes (*color*)
2. circuses (*color*)
3. parties
4. babies
5. buzzes (*color*)
6. inches (*color*)
7. keys
8. passes (*color*)
9. classes (*color*)
10. clowns
11. coaches (*color*)
12. watches (*color*)
13. fishes (*color*)
14. pitches (*color*)
15. finches (*color*)

Page 125
bush, bushes; pen, pens; bench, benches; egg, eggs; match, matches; miss, misses; valley, valleys; worry, worries; flower, flowers; princess, princesses; address, addresses; peach, peaches

Page 126
Sentences will vary.
1. men
2. women
3. children
4. sheep
5. mice
6. feet
7. oxen
8. geese

Page 127
1. doll's
2. Lena's
3. girls'
4. turtle's
5. Kate's
6. child's
7. boys'
8. penguin's
9. blouse's
10. pan's
11. man's
12. Jen's
13. lions'
14. toys'
15. play's

Page 128
1. plays
2. flies
3. makes
4. ran
5. popped
6. ran
7. fell
8. eat
9. stood
10. reads

Page 129
woke, jumped, landed, sat, rubbed, grumbled, fell, looked, wanted, see, ran, grabbed, blew, played, liked, sounded, heard, stopped, listened, came, like, grabbed, ran, sat, played, floated, felt, heard, stopped, listened, came, ran, played, liked, heard, called, went, took, put, put, told, went, tried, imagine, heard, stopped, listened, snored, moaned, stuck, heard, covered, fell

Page 130
Helping Verbs	Action Verbs
1. will	1. ride
2. is	2. ridden
3. were	3. pushed
4. can	4. move
5. has	5. driven
6. have	6. pulled
7. have	7. seen
8. will	8. go
9. is	9. going
10. will	10. drink

Page 131
1. painted
2. climbed
3. played
4. laughed
5. shouted
6. jumped
7. ran
8. saw
9. ate
10. came
11. made
12. built
13. slept
14. gave
15. took
16. brought
17. sang
18. held
19. went
20. wrote

Page 132
1. turned
2. cooked
3. rolled
4. watched
5. parked
6. filled
7. colored
8. folded
9. closed
10. looked
11. smile
12. fold
13. close
14. paint
15. climb
16. share
17. joke
18. match
19. laugh
20. play

Page 133
1. blew
2. came
3. sang
4. wore
5. took
6. cried
7. made
8. gave
9. fell
10. flew
11. catch
12. read
13. ride
14. drink
15. swing
16. shine
17. pay
18. write
19. sweep
20. tear

Page 134
1. was
2. were
3. was
4. were
5. was
6. were
7. were
8. was
9. were
10. was

Page 135
1. are
2. are
3. am
4. is
5. are
6. are
7. are
8. is
9. am
10. am

Page 136
1. S, has
2. P, run
3. P, jump
4. S, hops
5. P, sing
6. S, is
7. P, are
8. S, hops
9. S, is
10. S, has

Page 137
1. unusual, front
2. playful
3. green, long
4. funny, old
5. new, gray
6. tall, pretty.
7. smart, funny
8. silly
9. happy, large
10. small, black, shiny
11. choir, colorful, lively
12. kind, generous
13. orange, yellow
14. little, imaginary
15. quiet, barn

Answer Key *(cont.)*

Page 138
1. this; Which one?
2. old; What kind of?
3. French; What kind of?
4. Scottish; What kind of?
5. yellow; What kind of?
6. three; How many?
7. delicious, spinach; What kind of?
8. comic; What kind of?
9. soft; What kind of?
10. mean; What kind of?
11. clueless; What kind of?
12. those, black, small; What kind of?

Page 139
Adjectives will vary.

Page 140
1. a
2. an
3. a
4. an
5. a
6. a
7. an
8. an
9. a
10. a
11. An
12. a
13. a
14. An
15. A

Page 141
1. taller, tallest
2. sweeter, sweetest
3. smaller, smallest
4. messier, messiest
5. bigger, biggest
6. prettier, prettiest
7. harder, hardest
8. thicker, thickest

Page 142
1. how; quietly
2. when; tomorrow
3. when; later
4. where; here
5. how; fiercely
6. how; softly
7. how; gracefully
8. when; Yesterday
9. how; well
10. how; quickly

Page 143
1. He played baseball.
2. She swam across the pool.
3. They climbed the trees.
4. They rode their bikes to school.
5. The team surprised her with a trophy.
6. Kim saw it run across the street.
7. She read the new best seller.
8. He saw a strange shadow.
9. The girls walked to her house.
10. The family found them in a basket on their porch.
11. Where should I put them?
12. He put gas in the car.
13. They won the championship!
14. Where is it?
15. Please, give that to him.

Page 144
1. busy, active
2. nibble, chew
3. flavorful, tasty
4. joyful, happy
5. fall, trip
6. huge, enormous
7. worried, anxious
8. mad, angry
9. talk, chat
10. cry, weep

Page 145
1. neat, spotless
2. sad, unhappy
3. thin, skinny
4. look, see
5. plain, simple
6. strong, powerful
7. cold, chilly
8. big, large
9. cheap, stingy
10. quiet, calm
11. poor, needy
12. little, small
13. sharp, pointed
14. loud, noisy
15. rich, wealthy

Page 146
1. like, similar
2. snip, cut
3. plump, fat
4. fly, soar
5. bark, yelp
6. clown, jester
7. huge, gigantic
8. real, true
9. entire, whole
10. baby, infant

Page 147
1. laugh, cry
2. fast, slow
3. hurt, heal
4. shiny, dull
5. wake, sleep
6. girl, boy
7. fire, water
8. truth, lie
9. ugly, pretty
10. hard, soft

Page 148
Answers will vary but may include:
1. hard
2. sour
3. cold
4. later
5. lie
6. mean
7. murky
8. west

Page 149
1. hare, hair
2. our, hour
3. dough, doe
4. no, know
5. read, red
6. tale, tail

Page 150
1. might
2. not
3. popular
4. plum
5. bare
6. bawl
7. banned
8. franc
9. cymbal
10. chilly
11. scent
12. hymn
13. bazaar
14. blue
15. cereal

Page 151
1. Weather Flash . . . heavy rains due in an hour.
2. Next, on *The World Turns* . . . Elizabeth is never seen again.
3. News Extra! A wild horse and deer escape from zoo.
4. Watch Muscle Man weekly lift weights on Channel 2.
5. Special Announcement! Ice skating pair wins gold medals!
6. Try a new cereal just for kids! *Awesome Oats!*

Page 152
Some answers will vary.
Sunday, Monday, Tuesday, Wednesday, Thursday, Friday, Saturday
1. January
2. February
3. March
4. April
5. May
6. June
7. July
8. August
9. September
10. October
11. November
12. December

Page 153
Pacific Ocean, Grand Canyon, Mt. Rushmore, Amazon River, Sahara Desert, North Pole, San Diego Zoo, Lake Louise, Rocky Mountains, Hyde Park, Disneyland, Niagara Falls

Page 154
One, When, What, Mike, It's, Both, Ohhh, It's, Sure, Mike, Chris, Mike, He, The, Nobody, Mike, Chris, Next, The, No, You, Why, We, Well, The, They, They, George

Page 155
1. Uncle Jorge sat on the front porch.
2. I said, "Mom, what I really want to do is to stay home!"
3. My mom and my dad won't be home until 7 P.M.
4. His grandma made a quilt for his birthday.
5. My cousin and my grandma will be coming with my mom.

Answer Key *(cont.)*

6. Our grandparents have a surprise for Aunt Aimee.
7. I wrote "Dear Grandma," at the top of my stationery.
8. I wish my aunt lived closer to us; she looks just like Mom.
9. Then Dad stopped and looked behind him.
10. I like to go to Grandmother Norton's house in the summer.
11. My favorite cousin is Jimmy because he makes me laugh.
12. At the wedding we saw Aunt Marsha and Cousin Brad.
13. My mom and dad are taking me to dinner after the awards assembly.
14. At the reunion I saw Aunt Edith, Uncle Jacques, and Cousins Kathy, Meredith, Hector, and Samantha.
15. For my birthday I'm inviting Cousin Sarah, Cousin Leigh, Aunt Susie, and my uncle, whose name is Mike.

Page 156
1. isn't
2. let's
3. can't
4. he'll
5. aren't
6. we've

Page 157
1. couldn't
2. haven't
3. can't
4. aren't
5. isn't
6. wouldn't

Page 158
1. do not
2. would not
3. will not
4. are not
5. should not
6. he is
7. I have
8. they have
9. we are
10. she is
11. you will
12. did not
13. is not
14. was not
15. we will
16. I would

Page 159
cannot, You are, Do not, will not, could not, it is, it is, that is, Let us, it is, will not, must have, I had, must have, she would, did not, There have, who have, must have, should not, could not, It is, would have, that is, I had, she had, she would, I will, would have, was not, were not, Who is, we are, would have, was not, could not, should not, would not, What is, must not, were not, would have, she had, had not, she had, she would, Here is, it is, She has, She has, I am, I will

Page 160
1. !
2. . or !
3. ?
4. .
5. .
6. ?
7. ?
8. !
9. .
10. . or !
11. !
12. ! or .
13. ?
14. .
15. ?

Page 161
1. . . . Amy, Katy, and Melissa.
2. . . . basketball, baseball, and volleyball.
3. Katy, Melissa, and Tommy . . .
4. . . . a geologist, an astronaut, or a chemist.
5. . . . Skip, Tiger, and Rags.
6. . . . math, science, and art.
7. Tommy, Amy, Katy, and Melissa . . .
8. . . . his parents, his sisters, and his dogs.
9. . . . three birds, two cats, and one dog.
10. . . . Tommy, Amy, and Manuel.

Page 162
1. Mrs. Burnett, may we go out to recess now?
2. Yes, we are going out to recess now, Jason.
3. Mary, will you swing with Tommy and me?
4. Sure, Jason, I love to swing.
5. Mary is going to swing with us, Tommy.
6. No, Jason, I'm sliding with Matt.
7. Matt can swing with us, Tommy.
8. Jason, we can all swing first, and then we can all slide.
9. Jason, do you want to go on the slide first?
10. Tommy, what time is recess over?

Page 163
1. Amy Jones, my best friend, has a very large family.
2. Joe, her oldest brother, works for an airline company.
3. The youngest in the family, Tony, is only three years old.
4. The oldest daughters, Karen and Sue, often help with the younger children.
5. My other good friend, Nicole, and I spend a great deal of time at Amy's house.
6. Mrs. Jones, Amy's mother, says

that two more children are coming tomorrow.
7. Amy's dad, Mr. Jones, works hard to take care of seven children.
8. Rags and Slick, the Jones' pets, get a great deal of attention.

Page 164
1. Jerry was born on October 5, 1986.
2. My favorite Christmas was December 25, 1992.
3. Susan's mom came home from the hospital on April 6, 1994.
4. We took our summer vacation on July 21, 1993.
5. My grandfather was born on August 11, 1941.
6. On April 6, 1994, Susan's mom brought a new baby girl home from the hospital.
7. My grandfather remembers July 20, 1969, as an important date in history.
8. On July 21, 1993, my family went to Hawaii for our summer vacation.

Page 165
1. The state capital is in Austin, Texas.
2. My home is in Denver, Colorado.
3. Her grandparents live in Bangor, Maine.
4. Our tournament is in Ardmore, Oklahoma.
5. Disney World is in Orlando, Florida.
6. Her father is stationed in Fairbanks, Alaska.
7. Queen Elizabeth lives in London, England.
8. We rode the ferry in Seattle, Washington.

Page 166
1. April 15, 1972
2. July 27, 1640
3. September 13, 1910
4. Monday, January 31
5. Sunday, November 16
6. Anaheim, California
7. Albuquerque, New Mexico
8. Quebec, Canada
9. Bangor, Maine
10. Little Rock, Arkansas
11. Dear Joe,
12. Your friend,
13. Sincerely yours,

Answer Key *(cont.)*

14. Love,
15. Yours truly,
16. All birds have feathers, wings, and beaks.
17. The Shetland pony is small, friendly, and gentle.
18. A friendly, playful dog makes a good pet.
19. I have three cats named Boots, Muffin, and Tiger.
20. I like to color with pencils, markers, and crayons.

Page 167
1. No, Marlene does not like being squirted in the face.
2. Christopher, how long have you been on the telephone?
3. Well, just what did you have in mind?
4. Sure, Laura, I'd love another jelly donut.
5. My brother, the world's scariest boy, likes escargots.
6. The plane we are taking, a 747, will have plenty of room.
7. You realize, of course, that you will not be allowed out of the house in that outfit.
8. My orthodontist, Dr. Baugh, decorated his office for Halloween.
9. All right, if that's what you think, let's just eat all of the chocolate.
10. In the future we will be able to speak to our computers.
11. No kidding, you went rock climbing?
12. We went to Bouquet Canyon, a canyon near Valencia, to attend a harvest festival.
13. You could read, for example, some books about the historical period in which your novel takes place.
14. For Valentine's Day my dad gave me two pounds of my favorite treat, candy corn.
15. I don't care what you think, I'm going to go back there and help that little boy.

Page 168
1. cat's food
2. bird's nest
3. Miguel's bike
4. Kim's store
5. David's CD player
6. sister's book

7. brother's skateboard
8. baby's toys
9. teacher's desk
10. painter's brush
11. Nicky ran screaming into Manuel's house.
12. My dad knocked down a hornet's nest.
13. I wish I could drive my brother's car.
14. An alien ate Mariela's homework.
15. Grandpa's spaghetti is the best in the world.

Page 169
1. Ryan asked, "What do you want to play, Martha?"
2. Martha answered, "Let's play baseball."
3. "Okay, we'll play baseball first," said Ryan, "but let's play basketball after that."
4. Mom called, "The cookies are ready."
5. "Oh, boy," the boys yelled at the same time, "let's eat!"

Page 170
1. "What is that bizarre thing upon your head? It looks like an octopus," said Mr. Grimmy. (exact words)
2. The teacher told the students to read the poem, "The Raven" by Friday. (title)
3 I call my sister "Idget," but I have no idea why. (special word)
4. "Hey!" Jacques shouted, "Didn't you hear the coach? He said, 'Stop when you get to the fence!'" (quote within a quote)
5. "And then I will cover you with fragrant rose petals," Mama said, "and sing a lullaby." (exact words)
6. I found a book that said, "Dinosaurs may be more closely related to birds than to lizards." (exact words)
7. We have family nicknames, and my brother's is "Greasy Bear." (special word)
8. "Did you hear what Nicole said?" Amy asked us. "She said, `You guys are just too chicken to try it.' She doesn't know what she is talking about!" (quote within a quote)
9. I thought you would be too "cool"

to go on the merry-go-round with me. (special word)
10. She watched *Somewhere in Time* so many times she wore out the tape. (no quotation marks)
11. My brother always talks in his sleep. Last night he said, "Hurry and purple it before the snails get it!" (exact words)
12. After we watched *Twister,* we couldn't stop watching the clouds. (no quotation marks)
13. "Come with us," Dad said, "and we can stop for ice cream on the way." (exact words)
14. I need to find the root word for "transient." (special word)
15. Mom says we shouldn't say "Where's he at?" because it is not proper English. (special words)

Page 171
Dear Pen Pal,

I love to go to the circus! On May 6, 1999, the circus came to my hometown of Jackson, Wyoming. A parade marched through our streets, and soon the big top could be seen. Ken, my brother, and I went to watch the performers prepare for opening night. We saw clowns, acrobats, and even the ringmaster. What a sight! Have you ever seen anything like it? You should go if you ever get the chance.

I also really enjoy playing baseball. My favorite team is the New York Yankees, but I also like the Cardinals. When I grow up I want to be a baseball pitcher, first baseman, or shortstop. Do you like baseball? What do you want to do when you grow up? I wish you could see my cool baseball card collection, but Ken's collection is even better.

Oh, I almost forgot to tell you about my family! There are four people in my family. They are my mom, my dad, my brother, and me. Scruffy, my cat, is also a family member. In August 2000 my grandpa will probably move in with us. I can't wait for that! Didn't you say your grandma lives with you? I'll bet you really like that.

Well, that's all for now. Please write back to me soon. See you!
Your pal,
Brent

Answer Key *(cont.)*

Page 172
1. Blake
2. the paintbox
3. the colors
4. Blake
5. Green
6. Orange
7. Blake
8. Blake's favorite color
9. Mom
10. The painting

Page 173
1. Kids
2. Baseball
3. Swimming
4. I
5. Summertime
6. Jeremy
7. Mosquitoes
8. my skin, I
9. seashells
10. summer, it

Page 174
1. is very cold
2. jump into the water
3. splashes us
4. is cold
5. gets out of the water
6. does a handstand underwater
7. claps for him
8. has a leak in it
9. throws the inner tube onto the shore
10. sits on the inner tube
11. deflates with Tonia on it
12. laughs with Tonia
13. jumps into the water
14. swims as fast as he can
15. races Luke

Page 175
1. (Uncle Tony) invited us to the baseball game.
2. (His truck) carried us to the field.
3. (The parking lot) was crowded.
4. (We) finally found our seats.
5. (Uncle Tommy) bought popcorn and peanuts.
6. (Two batters) hit home runs.
7. (Our team) won the game.
8. (People) pushed to get out of the stadium.
9. (We) drove home late at night.
10. (My sister) was very tired.

Page 176
1. My books are on the table. My math book is on top.
2. They were closing the store. It was time to go home.
3. Watch out for the slippery ice! You could fall and hurt yourself.

4. I got a new blue dress. The blue shoes match perfectly.
5. My brother made the team! Will I be able to play baseball some day?
6. I like to go camping. The last time we went, we saw a bear.
7. My teacher was not at school. We had a substitute.
8. I don't like lima beans. I only want mashed potatoes.
9. Can you spend the night at my house? We can have pizza for dinner.
10. My dog has fleas. We had to get her some special medicine.

Page 177
Answers will vary.

Page 178
1. Bruce has many things in his room.
2. Answers will vary.
3. Is there a box of toys under the bed?
4. A rug is in front of the closet.
5. Answers will vary.
6. I can see trees from my window.
7. Answers will vary.
8. Answers will vary.
9. Answers will vary.
10. Latoya cleans her room every day.

Page 179
1. D
2. I
3. I
4. D
5. I
6. D
7. I
8. D
9. I
10. D

Page 180
1. pil´-low
2. fel´-low
3. piz´-za
4. sup-pose´
5. sur-round´
6. scis´-sors
7. col-lect´
8. hur-rah´
9. ad´-dress or ad-dress´
10. sil´-ly

Page 181
1. tur´-tle
2. bee´-tle
3. bub´-ble
4. can´-dle
5. jug´-gle
6. hus´-tle
7. baf´-fle
8. cra´-dle
9. bot´-tle
10. trou´-ble

Page 182
1. car-toon´
2. cin´-der
3. drop´-let
4. ex´-tra
5. ex-press´
6. im-print´ or im´-print
7. jun´-gle
8. sal´-ad
9. mag´-ic
10. pic´-ture

Page 183
1. hu´-mor
2. a´-ble
3. be-gin´
4. ki´-wi
5. pa´-per
6. lo´-cate
7. o´-pen
8. pro´-file
9. ro-sette´
10. e-rupt´

Page 184
1. responsible
2. understand
3. meaning
4. worth
5. material
6. engage
7. aware
8. arrange
9. circle
10. week
11. mountain
12. cycle
13. angle
14. sense
15. admiral

Page 185
1. sail
2. run
3. farm
4. buy
5. pharmacy
6. direct
7. dance
8. science
9. photograph
10. analyze
11. choreograph
12. biography

Page 186

ape	kick	satisfy
apple	kiss	season
banana	laugh	state
bear	limb	town
carrot	list	tuna
cheese	many	tune
cornhusk	mote	umbrella
dandelion	mother	under
dandy	neck	underneath
egg	noise	very
eggplant	other	violin
friend	otter	voice
frond	over	wig
grapes	pout	wisdom
grass	put	wonder
heaven	putt	xylophone
house	quilt	yeast
hover	quit	yes
ice	quitter	yesterday
icicle	raise	zebra
juice	roast	zoo
jump	salt	zoology

Answer Key *(cont.)*

Page 187

candy	grassy	rover
cane	house	salt
cart	join	same
cell	jump	science
cello	launch	scientist
dear	light	silent
deer	line	simple
dog	lion	sort
friend	loop	tune
gamble	lope	tunnel
game	lunch	umbrella
ghastly	moan	vest
ghost	moon	
grass	river	

Page 188

1. c   3. a   5. b
2. c   4. b

Page 189

1. They cleaned their rooms.
2. They washed the family's car.
3. They got ready to go to the zoo.
4. They visted the sharks.
5. They went to the wolf den.
6. They met their mother at the alligator exhibit.

Page 190

I woke up one morning feeling strange.
I got out of bed and looked in the mirror.
What a shock I got when I saw a plant growing out of my ears!
I ran to my mother to show her what had happened.
She said, "Those seeds you swallowed yesterday have planted inside you."
Then she looked in the phone book for a good gardener to come over to trim me.
I am feeling better now, but I still have to water myself every day.

Page 191

A. 2, 1, 5, 4, 3   E. 4, 2, 3, 1, 5
B. 1, 3, 5, 2, 4   F. 3, 5, 1, 2, 4
C. 4, 2, 1, 5, 3   G. 2, 1, 4, 3, 5
D. 3, 2, 4, 1, 5   H. 3, 5, 1, 2, 4

Page 192

1. football field   6. towels
2. bird   7. scissors
3. Beverly Hills   8. flowers
4. fortune cookies   9. tomato soup
5. diving board   10. spaghetti

Page 193

Julie and Juan want to work at the zoo.

Page 194

Answers will vary but should reflect these ideas:
1. Lola
2. loves to watch parrots
3. They are her favorite animals.
4. Lola loves to watch the parrots because they are her favorite animals.

Page 195

Answers will vary, but they should reflect the following ideas:
Mrs. Lee and her class are late for the bus.
The children enjoyed watching the penguins.

Page 196

1. It is about a very young boy named Max.
2. He watches baby penguins hatch.
3. He is nearby when they hatch.
4. Sentences will vary.
5. Pictures will vary.

Page 197

1. It is about George Washington.
2. He was a great leader.
3. He was a good general and president.
4. Sentences will vary.
5. Paragraphs will vary.

Page 198

1. She climbed down her bedpost.
2. She is glad her mother did not see the mess under her bed.
3. She arranges the dollhouse furniture.
4. They eat the girls' leftover cookies from her bedtime snack.
5. She actually finds cookie crumbs in her dollhouse.

Page 199

1. He was excited to pitch in the big game.
2. He had been practicing his pitching.
3. He rode his bicycle to the ballpark.
4. He warmed up in the bullpen.
5. He was named Most Valuable Player.

Page 200

1. Jack and Wendy do not like the Fun House.
2. They think it is too scary, and they want to leave.
1. Mary really wants the dress, and she is jealous.

2. Mary says that she does not like the dress, but she wants to know if there are any more. Also, by asking so much about it, she leads others to believe that she is really interested.

Page 201

1. *Alike:* eight years old, best friends, teaching each other their primary language, do homework together, popcorn is favorite snack, love Pete, enjoy the park, swing and slide with Pete
2. *Different:* Marta doesn't speak much English, Marta is from Mexico, Marta speaks Spanish well and Janis does not, Janis has a little brother and Marta has no siblings, Marta is a good skater, Janis has a scooter

Page 202

1. rooster   4. rose
2. movie   5. guitar
3. computer

Page 203–204

Answers will vary.

Page 205

1. F   6. O
2. O   7. O
3. O   8. F
4. F   9. F
5. F   10. O

1. Answers will vary.
2. Answers will vary.

Page 206

The following statements should be underlined (biased): 2, 4, 7, 8, and 9.

Page 207

1. excited   4. worried
2. sad   5. happy
3. funny

Page 208

Answers will vary.

Page 209

1. two
2. Tracy and his father
3. Tracy
4. "he" in first sentence

Page 210

1. check   4. check
2. no check   5. no check
3. check

Answer Key *(cont.)*

Page 211
1. 3
2. 1
3. 1
4. 3

Page 212
1. Alicia
2. Luke and Chris
3. movers
4. Sam
5. you and I
6. computer
7. Tom; sisters

Page 213
1. It scared or shocked her.
2. His father got serious and set rules or limits.
3. She was ready to leave.
4. He had not felt well.
5. He slept soundly.
6. He was going to be in trouble.
7. "Stop."
8. "Are you scared, nervous, or changing your mind?"
9. He loves to tell a story.
10. She doesn't know what is happening.

Page 214
1. Dinner is free.
2. John was in a bad mood.
3. My cousin can grow plants very well.
4. When I have money, I have to spend it.
5. One should apologize for wrongdoings.
6. Cathy didn't know how things were done yet.
7. Mother told us to clean the house.
8. Dad gets up early.
9. The child wasn't out of danger.
10. Crystal was sad.

Page 215
Some answers may vary.
1. Los Angeles
2. after noon
3. octagon
4. saw
5. Texas
6. bed
7. red
8. cherries
9. Easter
10. mother
11. pancakes
12. see
13. chicken
14. Egypt
15. temperature
16. 100
17. floor
18. pilot
19. hungry
20. hive

Page 516
Some answers may vary.
1. smell
2. tennis
3. Elizabeth
4. poem
11. read
12. Braces
13. right
14. Swim

5. driver
6. Roosevelt
7. foot
8. carpenter
9. den or cave
10. Frame
15. ankle
16. screwdriver
17. fin
18. fruit
19. Oink
20. queen

Page 217
1. little
2. foot
3. bee
4. floor
5. Car
6. girl
7. Door
8. eat
9. books
10. bottom
11. Green
12. waist
13. pilot
14. read
15. tree
16. eye
17. Night
18. December
19. cub
20. Nephew

Page 218
Some answers may vary.
1. holidays
2. girls' names
3. countries
4. fruits
5. farm animals
6. shades of purple
7. writing instruments
8. Disney characters
9. circus performers
10. colleges
11. rivers
12. directions
13. nursery rhymes
14. artists
15. former U.S. presidents
16. numbers
17. letters
18 baked goods
19. last names
20. tools

Page 219
animals: sloth, snipe, quetzal, meerkat, phoebe, peccary, toucan
fruits: strawberry, mango, quince, loganberry, papaya, guava, pineapple
flowers: primrose, gardenia, carnation, iris, crocus, impatiens, sweet William
sports: lacrosse, soccer, rugby, football, Ping-Pong, triathlon, kayaking
instruments: violin, bassoon, harp, trumpet, flute, mandolin, cello
clothing: moccasin, parka, poncho, trousers, tux, cummerbund, gown

Pages 220–221
Answers will vary.

Page 222
a. 108
b. 85
c. 55
d. 77
e. 76
f. 87
g. 148
h. 125
i. 42
j. 122

Page 223
a. 49 + 57 = $106
b. 26 + 32 = $58
c. 17 + 64 = $81
d. 32 + 57 = $89
e. 64 + 17 + 49 = $130
f. 26 + 57 + 32 = $115

Page 224
a. 83 + 24 + 16 = 123
b. 47 + 21 + 33 = 101
c. 14 + 32 + 24 = 70
d. 36 + 42 + 87 = 165

Page 225
a. 61
b. 106
c. 117
d. 37
e. 130
f. 81
g. 81
h. 110
i. 66
j. 63
k. 34
l. 93
m. 85
n. 130
o. 81
p. 137
q. 112
r. 183
s. 49
t. 109
u. 68
v. 110
w. 77
x. 130

Page 226
a. 143
b. 131
c. 91
d. 117
e. 186
f. 157
g. 123
h. 163
i. 145
j. 129
k. 185
l. 106
m. 156
n. 100
o. 93
p. 132
q. 201
r. 174
s. 150
t. 182
u. 174
v. 119
w. 111
x. 170

Page 227
1. 1599
2. 1233
3. 1852
4. 1408
5. 1316
6. 1402
7. 2157
8. 1871
9. 2174
10. 2061
11. 1074
12. 1767

Page 228
a. 14
b. 1
c. 7
d. 14
e. 30
f. 41
g. 26
h. 30
i. 60
j. 41

Answer Key (cont.)

Page 229

Across	Down
1. fourteen	1. fifteen
3. nineteen	2. twenty
7. seventeen	4. eighteen
9. sixteen	5. eleven
	6. twelve
	8. thirteen

Page 230

a. 1	m. 53
b. 22	n. 12
c. 71	o. 55
d. 17	p. 55
e. 26	q. 52
f. 53	r. 3
g. 57	s. 23
h. 34	t. 9
i. 30	u. 34
j. 41	v. 72
k. 4	w. 15
l. 31	x. 44

Page 231

a. 8	i. 44	q. 4
b. 33	j. 40	r. 37
c. 31	k. 72	s. 32
d. 16	l. 21	t. 64
e. 62	m. 64	u. 59
f. 28	n. 31	v. 26
g. 47	o. 14	w. 5
h. 6	p. 15	x. 14

Page 232

1. 6	9. 9
2. 9	10. 7
3. 13	11. 23
4. 10	12. 11
5. 7	13. 8
6. 19	14. 6
7. 18	15. 24
8. 5	16. 12

Page 233

Possible Solutions:

1. $6 + 4 - 1 - 2 + 6 + 2 = 15$
2. $9 + 1 - 3 + 1 - 4 + 1 = 5$
3. $9 - 3 + 4 - 1 + 2 + 3 = 14$
4. $5 - 1 + 1 + 3 + 4 + 6 = 18$
5. $9 - 8 + 6 + 3 - 5 + 3 = 8$
6. $2 - 1 + 8 + 9 - 3 + 5 = 20$
7. $5 + 3 + 2 - 4 + 1 + 5 = 12$
8. $4 + 9 + 3 - 7 + 3 - 1 = 11$
9. $7 - 6 + 2 + 8 - 7 - 1 = 3$
10. $9 + 9 - 9 + 2 - 2 - 8 = 1$

Page 234

$2 \times 2 = 4$	$12 \times 5 = 60$	$6 \times 1 = 6$	$6 \times 3 = 18$
$3 \times 8 = 24$	$7 \times 5 = 35$	$7 \times 7 = 49$	$7 \times 9 = 63$
$5 \times 1 = 5$	$11 \times 8 = 88$	$9 \times 0 = 0$	$9 \times 2 = 18$
$10 \times 0 = 0$	$10 \times 4 = 40$	$10 \times 6 = 60$	$10 \times 8 = 80$
$2 \times 3 = 6$	$11 \times 10 = 110$	$11 \times 12 = 132$	$12 \times 1 = 12$
$11 \times 5 = 55$	$6 \times 0 = 0$	$6 \times 2 = 12$	$6 \times 4 = 24$
$7 \times 4 = 28$	$7 \times 6 = 42$	$7 \times 8 = 56$	$10 \times 7 = 70$
$10 \times 8 = 80$	$12 \times 8 = 96$	$9 \times 1 = 9$	$9 \times 3 = 27$
$10 \times 3 = 30$	$10 \times 5 = 50$	$10 \times 7 = 70$	$10 \times 9 = 90$
$11 \times 9 = 99$	$11 \times 11 = 121$	$12 \times 0 = 0$	$12 \times 2 = 24$

Page 235

$96 \times 16 = 1,536$	$68 \times 88 = 5,984$	$56 \times 75 = 4,200$	$22 \times 67 = 1,474$
$90 \times 13 = 1,170$	$33 \times 31 = 1,023$	$84 \times 28 = 2,352$	$74 \times 17 = 1,258$
$47 \times 19 = 893$	$20 \times 62 = 1,240$	$70 \times 96 = 6,720$	$26 \times 93 = 2,418$
$25 \times 11 = 275$	$24 \times 19 = 456$	$58 \times 75 = 4,350$	$14 \times 72 = 1,008$
$26 \times 16 = 416$	$41 \times 40 = 1,640$	$50 \times 10 = 500$	$48 \times 30 = 1,440$
$40 \times 28 = 1,120$	$46 \times 20 = 920$	$21 \times 25 = 525$	$42 \times 48 = 2,016$
$82 \times 35 = 2,870$	$49 \times 71 = 3,479$	$77 \times 63 = 4,851$	$88 \times 50 = 4,400$
$60 \times 52 = 3,120$	$38 \times 45 = 1,710$	$79 \times 44 = 3,476$	$69 \times 18 = 1,242$
$71 \times 27 = 1,917$	$24 \times 35 = 840$	$86 \times 33 = 2,838$	$43 \times 31 = 1,333$
$32 \times 54 = 1,728$	$27 \times 32 = 864$	$13 \times 29 = 377$	$19 \times 22 = 418$

Page 236

$173 \times 6 = 1,038$	$533 \times 8 = 4,264$	$138 \times 2 = 276$	$833 \times 5 = 4,165$
$227 \times 3 = 681$	$388 \times 1 = 388$	$417 \times 8 = 3,336$	$524 \times 3 = 1,572$
$402 \times 1 = 402$	$620 \times 6 = 3,720$	$317 \times 4 = 1,268$	$468 \times 6 = 2,808$
$420 \times 8 = 3,360$	$662 \times 3 = 1,986$	$458 \times 7 = 3,206$	$947 \times 2 = 1,894$
$178 \times 9 = 1,602$	$714 \times 9 = 6,426$	$550 \times 6 = 3,300$	$767 \times 7 = 5,369$
$324 \times 8 = 2,592$	$835 \times 3 = 2,505$	$594 \times 5 = 2,970$	$632 \times 3 = 1,896$
$172 \times 4 = 688$	$152 \times 7 = 1,064$	$180 \times 4 = 720$	$221 \times 2 = 442$
$286 \times 8 = 2,288$	$254 \times 5 = 1,270$	$538 \times 1 = 538$	$489 \times 4 = 1,956$
$509 \times 4 = 2,036$	$851 \times 1 = 851$	$728 \times 6 = 4,368$	$141 \times 9 = 1,269$
$615 \times 2 = 1,230$	$674 \times 8 = 5,392$	$107 \times 3 = 321$	$213 \times 5 = 1,065$

Page 237

$23 \times 16 = 368$	$13 \times 38 = 494$	$89 \times 57 = 5,073$	$44 \times 76 = 3,344$
$90 \times 39 = 3,510$	$31 \times 11 = 341$	$24 \times 23 = 552$	$22 \times 51 = 1,122$
$17 \times 79 = 1,343$	$41 \times 96 = 3,936$	$74 \times 19 = 1,406$	$16 \times 39 = 624$
$35 \times 15 = 525$	$14 \times 79 = 1,106$	$48 \times 79 = 3,792$	$25 \times 17 = 425$
$14 \times 63 = 882$	$80 \times 54 = 4,320$	$70 \times 71 = 4,970$	$28 \times 93 = 2,604$
$56 \times 82 = 4,592$	$34 \times 24 = 816$	$21 \times 26 = 546$	$58 \times 48 = 2,784$
$73 \times 50 = 3,650$	$46 \times 27 = 1,242$	$67 \times 64 = 4,288$	$99 \times 56 = 5,544$
$50 \times 28 = 1,400$	$68 \times 40 = 2,720$	$39 \times 42 = 1,638$	$64 \times 48 = 3,072$
$81 \times 76 = 6,156$	$34 \times 83 = 2,822$	$96 \times 30 = 2,880$	$34 \times 23 = 782$
$51 \times 44 = 2,244$	$23 \times 36 = 828$	$18 \times 28 = 504$	$36 \times 20 = 720$

Page 238

$400 \div 16 = 25$	$180 \div 10 = 18$	$112 \div 2 = 56$	$288 \div 16 = 18$
$225 \div 15 = 15$	$136 \div 8 = 17$	$256 \div 16 = 16$	$171 \div 9 = 19$
$234 \div 18 = 13$	$95 \div 5 = 19$	$150 \div 6 = 25$	$231 \div 11 = 21$
$240 \div 12 = 20$	$248 \div 8 = 31$	$128 \div 32 = 4$	

Page 239

1. $5 + 7 = 12$	6. $4 \times 9 = 36$	11. $2 \times 8 = 16$	16. $144 \div 12 = 12$
2. $24 \div 4 = 6$	7. $10 \times 8 = 80$	12. $3 + 2 = 5$	17. $21 \div 3 = 7$
3. $9 + 3 = 12$	8. $15 \div 5 = 3$	13. $22 - 6 = 16$	18. $90 \div 10 = 9$
4. $18 - 6 = 12$	9. $11 \div 4 = 7$	14. $9 + 1 = 10$	19. $12 \times 11 = 132$
5. $4 + 9 = 13$	10. $8 + 16 = 24$	15. $3 \times 3 = 9$	20. $14 \times 1 = 14$

Answer Key *(cont.)*

Page 240
1. 1/3
2. 1/4
3. 5/8
4. 3/5
5. 7/10
6. 2/6 = 1/3
7. 3/4
8. 1/2

Page 241

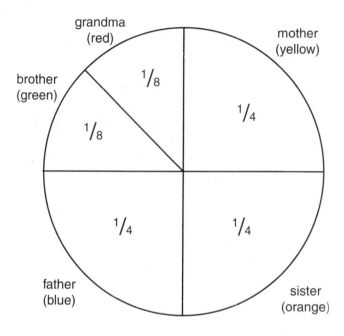

Page 242
1. watermelon
2. grapes
3. 1) watermelon, 2) peaches, 3) plums, 4) apricots, 5) grapes
4. 1/2; 1/4; 1/8
5. Answers will vary.

Page 243
1. 30 minutes; five minutes; five minutes; 10 minutes; 10 minutes
2. Answers will vary.
Graphs will vary.

Page 244
Answers are approximate measurements.
1. 4 meters
2. 9 meters
3. 12.5 meters
4. 13 meters
5. 15.5 meters

Page 245
Answers will vary but may include:
1. a
2. f
3. c, e
4. b, d
5. d
6. d
7. b, d
8. f
9. c, e
10. a

Page 246
Answers are approximate measurements.
1. 18 miles
2. 10 miles
3. 35 miles
4. 18 miles
5. 16 miles
6. 10 miles
It is farther from Pleasantown to Mountaintown.

Page 247
1. 1,750
2. 550
3. 450
4. 1,150
5. 1,400
6. 1,050
7. 850
8. 600
9. 600
10. 600

Page 248
1. one cent
2. five cents
3. ten cents
4. Answers will vary, but the first number should always be divided by five to get the second number.
5. Answers will vary, but the first number should always be divided by two to get the second number.
6. Answers will vary, but the first number should always be divided by ten to get the second number.
7. one nickel
8. one dime
9. one dime
10. 16 cents

Page 249
1. 1 silver dollar
2. 3 q, 2 d, 1 n
3. 2 q, 5 d
4. 10 d
5. 5 d, 10 n
6. 2 q, 4 d, 10 p
7. 7 d, 5 n, 5 p
8. 9 d, 10 p
9. 1 q, 3 d, 6 n, 15 p
10. 3 q, 25 p

Page 250
Answers will vary. Accept all that add to fifty cents.

Page 251
Answers will vary. Accept all that add to one dollar.

Page 252
Lucy = B
Gwen = C-
Cara = A
Martin = C
Donald = D

Page 253
Ted Agee, 9
Theodore Chin, 8
Teddy Dalton, 10

Answer Key *(cont.)*

Page 254
Chad = Reds
Danny = Cardinals
Andrew = White Sox
Ryan = Dodgers
Will = A's

Page 255
Katelyn—roller coaster, bratwurst
Kenny—Ferris wheel, hot dogs
Emily—bumper cars, hamburger
Howie—carousel, corndog

Page 256
Jane = 5   Annie = 6
Daisy = 2   Penny = 8
Carrie = 9   Tammy = 1
Joanne = 3   Lindsey = 7
Gertie = 4

Page 257
1. southeast   5. south
2. west   6. north
3. northeast   7. east
4. southwest   8. northwest

Page 258
Home = last row fourth house from
    the left

Page 259
1. true
2. false; western and southeastern
3. false; northeast
4. false; only one, the others are
    reached by local roads
5. true
6. true
7. false; west of lake, east of
    railroad
8. true

Page 260
example: silver
A1, white; D3, gray; B4, red; D2,
ivory
C4, silver; A2, yellow; D1, black; C2,
purple
B3, tan; A4, gold; C3, brown; B1,
pink
D4, lavender; B2, green; A3, orange;
C1, blue
shaded: A1, A3, B3, C2
striped: B2, C1, C3
unmarked: A2, B1

Page 261
1. E2
2. F3
3. C1, D1, E1
4. E5

5. E3
6. A3, A4, B3, B4
7. F1, F2
8. A5, A6
9. D5
10. C4
11. E6
12. B1
13. D4
14. B5
15. C6
16. C2

Page 262
1. 35 and 40
2. 27
3. Wayne
4. Glen Ridge, 33
5. a. 15
   b. 37
   c. 27
   d. 48

Page 263
1. a. 31
   b. 45
   c. 37
   d. 88
   e. 51
   f. 85
2. a. 6
   b. 14
   c. 29
   d. 45
   e. 66
   f. 29
3. a. 99
   b. 62
   c. 66
   d. 59
   e. 45
   f. 71

Page 264
1. east
2. Ekalaka
3. Boyes, Hammond, Alzada
4. Boxelder Creek
5. Medicine Rocks

Page 265
1. Far North
2. Southwestern
3. Pacific Coast
4. Plains

Page 266
1. Brunswick
2. fruit
3. pecans, peanuts, tobacco (Other
   choices are possible.)

4. berries
5. corn
6. marble, granite

Page 267
1. Sacramento, Oakland, San
   Francisco, San Jose, Los
   Angeles, San Diego
2. Needles, Barstow
3. 75 to 100
4. Crescent City, Redding,
   Bakersfield
5. Answers will vary. Accept
   logically explained answers, such
   as desert conditions in Needles
   and Barstow.

Page 268
1. Boston
2. Plymouth, New Bedford
3. Boston: Below 22 F, Below -6 C
   Lowell: 22 to 26 F, -6 to -3 C
   Pittsfield: 26 to 30 F, -3 to -1 C

Page 269
1. D3, A1, C3
2. A1, D1
3. State Highway 106
4. B1, B2, C1, C2
5. Mount McGee, Remington,
   Carlton
6. 16, 22
7. coastline

Page 270
Answers are in miles.
1. 2786
2. 1440
3. 206
4. 2037
5. 802
6. 840
7. 1329
8. 1058
9. 2873
10. 2976
11. 963
12. 417

Page 271
1. obsidian
2. sedimentary
3. metamorphic

Page 272
1. David Peterson
2. $5.80—Kathryn Ross
3. Barbara Marshall
4. no
5. no
6. 614
7. $48.00

Answer Key *(cont.)*

Page 273
1. 5 pianos, 10 flutes, 30 guitars, 15 drums, 5 trumpets
2. 25, 20, 15, 25
3. Accept any reasonable response.

Page 274
1. acoustic and electric guitar
2. tuning keys, fingerboard, frets, and bridge
3. soundboard and sound hole
4. pickups, base, treble, and volume controls

Page 276
#1 = M, #2 = W, #3 = V

Page 277
1. no
2. 5:00 P.M.
3. no
4. *A Lad*, *Dan*, and *The Mystery Garden*
5. *The Sandy Lot* and *The Mystery Garden*
6. Answers will vary.

Page 278
Hawaii, Washington, Nevada, Wyoming, Oklahoma, Arkansas, Illinois, Kentucky, Georgia, West Virginia, New York, Vermont, New Hampshire, Maine

Page 279
Finland, Germany, England, Venezuela, Peru, Mexico, New Zealand, Australia, Mongolia, India, Pakistan, Saudi Arabia, Egypt, Italy, France, Ireland, Iceland, Canada

Page 280
Los Angeles—United States
Glasgow—Scotland
Seoul—South Korea
Bombay—India
Nagano—Japan
Nice—France
Frankfurt—Germany
Florence—Italy
Toronto—Canada
Lima—Peru
Rio de Janeiro—Brazil
Bogota—Colombia
Lisbon—Portugal
Cairo—Egypt
Jerusalem—Israel
Copenhagen—Denmark
Canberra—Australia
Dublin—Ireland
Cape Town—South Africa

Acapulco—Mexico

Page 281
Alabama

Page 282
Utah

Page 283
Argentina

Page 284
Nigeria

Page 286
Nouns:
1. summer time year
2. weather children swimming
3. schools people time vacation
4. days hours sunlight
5. pool beach lake
6. teacher Mr. Dawson Metropolitan Museum of Art New York City July
7. care concern visitors
8. friends Tim Carol Statue of Liberty Ellis Island
9. scent flowers Central Park lunch
10. hamburgers grill backyard

Person:
Ms. Lizt
Dr. Forest

Place:
France
city
building
Texas

Thing:
clouds
shoelaces
bicycles
sounds
glasses
table

Idea:
happiness
science
loyalty
fairness
love
pain

Page 287
1. action
2. action
3. linking
4. linking
5. linking
6. action
7. linking
8. action
9. action
10. action
11. action
12. linking
13. linking
14. linking

Page 289
A.1. beautiful
2. slowly
3. thinly
4. very
B.1. pretty
2. big
3. green
4. happy
5. thin
6. round
7. wet
8. excellent
9. broken
10. smelly
C.1. slowly
2. quickly
3. quickly
4. down
5. joyfully
6. sloppily
7. closely
8. loudly
9. badly
10. wildly

Page 290
Part 1
1. All birds have feathers, wings, and beaks.
2. My sister is sleepy, grumpy, and clueless.
3. I would have done my homework, but I was abducted by aliens, was left in Siberia, and had to wait for the Marines to rescue me.
4. I ordered a pizza with cheese, pickles, and sliced cherries.
5. Please go to the store and get flypaper, chopsticks, and kumquats.
6. I went to the door with rollers in my hair, a mud mask on my face, and wearing my bathrobe.
7. My dog has brown spots, a short tail, and fuzzy feet.
8. My little brother can't go anywhere without his blanket, his stuffed duck, and his rabbit's foot key chain.
9. When I go to college, I am taking a stereo, a microwave, and a treadmill.
10. For her birthday, Mindy wants some edible flowers, sparkly socks, and a pony.

Answer Key *(cont.)*

Part 2

1. My rabbit has long, floppy ears.
2. A large, heavy sparrow could weigh 200 pounds.
3. My teacher has a green, pointy nose.
4. My dad used to have curly, frizzy hair.
5. A friendly, playful giraffe ate all my spaghetti.

Page 291

A.

1. My parents bought their first home on January 13, 1976.
2. My mon was born on March 31, 1948.
3. We went to Disneyland on Tuesday, August 18, and it was really crowded!
4. My brother's birthday is November 17, 1973.
5. On Saturday, April 19, we are flying to my grandma's house.
6. I get my tonsils out on Monday, September 16, and then I can eat lots of ice cream.
7. Our puppies were born on February 14, 1997.
8. It rained cats and dogs on January 18, 1995.

C.

1. Yesterday, I met a girl from Canberra, Australia.
2. A hurricane went on shore at Acapulco, Mexico.
3. I've never been to Seattle, Washington.
4. It can get very cold in Buffalo, New York.
5. Yesterday I received e-mail from Bordeaux, France.
6. Many movie stars live in La Canada-Flintridge, California.
7. Alexandria, Virginia, is an interesting historic town.
8. You can take a great train ride in Durango, Colorado.
9. Have you been on the roller coasters in St. Louis, Missouri?
10. The mountains are really high in Vail, Colorado.

Page 292

1. F
2. Father's Day, Fourth of July
3. Saturday, Sunday; Tuesday, Thurdsay
4. January, June, July; March, May; April, August

Page 293

1. Amanda Panda
2. Jeffrey R. Hardy
3. Carlos Custard Appleseed
4. Gilbert McGillicutty
5. Leslie Q. Presley

Page 294

1. !
2. .
3. ?
4. .
5. . or !
6. ?
7. ?
8. !
9. .
10. . or !
11. !
12. ! or .
13. ?
14. .
15. ?

Page 295

1. The first day of school is exciting.
2. Freddy Wilson's frog Peepers hopped into Mrs. Woolsey's purse.
3. As I walked outside, I smelled smoke.
4. In the play, Robin Hood was played by Lieutenant Bronksy.
5. The fourth Thursday in November is Thanksgiving.
6. I like Halloween best when it is on a Saturday.
7. Aunt Susan went to Yellowstone National Park.
8. Connie lives on Maple Street in Bismark, North Dakota.
9. Brazil, Argentina, and Peru are in South America.
10. The Mediterranean Sea and the Atlantic Ocean touch Spain.
11. The letter was signed, "Love always, Esther."

12. Davis Medical Center opened in January last year.
13. One of the religions practiced by many African people is Islam.
14. Italians and Germans belong to the Caucasian race.
15. Last Tuesday Ruben walked his dog Spotty down Tulip Street to Central Park.

Page 296

A.

1. c		4. b
2. d		5. a
3. e		

B.

1. His accomplishments were as follows: He was a painter, a publisher, a writer, an inventor, a scientist, a diplomat, a statesman, and an inspiration to others.
2. He decided to devote himself to the study of science.
3. He proved that lightning was electricity and that things could be positively or negatively charged with electricity.
4. He did not patent his inventions. He wanted to share them freely with the world.
5. Answers will vary.

Page 297

A.

1. c		4. a
2. d		5. b
3. e		

B.

1. The name of the poem was "The Defense of Fort McHenry."
2. The bombardment of Fort McHenry was taking place.
3. It became the official national anthem on March 3, 1931.
4. President Herbert Hoover signed the bill.
5. Answers will vary.

Page 298

A.

1. b		4. e
2. c		5. a
3. d		

Answer Key *(cont.)*

B.
1. A system of dashes and dots is used.
2. Samuel Morse developed this code.
3. No, is not used a telephone to send messages with Morse code.
4. Morse code is most commonly used in emergency situations.
5. Answers will vary.

Page 299

A.
1. b   4. d
2. c   5. a
3. e

B.
1. You can find them at Stanley Park in Vancouver, B.C., and at Thunderbird Park in Victoria, British Columbia.
2. Totem poles have been used by Native Americans as a way to record history.
3. Animals, birds, fish, plants, or other natural objects that would represent a Native American tribe are carved on totem poles.
4. The family's symbol is at the top of the pole.
5. Answers will vary.

Page 300

A.
1. c   4. a
2. d   5. b
3. e

B.
1. The Frisbie company began in the late 1800s.
2. They threw them to each other.
3. It was marketed as the Pluto Platter.
4. The sales of the Frisbee took off in the 1960s.
5. Answers will vary.

Page 301

A.
1. d   4. c
2. e   5. a
3. b

B.
1. They were looking for a product to eliminate moisture from electrical circuitry and to prevent corrosion on airplanes.
2. Norman Larsen, president and head chemist at the Rocket Chemical Company, invented it.
3. It was a water displacement (WD) formula developed on his fortieth try.
4. The Friendship VII was covered with it.
5. Answers will vary.

Page 302

A.
1. c   4. e
2. b   5. a
3. d

B.
1. John Lennon started the group.
2. The name of the first group was "the Quarrymen."
3. Ringo Starr replaced Pete Best.
4. The Ed Sullivan show made them famous in America.
5. Answers will vary.

Page 303

A.
1. c   4. a
2. d   5. b
3. e

B.
1. Butchart Gardens is located in Victoria, British Columbia.
2. You can find Japanese gardens, a rose garden and a sunken garden.
3. People go and count how many flowers and buds they see.
4. Children are given an hour off of school to help count.
5. Answers will vary.

Page 304

A.
1. c   4. b
2. d   5. a
3. e

B.
1. Spider-Man is Peter Parker, the freelance photographer.
2. He got his special powers by being bitten by a spider that had been exposed to huge amounts of radiation.

3. He made a red and blue uniform for himself to wear when he was Spider-Man.
4. His uncle was killed by a burglar and as a result Spider-Man decided to devote his life to fighting crime.
5. Answers will vary.

Page 305

A.
1. b   4. c
2. e   5. a
3. d

B.
1. The first Olympics were in 776 B.C.
2. They have changed over the years.
3. The first Olympic Games were held in Greece.
4. No, the winter and summer games are held 2 years apart.
5. Answers will vary.

Page 306

A.
1. e   4. b
2. d   5. a
3. c

B.
1. Barbie made her debut in 1959.
2. Ruth Handler invented Barbie.
3. She invented Barbie for her daughter who preferred to play with dolls designed for teens.
4. Ruth Handler went on to be president of Mattel, Inc.
5. Answers will vary.

Page 307

A.
1. d   4. c
2. a   5. b
3. e

B.
1. It was the fastest selling toy for 6 months.
2. The craze did not last very long.
3. The Hula-Hoop was based on wooden hoop used by Australian youths.
4. Richard Knerr, a partner in the Wham-O toy manufacturing company, invented it.
5. Answers will vary.

Answer Key *(cont.)*

Page 308

A.

1. d   4. b
2. e   5. c
3. a   6. f

B.

1. In the mid 1980s fur trade was thriving.
2. The sea otter was prized for its pelt and demand was high.
3. It is illegal to hunt sea otters today.
4. The sea otters off the coast of California are increasing.
5. Answers will vary.

Page 309

A.

1. b   4. f
2. e   5. d
3. c   6. a

B.

1. No one knows the identity of the real Spider Woman.
2. No one knows if she was born with special powers or acquired them later.
3. She concentrates intensely to create a web and does not need any separate devices.
4. She can sense danger as well as an ordinary person and no better than one.
5. A criminal can only break loose from a web that is weaker and far away from Spider-Woman.
6. Answers will vary.

Page 310

A.

1. b   4. a
2. d   5. c
3. e

B.

1. Walter Elias Disney was born on December 5, 1901.
2. Walt's wife, Lillian, thought his original name, Mortimer the Mouse was too stuffy. She made it up.
3. Walt went into business with his brother, Roy.
4. Mickey Mouse's first movie was *Steamboat Willie*.
5. Answers will vary.

Page 311

A.

1. c   4. e
2. d   5. a
3. f   6. b

B.

1. Construction began for a major trans-Amazon highway.
2. Huge areas of the Amazon rain forest were cut down and burned.
3. Each family would be given a 240-acre piece of land, housing, and a small salary for a few months.
4. Schools, health facilities and other services would be available for these families.
5. The plan was a failure. Life in the rain forest was too difficult.
6. Answers will vary.

Page 312

A.

1. f   4. d
2. b   5. c
3. e   6. a

B.

1. Robin Hood was a legendary English hero.
2. A group of outlaws rescues him.
3. His faithful followers were Maid Marian, Friar Tuck, and Little John.
4. He treats them with contempt.
5. He treats them with respect.
6. Answers will vary.

Page 313

A.

1. a   4. d
2. e   5. b
3. c

B.

1. Kristi was born in Hayward, California, in 1971.
2. She was 6 years old.
3. She decided to concentrate on her singles career.
4. She won the gold medal.
5. Answers will vary.

Page 314

A.

1. c   4. e
2. d   5. b
3. a

B.

1. The zeppelins were 40 times bigger than blimps.
2. The largest and most luxurious zeppelin ever built was the Hindenburg.
3. The Hindenburg was going to America in 1937.
4. When it landed there was a loud thump, and the tail section burst into flames.
5. Answers will vary.

Page 315

A.

1. a   4. b
2. e   5. c
3. d

B.

1. The first book was *Are You there God? It's Me, Margaret*.
2. She was an A student and did as she was told.
3. She liked to read Nancy Drew mysteries, biographies, and horse stories.
4. She met and married John W. Blume and took his last name.
5. Answers will vary.

Page 316

A.

1. b   4. c
2. d   5. a
3. e

B.

1. She helped to hunt for food.
2. She met him in a shooting match.
3. She could shoot a dime that was in her husband's hand or a cigarette that was in his mouth. She also could shoot a playing card thrown in the air 90 feet away from her.
4. Her nickname was "Little Sure Shot."
5. Answers will vary.

Page 317

A.

1. b   4. a
2. d   5. c
3. e

Answer Key *(cont.)*

B.
1. The statue symbolizes welcome and a promise of freedom for immigrants to the Untied States.
2. The statue was given to the United States by the people of France in 1884.
3. Frédéric Bartholdi designed and sculpted it.
4. Bartholdi named the statue Liberty Enlightening the World.
5. The seven spikes stand for the seven seas, the seven continents, and the seven liberties.

Page 318
A.
1. c
2. d
3. b
4. e
5. a

B.
1. He became a writer when his brother bet that he couldn't compose a verse.
2. During WWI he wrote his first children's book and a play to entertain the troops.
3. He wrote *Winnie-the-Pooh* in 1926.
4. Walt Disney Company made it into a movie.
5. Answers will vary.

Page 319
A.
1. b
2. d
3. e
4. c
5. a
6. f

B.
1. Ancient people used the stars to guide their way and lives.
2. We call them constellations.
3. The constellations written about were the Big Dipper, the Bear, the Wagon, the Plow, Seven Rishis, and Cassiopeia.
4. Many of the stars names were based on ancient stories and myths.
5. She claimed that she was more beautiful than the lovely sea nymphs.

Page 320
A.
1. e
2. c
3. d
4. a
5. b

B.
1. Hercules' father was Zeus.
2. When he was a baby he killed two serpents who were about to attack him.
3. Hercules learned wrestling, archery and fencing. (you only need two)
4. He was banished from Thebe because of his bad temper.
5. He had to serve King Eurystheus for 12 years and accomplish many difficult tasks.
6. Individual answers.

Page 321
A.
1. c
2. e
3. d
4. b
5. a

B.
1. He was a pilot for the US Navy.
2. The name of the space flight was Gemini 8.
3. After docking, the two spacecrafts went into a violent roll. They were able to deal with it and save the mission.
4. He retired in 1971 and became an aerospace engineering professor.
5. Answers will vary.

Page 322
A.
1. b
2. d
3. e
4. f
5. a
6. c

B.
1. He was born in Baltimore.
2. As a child he got into trouble and went to a Catholic boy's school where he played baseball.
3. He played as a pitcher, an outfielder, and a left-handed pitcher.
4. In 1920 he broke the 1884 record of 24 home runs in one season by hitting 54.

5. Yankee Stadium was also called "the house that Ruth built."
6. Answers will vary.

Page 323
A.
1. e
2. b
3. f
4. d
5. c
6. a

B.
1. When Elvis was eight, he won his first talent contest.
2. He recorded his first song as a present for his mother.
3. He was drafted into the army.
4. He started doing live tours.
5. He made over 40 albums in his lifetime.
6. Answers will vary.

Page 324
A.
1. c
2. b
3. d
4. a
5. e

B.
1. Baseball was his favorite sport.
2. He could not play in college at first because his grades and his playing were not good enough.
3. He started as a pitcher for the Los Angeles Dodgers minor-league team.
4. He was not a great player, however, his coach felt that he had potential and convinced him to keep working on his pitch.
5. Answers will vary.

Page 326
A.
1. b
2. d
3. e
4. f
5. c
6. a

B.
1. Merlin, the magician, raised Arthur.
2. He easily pulled it from the stone and became king of Britain.
3. He was a fair and wise ruler.
4. This table was round and could seat 1,600 knights without anyone knight having a better seat than another. Arthur felt that this would keep his knights from arguing.

Answer Key *(cont.)*

5. When Arthur returned home from conquering most of western Europe, he had to fight and kill his nephew, Mordred. He was injured badly and later died.
6. Answers will vary.

Page 328

1. Beethoven was born in Bonn, Germany, in 1770.
2. He began to study music when he was four years old.
3. His father wanted him to be a musician.
4. Beethoven went on his first concert tour when he was 11 years old.
5. Beethoven was 17 years old when Mozart heard him play.
6. He went to Vienna, Austria.
7. Beethoven studied with Haydn, another great musician and composer.
8. Beethoven wrote about 300 pieces of music.
9. His compositions included sonatas, symphonies, concertos, and operas.
10. Beethoven gradually lost his hearing after an illness.

Page 329

1. Austria	11. musician
2. Bonn	12. notation
3. composer	13. opera
4. composition	14. orchestra
5. concerto	15. piano
6. Germany	16. sonata
7. harmony	17. symphony
8. Haydn	18. tempo
9. melody	19. Vienna
10. Mozart	20. violin

Page 330

```
S D F G H J K P Q W E A U S T R I A X C
A C O M P O S I T I O N Z X C S T V O P
M O O N B V C A C E X Z O V I O L I N I
L M K N J H G N G F M D S T A N Q E E R
U P Y T C T R O S E R P F G A A H N H U
B O N N M E L O D Y A S O D F T H N A Y
G S T O P E R A R G M E D C V A I A Y T
A E S D F G H T K L E P M N B V C O D A
Q R W E R T Y O O I O R H P L K J H N C
A M U S I C I A N Q U I M O Z A R T S D
A S D F G H J K L P O I U A N Y T R E W
O R C H E S T R A H A R M O N Y A S D F
Q A Z X S W E D C V F R T G B Y J U I L
```

Page 332

1.	15	26.	13
2.	9	27.	14
3.	17	28.	11
4.	13	29.	7
5.	5	30.	10
6.	8	31.	15
7.	14	32.	4
8.	7	33.	9
9.	16	34.	14
10.	10	35.	1
11.	13	36.	14
12.	6	37.	9
13.	6	38.	17
14.	5	39.	10
15.	8	40.	13
16.	4	41.	10
17.	11	42.	9
18.	10	43.	12
19.	7	44.	9
20.	12	45.	3
21.	7	46.	6
22.	18	47.	8
23.	6	48.	13
24.	8	49.	16
25.	12	50.	11

Page 333

51.	8	76.	5
52.	11	77.	12
53.	14	78.	9
54.	7	79.	10
55.	4	80.	5
56.	2	81.	0
57.	15	82.	7
58.	6	83.	15
59.	2	84.	10
60.	8	85.	3
61.	12	86.	2
62.	9	87.	9
63.	3	88.	8
64.	12	89.	6
65.	16	90.	11
66.	5	91.	13
67.	9	92.	8
68.	11	93.	3
69.	5	94.	10
70.	9	95.	7
71.	7	96.	8
72.	10	97.	6
73.	4	98.	10
74.	14	99.	2
75.	11	100.	12

Answer Key *(cont.)*

Page 334
1. 6
2. 12
3. 5
4. 13
5. 10
6. 11
7. 17
8. 19
9. 15
10. 16
11. 14
12. 19
13. 10
14. 12
15. 20
16. 16

Page 335
1. 26
2. 6
3. 18
4. 15
5. 9
6. 17
7. 15
8. 22
9. 18
10. 23
11. 20
12. 16

Page 336
1. 52
2. 49
3. 52
4. 38
5. 33
6. 35
7. 42
8. 46
9. 50
10. 38
11. 46
12. 31
13. 37
14. 40
15. 22
16. 27

Page 337
1. 19
2. 20
3. 17
4. 49
5. 60
6. 53
7. 30
8. 75
9. 78
10. 87
11. 45
12. 61
13. 58
14. 22
15. 63
16. 19
17. 35
18. 87
19. 87
20. 50
21. 57
22. 42
23. 97
24. 56
25. 98

Page 338
1. 121
2. 154
3. 131
4. 94
5. 81
6. 89
7. 44
8. 120
9. 91
10. 39
11. 124
12. 47
13. 125
14. 138
15. 107
16. 196
17. 111
18. 67
19. 54
20. 127
21. 120
22. 119
23. 160

24. 135
25. 73

Page 339
1. 169
2. 177
3. 191
4. 157
5. 132
6. 179
7. 111
8. 148
9. 188
10. 195
11. 193
12. 81
13. 218
14. 192
15. 187
16. 176

Pageq 340
1. 266
2. 300
3. 182
4. 265
5. 182
6. 196
7. 212
8. 128
9. 358
10. 303
11. 248
12. 91

Page 341
1. 898
2. 825
3. 1,072
4. 873
5. 988
6. 1,019
7. 1,336
8. 861
9. 389
10. 1,117
11. 1,090
12. 621
13. 843
14. 1,402
15. 1,012
16. 1,670

17. 823
18. 1,822
19. 967
20. 938
21. 1,248
22. 925
23. 623
24. 947
25. 1,314

Page 342
1. 2,035
2. 1,879
3. 2,160
4. 1963
5. 1,431
6. 1,762
7. 1,260
8. 2,275
9. 1,661
10. 1,744
11. 1,994
12. 1,622
13. 1,700
14. 1,832
15. 2,013
16. 1,023

Page 343
1. 1,404
2. 2,675
3. 1,096
4. 1,824
5. 3,184
6. 1,825
7. 1,671
8. 2,210
9. 3,056
10. 2,359
11. 2,678
12. 2,361

Page 344
1. 17,339
2. 14,490
3. 15,499
4. 5,737
5. 13,216
6. 10,335
7. 6,869
8. 16,045
9. 4,685

Answer Key *(cont.)*

10. 14,358
11. 10,519
12. 7,336
13. 8,610
14. 8,323
15. 12,244
16. 7,787
17. 7,753
18. 8,040
19. 9,097
20. 12,031
21. 8,415
22. 10,786
23. 16,877
24. 7,129
25. 5,166

Page 345
1. 19,555
2. 14,017
3. 9,155
4. 15,563
5. 16,152
6. 17,552
7. 15,169
8. 15,388
9. 15,817
10. 12,793
11. 14,186
12. 24,204
13. 24,649
14. 17,700
15. 25,076
16. 13,821

Page 346
1. 27,788
2. 27,827
3. 24,036
4. 25,815
5. 12,814
6. 29,265
7. 25,490
8. 23,657
9. 28,244
10. 12,801
11. 25,132
12. 18,138

Page 347
1. 76
2. 11
3. 120
4. 9
5. 15
6. 4,670
7. 39
8. 17
9. 181
10. 1,778
11. 140
12. 19
13. 180
14. 1,843
15. 18
16. 16
17. 158
18. 101
19. 3,449
20. 110

Page 348
1. 9
2. 8
3. 8
4. 6
5. 5
6. 8
7. 5
8. 6
9. 8
10. 5
11. 7
12. 5
13. 0
14. 4
15. 4
16. 3
17. 6
18. 6
19. 7
20. 9
21. 5
22. 9
23. 4
24. 3
25. 6
26. 6
27. 6
28. 5

29. 7
30. 4
31. 9
32. 2
33. 9
34. 9
35. 1
36. 7
37. 3
38. 9
39. 7
40. 4
41. 9
42. 0
43. 3
44. 7
45. 3
46. 6
47. 5
48. 8
49. 9
50. 4

Page 349
51. 7
52. 8
53. 4
54. 4
55. 1
56. 2
57. 7
58. 3
59. 1
60. 6
61. 5
62. 2
63. 1
64. 8
65. 7
66. 0
67. 4
68. 7
69. 3
70. 1
71. 1
72. 1
73. 0
74. 8
75. 2
76. 2
77. 4

78. 5
79. 8
80. 1
81. 0
82. 3
83. 8
84. 3
85. 2
86. 9
87. 6
88. 1
89. 2
90. 3
91. 5
92. 2
93. 0
94. 1
95. 2
96. 0
97. 1
98. 2
99. 0
100. 7

Page 350
1. 35
2. 14
3. 34
4. 44
5. 41
6. 75
7. 13
8. 81
9. 91
10. 85
11. 88
12. 46
13. 94
14. 50
15. 53
16. 70
17. 41
18. 21
19. 67
20. 53
21. 32
22. 79
23. 8
24. 90
25. 25

Answer Key (cont.)

Page 351
1. 360
2. 625
3. 219
4. 349
5. 581
6. 823
7. 533
8. 247
9. 534
10. 340
11. 118
12. 381
13. 457
14. 262
15. 930
16. 764
17. 339
18. 879
19. 533
20. 595
21. 678
22. 357
23. 657
24. 826
25. 553

Page 352
1. 845
2. 159
3. 257
4. 821
5. 888
6. 201
7. 233
8. 759
9. 406
10. 461
11. 532
12. 555
13. 167
14. 223
15. 708
16. 585
17. 887
18. 233
19. 840
20. 816
21. 146
22. 748
23. 250

24. 708
25. 443

Page 353
1. 4,213
2. 3,311
3. 2,322
4. 4,227
5. 4,173
6. 2,860
7. 4,251
8. 9,332
9. 1,612
10. 1,831
11. 5,162
12. 2,131
13. 6,305
14. 9,050
15. 7,130
16. 9,233
17. 7,634
18. 3,630
19. 7,246
20. 8,242
21. 2,234
22. 8,112
23. 7,570
24. 9,640
25. 1,171

Page 354
1. 9,331
2. 1,243
3. 9,117
4. 5,651
5. 8,312
6. 4,125
7. 2,451
8. 7,123
9. 9,841
10. 6,153
11. 4,041
12. 3,246
13. 1,533
14. 4,510
15. 5,330
16. 8,015
17. 6,311
18. 3,271
19. 7,174
20. 6,404

21. 4,153
22. 759
23. 1,647
24. 4,266
25. 6,633

Page 355
1. 62
2. 24
3. 330
4. 785
5. 7,146
6. 8,448
7. 75
8. 2,788
9. 9,605
10. 8,922
11. 125
12. 7,767
13. 8
14. 6,594
15. 1,148
16. 815
17. 40
18. 854
19. 29
20. 68

Page 356
1. 0
2. 169
3. 2
4. 532
5. 2
6. 1,833
7. 8,557
8. 5,783
9. 115
10. 5
11. 209
12. 5
13. 189
14. 3,204
15. 4,452
16. 524
17. 118
18. 3
19. 3,916
20. 6,758

Page 357
1. 36
2. 0
3. 21
4. 28
5. 72
6. 48
7. 35
8. 12
9. 0
10. 30
11. 8
12. 36
13. 14
14. 6
15. 8
16. 12
17. 0
18. 15
19. 5
20. 54
21. 7
22. 16
23. 21
24. 7
25. 30
26. 20
27. 42
28. 42
29. 54
30. 2
31. 25
32. 56
33. 14
34. 0
35. 3
36. 81
37. 9
38. 18
39. 24
40. 36
41. 0
42. 8
43. 27
44. 0
45. 9
46. 15
47. 6
48. 10
49. 63
50. 8

Answer Key *(cont.)*

Page 358

51. 1
52. 56
53. 64
54. 48
55. 18
56. 0
57. 6
58. 4
59. 4
60. 0
61. 0
62. 12
63. 28
64. 12
65. 40
66. 45
67. 63
68. 0
69. 0
70. 27
71. 3
72. 9
73. 18
74. 24
75. 24
76. 32
77. 24
78. 49
79. 45
80. 40
81. 0
82. 6
83. 0
84. 72
85. 0
86. 0
87. 4
88. 16
89. 20
90. 32
91. 0
92. 0
93. 18
94. 1
95. 35
96. 0
97. 16
98. 5
99. 0
100. 10

Page 359

1. 378
2. 792
3. 288
4. 90
5. 584
6. 405
7. 45
8. 616
9. 176
10. 231
11. 375
12. 552
13. 36
14. 304
15. 567
16. 225
17. 108
18. 36
19. 144
20. 70
21. 90
22. 490
23. 864
24. 150
25. 272

Page 360

1. 44
2. 273
3. 276
4. 295
5. 104
6. 51
7. 252
8. 291
9. 44
10. 284
11. 84
12. 78
13. 175
14. 255
15. 290
16. 388
17. 162
18. 33
19. 258
20. 96
21. 455
22. 266
23. 344

24. 192
25. 285

Page 361

1. 770
2. 1,771
3. 484
4. 3,074
5. 5,170
6. 3,216
7. 2,590
8. 8,008
9. 561
10. 3,869
11. 3,162
12. 8,118
13. 2,914
14. 1,116
15. 1,260
16. 7,722
17. 2,523
18. 2,432
19. 4,686
20. 1,092
21. 522
22. 3,416
23 713
24. 1,298
25. 7,275

Page 362

1. 1,568
2. 3,872
3. 2,664
4. 3,038
5. 576
6. 3,626
7. 4,158
8. 1,421
9. 3854
10. 1,748
11. 3,752
12. 2,964
13. 2,788
14. 2,596
15. 2,304
16. 6,461
17. 5,621
18. 1,914
19. 2,233
20. 4,704

21. 2,945
22. 2,700
23. 4,118
24. 6,935
25. 4,264

Page 363

1. 3,080
2. 3,875
3. 1,260
4. 5,553
5. 5,391
6. 2,802
7. 1,284
8. 1,982
9. 930
10. 1,010
11. 3,846
12. 1,738
13. 1,816
14. 4,270
15. 864
16. 3,528
17. 602
18. 6,147
19. 2,648
20. 3,664
21. 4,788
22. 1,089
23. 6,699
24. 1,718
25. 2,370

Page 364

1. 1,981
2. 2,076
3. 7,384
4. 1,592
5. 2,384
6. 4,055
7. 1,848
8. 1,236
9. 1,074
10. 2,559
11. 5,456
12. 1,053
13. 1,272
14. 7,956
15. 3,716
16. 393
17. 2,422

Answer Key *(cont.)*

18. 4,010
19. 597
20. 7,640
21. 1,728
22. 3,328
23. 2,184
24. 1,125
25. 3,405

Page 365
1. 2,547
2. 4,476
3. 985
4. 738
5. 896
6. 5,481
7. 4,374
8. 2,205
9. 6,376
10. 1,812
11. 1,028
12. 4,398
13. 4,254
14. 4,988
15. 261
16. 2,680
17. 228
18. 3255
19. 576
20. 4590
21. 498
22. 4004
23. 109
24. 5769
25. 4522

Page 366
1. 37,351
2. 47,124
3. 5,248
4. 24,012
5. 32,034
6. 11,856
7. 10,934
8. 29,634
9. 34,056
10. 38,184
11. 23,304
12. 58,044
13. 83,979
14. 52,785

15. 31,140
16. 25,704
17. 9,177
18. 4,995
19. 13,498
20. 15,950
21. 20,925
22. 13,545
23. 34,892
24. 25,428
25. 7,696

Page 367
1. 18,531
2. 4,131
3. 29,481
4. 51,810
5. 21,600
6. 4,408
7. 16,215
8. 80,132
9. 76,930
10. 28,028
11. 53,361
12. 26,109
13. 34,336
14. 41,922
15. 15,916
16. 13,365
17. 32,580
18. 54,096
19. 49,329
20. 7,228
21. 10,336
22. 14,055
23. 25,637
24. 31,668
25. 20,460

Page 368
1. 45
2. 162
3. 368
4. 27
5. 2,208
6. 6
7. 270
8. 155
9. 60
10. 388
11. 6,992

12. 230
13. 170
14. 9
15. 3,713
16. 140
17. 88
18. 56
19. 114
20. 35

Page 369
1. 8,625
2. 2,548
3. 48,546
4. 56
5. 25
6. 1,100,337
7. 23,324
8. 86,044
9. 1,925
10. 43,798
11. 3,598,771
12. 12,643
13. 54
14. 7,209
15. 27
16. 2,924
17. 37,422
18. 12
19. 12
20. 45

Page 370
1. 5
2. 7
3. 8
4. 7
5. 5
6. 8
7. 6
8. 3
9. 5
10. 0
11. 4
12. 8
13. 5
14. 7
15. 4
16. 9
17. 0
18. 6

19. 7
20. 5
21. 2
22. 7
23. 9
24. 9
25. 2
26. 6
27. 8
28. 4
29. 0
30. 3
31. 9
32. 4
33. 4
34. 3
35. 9
36. 6
37. 9
38. 9
39. 5
40. 7

Page 371
41. 1
42. 4
43. 8
44. 1
45. 3
46. 3
47. 1
48. 6
49. 0
50. 2
51. 3
52. 9
53. 3
54. 5
55. 4
56. 0
57. 6
58. 0
59. 6
60. 2
61. 7
62. 9
63. 3
64. 4
65. 3
66. 0
67. 2

Answer Key *(cont.)*

68. 6
69. 8
70. 1
71. 0
72. 1
73. 8
74. 5
75. 6
76. 7
77. 2
78. 4
79. 8
80. 5
81. 3
82. 8
83. 2
84. 1
85. 1
86. 1
87. 0
88. 2
89. 7
90. 1

Page 372
1. 3 r1
2. 1 r2
3. 1 r1
4. 5
5. 2
6. 2 r2
7. 2
8. 1r1
9. 1 r3
10. 2 r1
11. 2 r1
12. 4
13. 1 r1
14. 6
15. 3
16. 1 r3
17. 1
18. 1 r3
19. 1
20. 9

Page 373
1. 4
2. 2 r2
3. 1
4. 4

5. 1 r2
6. 1 r3
7. 3 r1
8. 2
9. 1 r2
10. 1 r2
11. 7
12. 1 r3
13. 1 r3
14. 2 r1
15. 2 r1
16. 1 r1
17. 4
18. 6
19. 1 r1
20. 1 r2

Page 374
1. 19
2. 11 r1
3. 27
4. 9 r5
5. 10 r2
6. 21 r1
7. 6
8. 93
9. 5 r3
10. 27
11. 16 r3
12. 20 r2
13. 15 r4
14. 21
15. 9 r3
16. 22
17. 1 r4
18. 14 r2
19. 9 r1
20. 13 r2

Page 375
1. 5
2. 4 r3
3. 11 r6
4. 10 r7
5. 8 r4
6. 15 r1
7. 9 r4
8. 8 r7
9. 20 r2
10. 13 r4
11. 11 r 2

12. 16 r2
13. 46
14. 37 r1
15. 25 r1
16. 13 r1
17. 7 r4
18. 2 r6
19. 33 r1
20. 11 r5

Page 376
1. 442
2. 311
3. 269 r1
4. 124
5. 725
6. 31 r1
7. 233 r1
8. 133
9. 135 r1
10. 170 r4
11. 90 r8
12. 79 r2
13. 52 r2
14. 47
15. 190 r2
16. 191 r2
17. 106 r8
18. 122 r1
19. 162 r4
20. 120 r5

Page 377
1. 42 r1
2. 111 r2
3. 80 r1
4. 55 r6
5. 18 r1
6. 93 r2
7. 39 r1
8. 53
9. 49 r6
10. 118 r2
11. 94
12. 187 r2
13. 83 r2
14. 92 r1
15. 515
16. 46 r1
17. 39
18. 419 r1

19. 218
20. 107 r6

Page 378
1. 36 r7
2. 25 r4
3. 25 r6
4. 79 r1
5. 108 r2
6. 128 r2
7. 66 r2
8. 174 r3
9. 110 r1
10. 184 r3
11. 355 r1
12. 192 r1
13. 77 r6
14. 47 r3
15. 35
16. 69
17. 133
18. 217 r2
19. 93 r2
20. 78

Page 379
1. 9 r31
2. 5 r71
3. 9 r18
4. 7 r18
5. 20 r16
6. 34 r10
7. 18 r3
8. 7 r53
9. 9 r22
10. 16 r5
11. 12 r21
12. 6 r39
13. 19 r38
14. 2 r13
15. 4 r27
16. 10 r52
17. 10 r24
18. 6 r12
19. 5 r71
20. 5 r29

Page 380
1. 9 r1
2. 12 r3
3. 6 r5
4. 49 r13

Answer Key (cont.)

5. 57 r9
6. 10 r61
7. 5 r34
8. 54 r3
9. 27 r21
10. 14 r31
11. 20 r1
12. 3 r48
13. 11 r12
14. 54 r12
15. 29 r16
16. 37 r2
17. 18 r9
18. 19 r13
19. 16 r2
20. 37 r2

Page 381

1. 9 r24
2. 7 r48
3. 4 r14
4. 26 r2
5. 8 r59
6. 13 r37
7. 3 r54
8. 6 r35
9. 18 r13
10. 27 r8
11. 26 r8
12. 11 r65
13. 11 r20
14. 16 r2
15. 12 r18
16. 45 r3
17. 10 r27
18. 3 r28
19. 10 r28
20. 4 r85

Page 382

1. 1 3/4
2. 2 1/7
3. 2 2/5
4. 1 2/5
5. 1 2/3
6. 1 7/9
7. 3 1/3
8. 1 1/13
9. 1 1/11
10. 4 1/2
11. 1 1/3

12. 3 1/2
13. 1 5/8
14. 1 1/5
15. 2 2/3
16. 1 1/4
17. 3 1/5
18. 1 9/10
19. 1 1/4
20. 1 1/6
21. 1 1/3
22. 1 1/2
23. 2 1/2
24. 1 1/3
25. 1 7/11
26. 1 4/5
27. 1 1/8
28. 1 1/2
29. 1 1/7
30. 1 2/7
31. 2 1/5
32. 1 1/5
33. 1 5/9
34. 1 1/2
35. 1 1/4
36. 1 5/13
37. 1 1/6
38. 1 1/8
39. 2 3/8
40. 3 1/2

Page 383

1. 24/5
2. 16/5
3. 19/7
4. 22/3
5. 37/4
6. 12/7
7. 19/2
8. 49/5
9. 21/8
10. 48/5
11. 38/8
12. 15/9
13. 75/9
14. 61/8
15. 51/6
16. 53/9
17. 17/6
18. 23/5
19. 22/6
20. 9/5

21. 26/6
22. 89/9
23. 43/6
24. 4/3
25. 14/3
26. 33/6
27. 59/7
28. 57/9
29. 14/4
30. 49/8
31. 28/3
32. 64/9
33. 15/6
34. 17/2
35. 69/7
36. 13/8
37. 27/4
38. 47/8
39. 73/9
40. 34/5

Page 384

1. 3
2. 3 2/3
3. 7 1/2
4. 1 1/2
5. 6 1/3
6. 5
7. 5 3/4
8. 11
9. 3 1/2
10. 8
11. 3 3/8
12. 8 4/7
13. 5 3/8
14. 15
15. 23
16. 134 1/2

Page 385

1. 1 13/24
2. 1 33/56
3. 2/3
4. 1 27/40
5. 14/15
6. 1 2/15
7. 29/30
8. 1 11/21
9. 1 1/36
10. 32/45
11. 1 31/45

12. 1 11/40
13. 1 7/15
14. 31/42
15. 1 4/63
16. 1 11/36

Page 386

1. 1 1/14
2. 1 3/8
3. 59/72
4. 1 7/15
5. 5/8
6. 1 3/14
7. 1 1/12
8. 19/28
9. 1 16/45
10. 1 1/24
11. 1 5/14
12. 1 1/7
13. 5/6
14. 11/30
15. 1 19/56
16. 1 2/35

Page 387

1. 7 1/18
2. 13 1/4
3. 12 3/5
4. 8 4/9
5. 11
6. 10 53/72
7. 7 47/63
8. 10 13/63
9. 4 5/24
10. 7 5/6
11. 8 7/12
12. 9 16/21
13. 6 1/2
14. 16 8/9
15. 7 67/72
16. 16 1/30

Page 388

1. 1/12
2. 5/8
3. 3/8
4. 1/3
5. 2/3
6. 0
7. 4/5
8. 1/2
9. 1/2

Answer Key *(cont.)*

10. 1/5
11. 8/11
12. 3/5
13. 1/10
14. 1/4
15. 1/3
16. 1/14

Page 389
1. 1/14
2. 4/15
3. 1/45
4. 4/9
5. 19/36
6. 11/56
7. 8/21
8. 3/35
9. 3/40
10. 1/2
11. 1/6
12. 5/72
13. 2/3
14. 4/9
15. 1/72
16. 7/24

Page 390
1. 1/5
2. 10/27
3. 1/10
4. 1/3
5. 16/63
6. 2/3
7. 9/32
8. 1/18
9. 2/5
10. 3/8
11. 14/27
12. 7/24
13. 10/27
14. 1/12
15. 2/15
16. 1/3
17. 3/7
18. 2/35
19. 4/15
20. 2/27
21. 4/9
22. 1/12
23. 3/16
24. 1/2

Page 391
1. 8/21
2. 2/5
3. 4/27
4. 1/20
5. 5/18
6. 5/24
7. 2/7
8. 7/32
9. 35/48
10. 2/9
11. 56/81
12. 8/81
13. 1/6
14. 4/21
15. 1/4
16. 10/27
17. 1/4
18. 1/16
19. 5/14
20. 2/9
21. 1/3
22. 7/24
23. 1/8
24. 1/15

Page 392
1. 2/5
2. 2 1/3
3. 5/14
4. 27/35
5. 5/6
6. 9/28
7. 5/8
8. 5/16
9. 32/35
10. 3/7
11. 5/6
12. 3/16
13. 1/3
14. 1 5/9
15. 3/5
16. 1/4
17. 1 1/8
18. 1 1/3
19. 1 2/3
20. 3/10
21. 1 1/2
22. 1 2/3
23. 1 13/15
24. 1 1/3

Page 393
1. 6
2. 1 1/3
3. 7/12
4. 1 1/8
5. 1 1/2
6. 3
7. 1 1/35
8. 3 15/16
9. 1 1/6
10. 1/5
11. 6/7
12. 1 2/3
13. 35/36
14. 1
15. 3/5
16. 5/9
17. 1 1/8
18. 1 1/4
19. 8/15
20. 27/28
21. 1 1/2
22. 1/2
23. 3/4
24. 16/63

Page 394
1. 3/16
2. 5/6
3. 2 2/3
4. 3/14
5. 1 1/8
6. 1 11/24
7. 1 1/5
8. 1 1/4
9. 9/14
10. 2/3
11. 2/3
12. 1 1/8
13. 1 1/2
14. 2 1/4
15. 1 1/3
16. 5
17. 1 7/9
18. 1 3/4
19. 2/3
20. 7/9
21. 1/6
22. 2
23. 1 3/32
24. 1

Page 395
1. <
2. >
3. <
4. >
5. >
6. <
7. <
8. >
9. >
10. >
11. <
12. <
13. >
14. <
15. >
16. <
17. >
18. >
19. <
20. >
21. <
22. <
23. <
24. <
25. <
26. <
27. <
28. <
29. >
30. >
31. >
32. >
33. <

Answer Key (cont.)

Page 396
1. 5 birds, 10 fish, 30 dogs, 15 cats, 5 rabbits
2. 25, 20, 15, 25
3. Accept any reasonable explanation.

Page 399
1. watermelon
2. grapes
3. watermelon, peaches, plums, apricots, grapes
4. watermelon 1/2, peaches 1/4, plums 1/8

Page 400
1. homework, 30 minutes; snack, 5 minutes; clothes, 6 minutes; video game, 9 minutes; walking the dog, 10 minutes
2. Answers will vary. Check as a class exercise.

Page 401
1. 25 cups
2. 55 cups
3. 10 quarts
4. 20 cups
5. 10 pints
6. 23 cups
7. skunk cabbage
8. mushrooms
9. 12 1/2 cups
1. 5 pounds
2. 320 ounces
3. 10 pounds
4. 13 1/2 pounds
5. 110 pounds

Page 402
1. 2786 miles
2. 1440 miles
3. 206 miles
4. 2037 miles
5. 802 miles
6. 840 miles
7. 1329 miles
8. 1058 miles
9. 2873 miles
10. 2976 miles
11. 963 miles
12. 417 miles

Page 403
1. David Peterson
2. $5.80—Kathryn Ross
3. Barbara Marshall
4. no
5. no
6. 614
7. $48.00

Page 406
a new bicycle

Page 407
steal its chair

Page 408
1. $.94
2. $.84, $.08
3. 2792
4. 30,251
5. 483
6. 48,404
7. $3.60
8. $14.35
9. 84
10. 214

Page 409
1. a. 50   b. 4th grade
2. a. 98 km   b. no
3. a. $284.95   b. yes
4. a. 7   b 13
5. a. $3.07   b. $29.19
6. a.$37.36   b. $34.64

Page 410
1. 43
2. 576
3. $10.76 each
4. 855 holes
5. 14
6. 5
7. $7.11
8. 9
9. $19.83
10. 264

Page 411
1. 90
2. 5
3. 33
4. 180
5. 73
6. 249, 11 left over
7. 78, 3 left over
8. 20
9. 3
10. 6

Page 412
1. south
2. north
3. west
4. east
5. north (top) south (bottom)
6. east (left) west (right)
7. west (left), east (right), and south (bottom)
8. west (left), north (top), east (right), and south (bottom)

Page 413
Ending square is bottom left corner square.

Page 414
1. point A: 5 miles—F, 9 kilometers—E, 4 kilometers—C
2. point B: 2 kilometers—A, 12 kilometers—G, 7 kilometers—E
3. 3 miles—D, 6 miles—A, 1 mile—F

Page 415
1. 900
2. 200
3. 500
4. 1400
5. 800
6. 500
7. 1500
8. 700

Page 416
1. 20 miles
2. 10 miles
3. 40 miles
4. 20 miles
5. 20 miles
6. 10 miles

Page 417
4.A. North America
   B. South America
   C. Antarctica
   D. Europe
   E. Africa
   F. Asia
   G. Australia

Answer Key *(cont.)*

Page 418
1. Southern, Eastern
2. Northern, Eastern
3. Northern, Western
4. Northern, Western
5. Northern, Eastern
6. Northern, Western
7. Northern, Eastern
8. Northern, Eastern
9. Northern, Western
10. Southern, Western
11. Northern, Eastern
12. Northern, Western
13. Northern, Eastern
14. Southern, Western
15. Southern, Eastern
16. Southern, Eastern

Page 419
1. latitude
2. longitude
3. latitude
4. longitude

Page 420
1. Grand Junction
2. Sterling
3. Denver
4. Lamar
5. Durango
6. Colorado Springs
7. Glenwood Springs
8. Campo
9. Craig
10. Kanorado

Page 421
3. Continents:
   North America
   South America
   Asia
   Australia
   Antarctica
   Europe
   Africa
   Oceans:
   Pacific
   Atlantic
   Arctic
   Indian

Page 422
1. J
2. G
3. B
4. D
5. F
6. C
7. I
8. H
9. E
10. A

Page 424
1. Where
2. There eight
3. toe
4. grown
5. would
6. which roll
7. hair tail
8. know sew
9. air
10. road steel
11. Too sea
12. fair pair
13. hear planes
14. Four boars
15. They're seen
16. role witch

Grammar

Page 425
1. The snow | was falling heavily during the night, depositing one foot on the ground.
2. The streets and highways | were closed for many hours.
3. All the schools in the area | had delayed opening for two hours.
4. Most of the elementary school students | did not attend school at all.
5. Many high school students | were stranded on an overturned bus.
6. A helicopter and an ambulance | transported the injured students to the hospital.
7. Another major storm | pounded the area, dumping another four feet of snow.
8. The board of education | decided to close the schools for two weeks.
9. At first the children | enjoyed ice skating, building snowmen, and sledding.
10. The regular school year | was extended for two weeks into the month of July.
11. The Little League baseball game schedule | was revised and altered.
12. The local pools and beaches | changed their lifeguard schedules.
13. Many vacation plans | needed to be adjusted or cancelled.
14. The highlight of the summer, the county fair, | continued as planned.

Page 426
1. is the strongest muscle in the body— (is)
2. is enclosed in the skull— (is enclosed)
3. attaches the eye to the brain— (attaches)
4. broke his femur during the baseball game— (broke)
5. could distinguish color at an early age— (could distinguish)

Simple Subject	*Simple Predicate*
1. puzzles—	help develop
2. clues—	are
3. students—	check
4. Maryanne—	keeps
5. cryptogram—	is
6. puzzle—	has
7. puzzle—	includes
8. puzzle solver—	hunts
9. children—	like
10. Summertime—	is
11. Michael/Joe—	join
12. Joan—	read
13. Heather—	was
14. lifeguards—	awarded
15. librarian—	distributed

Answer Key *(cont.)*

Page 427
1. <u>equipment</u> <u>is</u>—inverted
2. <u>whales</u> <u>are</u>—inverted
3. <u>Susan</u> <u>greeted</u>—natural
4. <u>tiger</u> <u>climbed</u>—inverted

Page 428
1. (you)
2. we
3. you
4. animals
5. (you)
6. (you)
7. relatives
8. priests
9. Jessica
10. Sam
11. mural
12. pyramids

Page 429
1. summer time year
2. weather children swimming
3. schools people time vacations
4. days hours sunlight
5. pool beach lake
6. teacher Mr. Dawson Metropolitan Museum of Art New York City July
7. care concern visitors
8. friends Tim Carol Statue of Liberty Ellis Island
9. scent flowers Central Park lunch
10. hamburgers grill backyard

Person	Place	Thing	Idea
Ms. Lizt	France	clouds	happiness
Dr. Forest	city	shoelaces	science
	building	bicycles	loyalty
	Texas	sounds	fairness
		glasses	love
		table	pain

Page 430
1. President of the United States—proper
   George Washington—proper
2. Eiffel Tower—proper
   attraction—common
   Paris—proper
3. John Glenn—proper
   astronaut—common
4. bridges—common
   Golden Gate Bridge—proper
   California—proper
   George Washington Bridge—proper
   New York—proper
5. Space Needle—proper
   attraction—common
   Seattle, Washington—proper

1. D
2. F
3. H
4. J
5. G
6. A
7. C
8. I
9. E
10. B

1. P
2. C
3. C
4. P
5. P
6. P
7. P
8. C
9. C
10. P

Page 431
1. foxes
2. knives
3. apples
4. stereos
5. ladies
6. families
7. monkeys
8. giraffes

1. singular, plural
2. plural, plural, plural, singular
3. singular, singular, singular
4. plural, plural
5. plural, plural, plural, plural, singular
6. plural, plural
7. singular, plural
8. plural, singular, singular, plural
9. plural, plural, plural
10. singular, singular

Page 432
1. Mr. Briggs' or Briggs's
2. men's
3. birds' or bird's
4. sister's
5. puppies'
6. mouse's
7. libraries'
8. women's
9. Fred's
10. guitar's
1. girls'
2. teacher's
3. babies' or baby's
4. players'
5. deer's
1. cat's, cats'
2. mouse's, mice's
3. runner's, runners'

Page 433
Days of the Week
Sun.
Mon.
Tues.
Wed.
Thur.
Fri.
Sat.
Months
Jan.
Feb.
Mar.
Apr.
May
Je
Jul
Aug.
Sept.
Oct.
Nov.
Dec.
Titles
Mr.
Dr.
Rev.
Pres.
Sen.

Answer Key *(cont.)*

Gov.
Capt.
Gen.
Prof.
Jr.
Sr.
Streets
Dr.
Ave.
Rd.
Blvd.
Pkwy.
Hwy.
St.
Pl.
Ln.
Places
Ft.
Mt.
Riv.
Nat'l Pk.
States
NY
NJ
CA
TX
WN
IL
KY
General
° C
° F
U.S.N.
D.A.

Page 434

1. I
2. We
3. he
4. They
5. she
6. She, I
7. he
8. They
1. she
2. he
3. It
4. he
5. They

Carl and he like to water-ski in the summer.
He and I like to water-ski in the summer.

Page 435

1. My
2. mine, yours
3. Your, mine
4. her
5. My, our
6. his
7. Their
8. their
1. themselves
2. ourselves
3. herself
4. himself
5. yourselves
6. herself
7. yourself
8. ourselves

Page 436

1. it
2. her
3. him
4. them
5. us
6. her, him
7. me
8. us

1–6. Answers will vary.

Page 437

1. she, Wanda
2. it, Biking
3. they, Craig and Bill
4. she, Carla
5. her, Louise
6. their, Bob and Jim

1. their
2. it
3. He
4. her
5. their
6. she
7. their
8. He

Page 138

1. Everybody
2. Neither
3. anyone
4. Each
5. Somebody
1. no one, his
2. one, she
3. each, his
4. either, his

Page 439

1. flashed—PA
2. raced—PA
3. is—linking
4. looked-linking
5. smelled—linking
6. captured—PA
7. are—linking
8. covered—PA
9. skidded—PA
10. formed—PA
11. pulled—PA
12. appears—linking
13. seems—linking
14. became—linking

Page 440

1. has sketched
2. have visited
3. is elected
4. can serve
5. will be needed
6. has planted
7. were dressed
8. has been closed
9. will reopen
10. are circling
11. could control
12. have collected
13. will be going
14. have won

Page 441

1. will take off—future
2. left—past
3. landed—past
4. was—past
5. steers—present
6. waits—present
7. meets—present
8. beats—present
9. will shine—future
10. played—past
11. rises
12. protected
13. launched
14. will circle
15. roamed

Page 442

1. drove, us
2. brought, it
3. read, newspaper
4. picked, apples
5. collected, papers
6. found, us
1. A. bought
   B. CD
   C. Us

Answer Key *(cont.)*

2. A. send
   B. letter
   C. Him

Page 443

Subject	Predicate	Predicate Adjective
1. soup	was	hot, delicious
2. room	was	dark, cool
3. Statue of Liberty	is	famous
4. wind	was	fierce, cold
5. We	felt	happy
6. Jodi	felt	relaxed
7. lights	are	colorful
8. game	was	unbelievable
9. whistle	sounds	low
10. rain	was	cool, chilling

1–5. Answers will vary.

Page 444

1. rush(es) rushed rushed
2. ruin(s) ruined ruined
3. pass(es) passed passed
4. try(tries) tried tried
5. grade(s) graded graded
6. provide(s) provided provided
7. slip(s) slipped slipped
8. roam—present
9. climbed—past participle
10. live—present
11. killed—past participle
12. studied—past

Page 446

1. said	2. ran	3. chosen
4. stolen	5. grow	6. written
7. took	8. fallen	9. flew
10. froze	11. saw	12. ridden
13. broken	14. froze	15. eaten
16. gave	17. grew	18. caught

Page 447

1. given
2. known
3. spoken
4. torn
5. ran/runs
6. written
7. gone

1. go(es) went gone
2. come(s) came come
3. throw(s) threw thrown
4. eat(s) ate eaten
5. fly(ies) flew flown
6. forget(s) forgot forgotten
7. begin(s) began begun
8. buy(s) bought bought
9. hear(s) heard heard

Correct Principal Parts: 2, 6, 9, 10, 13, 14, 16, 19

Page 448

1. May	2. can	3. laid
4. lie	5. left	6. Let
7. Leave	8. set	9. sat
10. raised	11. rises	12. raised
13. risen	14. learn	15. taught
16. teach	17. learned	18. taught
19. Let	20. Can	

Page 449

1. holds		1. is
2. protect		2. are
3. places		3. have
4. cross		4. Were
5. gives		5. have

Page 450

Subject	Verb
1. one	hurts
2. neither chicken nor fish	tasted
3. Jim and Steve	play
4. dog	seems
5. people	are
6. You	are
7. you	have heard
8. Everyone	loves
9. James and Carla	have
10. All	were
11. Someone	took
12. English and science	are
13. No one	knows
14. Either Lisa or I	will call
15. Aunt Maggie and Uncle Fred	ran

Page 451

1. favorite—which kind
2. front—which kind
3. Eight—how many
4. cloudy, rainy—which kind
5. chocolate—which kind
6. well-baked cheese-covered—which kind
7. Nine—how many
8. cute little Dalmation—which kind
9. The—which one
10. flashing, two—which kind, how many
11. tourist—which kind
12. long, winding—which kind
13. many large, small—how many, which kind
14. Five hot, tired, happy—how many—which kind (3)
15. Several—how many

1. The big hairy
2. six
3. wet
4. this

Answer Key *(cont.)*

Page 452
1. these
2. Those
3. This
4. this
5. this
6. These
7. those
8. those
9. The
10. the
11. These
12. them
13. those
14. Those

Page 453
1. small
2. funnier
3. bigger
4. tallest
5. more thrilling
6. most difficult
7. better
8. fewest

1. better
2. happy
3. biggest
4. lonelier
5. more enjoyable
6. most
7. nice

Page 454
1. accidentally—was discovered
2. usually—is prescribed
3. badly—were treated
4. very—famous
5. really—slender
6. best—grow
7. greatest—English
8. swiftly—rode
9. always—delivered
10. financially—were ruined
11. elaborately—how
12. usually—when
13. thickly—how
14. Often—when
15. here—where

Page 455
1. firmer—C
2. fastest—S
3. usually—P
4. less—C
5. most often—S
6. steadily
7. farther
8. higher
9. hardest
10. most skillfully

Page 456
1. adjective—teacher
2. adverb—waited
3. adverb—ended
4. adjective—desserts
5. adverb—paints
6. slowly—steadily
7. smoothly—quickly
8. terribly—fierce
9. suddenly—ferociously
10. famous—amazing
11. beautifully—beautiful
12. sure—surely
13. attentive—attentively
14. real—really

Page 457
1. good
2. well
3. badly
4. good
5. well
6. good
7. any
8. ever
9. anything
10. anywhere
11. any
12. any

Page 458
1. I enjoy going to the theater and ice skating.
2. I eat lunch with Mary and Brian in the school cafeteria.
3. Debra can swim faster than Henry, but Henry won the race.
4. I don't like to go mountain climbing, and I don't like building things.
1. "Oh!" said Sylvia . . . forward.
2. Ouch! The hammer hit my finger.
3. Hey, wait for me.
4. Oh no! What did I do with my homework?
5. Well, that might just work.
6. Ah, I see what you mean.
7. Ssh, be quiet so he doesn't hear you.
8. Ugh! What an ugly shirt!
9. Wow! I've never seen a bug like that before.

Page 459
1. alongside
2. into
3. around
4. over
5. in front of
6. among
7. against
8. beneath
9. through
10. across

1. C
2. I
3. H
4. D
5. E
6. B
7. G
8. J
9. A
10. F

Page 460
1. around the playground
2. one the next block
3. except the broccoli
4. out of the front door
5. over the foul line
6. like me
7. since breakfast
8. with a shout of hello
9. from Aunt Rose
10. Into the mailbox
11. near the road
12. Alongside the stable

Answer Key *(cont.)*

Page 461

1. C	2. D
3. B	4. A
5. J	6. G
7. H	8. I
9. F	10. E

uncooperative	illogical	irregular
disapprove	incorrect	misunderstand
improper	nonsense	unbalance
power (ful)	farm (er)	count (less)
soft (ness)	Swed (ish)	produc (tion)
respons (ible)	fool (ish)	appli (cant)
govern (ment)	art (ist)	tight (en)
danger (ous)	accept (ance)	
humid (ity)	gent (ly)	

auto | matic	multi | media	kilo | watt
micro | surgery	thermo | meter	tele | vision
geo | logy	peri | scope	photo | graph
geo | graphy	photo | genic	auto | graph
tele | phone	tele | scope	tri | pod
thermo	auto	multi
meter	photo	ology
geo	tele	micro
scope	phone	kilo

Page 462

1. Two—to	2. rode—road
3. knights—nights	4. know
5. wear—new	6. won—role
7. sun—pier	8. steak
9. steel	10. pair
11. clothes	12. plane
13. birth	14. toes
15. guests	

Page 464

1. The Eiffel Tower is located in Paris, France.
2. Rhode Island, Delaware, Connecticut, Hawaii, and New Jersey are the five smallest states by area in the U.S.
3. *The Nutcracker*, a famous ballet, is performed during the Christmas season.
4. Edgar Allan Poe wrote the thrilling short story "The Fall of the House of Usher."
5. The flight is scheduled to depart from La Guardia Airport at 10:30 A.M. and arrive in San Francisco at 5:30 P.M.
6. I am going to receive the magazine *Car and Driver* on the first Tuesday of March.
7. The novel The *Castle in the Attic* is an adventure story based on the Middle Ages.
8. The Statue of Liberty, a gift to the United States from France, is visible from New York City.
9. Did you see the Thanksgiving Day Parade as it proceeded down Fifth Avenue?
10. The Taj Mahal, an Indian tomb, is an example of the blending of Hindu and Muslim architecture.
11. Dr. Erica Weiss
12. *Sports Illustrated*
13. Mr. James Frank
14. Dallas, Texas
15. Park Place
16. George Washington Bridge
17. 5:40 A.M.
18. *The Island of the Blue Dolphins*
19. Pres. Ronald Reagan
20. The Civil War

Page 465

1. How do male humpbacks communicate to the female humpback whales?
2. What an incredible landing the pilot made!
3. Great! Your performance on the test was nearly perfect!
4. The New York Knicks played the Chicago Bulls in Madison Square Garden.
5. The Super Bowl was broadcast at 6:00 P.M. on Jan. 31, 1999.
6. Which president was elected first, Franklin D. Roosevelt or Rutherford B. Hayes?
7. Mrs. B. B. Johnson, Jr. was chosen to lead the parade.
8. Watch out! A deer is crossing the highway.
9. Oh, no! The elephants are stampeding the audience!
10. Wow! My bedroom will be 20 ft. long and 15 ft. wide.
11. Mr. James Mulligan
12. Mt. Rushmore
13. the year 456 B.C.
14. P.O. Box 345
15. Rev. Jesse Jackson
16. J. H. Thompson and Co.
17. I. Museums of New York
    A. Guggenheim
    B. Metropolitan Museum of Art
    C. Museum of Natural History

Page 466

1. "Please give our guest a warm welcome," said the host of the talk show.
2. "Governor, how will the new tax increase affect the local schools?" asked the reporter.
3. "Be careful driving to work," warned the meteorologist. "Freezing temperatures have caused black ice to form on the roads."
4. Mars, Jupiter, Venus, and Saturn are planets in our solar system.
5. The baby's tears wouldn't stop for hours.
6. The *Titanic* sank in the Atlantic Ocean on April 15, 1912.

Answer Key *(cont.)*

Page 468
Vocabulary
1. confident
2. glider
3. aerodynamic
4. exceeded

Comprehension
1. Most people believed that flight was not possible because the machines used to fly were heavier than air.
2. Three achievements Orville Wright made prior to 1886 were
   a. he built a printing press
   b. he started a printing business
   c. he developed a weekly newspaper edited by Wilbur
3. Both brothers were involved in
   a. a weekly newspaper
   b. renting and selling bicycles
   c. manufacturing bicycles
4. When Otto Lilienthal, a pioneer glider died, the brothers, upon reading about his work, became interested in aerodynamics.
5. 1900, Kill Devil Hill near Kittyhawk, North Carolina.
6. They felt that the data that they had on air pressure and curved surfaces was inaccurate, so they built a wind tunnel to make their own pressure tables.

Page 469
1900	D 1901	B 1902 F
1903	E 1905	C 1908 A

Page 471
Vocabulary
1. C   2. E   3. B
4. F   5. A   6. D

Comprehension
1. April 1912; The vessel was luxurious, having the best of everything. It was believed to be unsinkable.
2. The hull had sixteen watertight compartments and even if two compartments flooded, the ship would still float.
3. Mr. and Mrs. John Jacob Astor and Isidor and Ida Strauss
4. It departed from Southampton, England, and was to arrive in New York City.
5. They only had room for 1,200 people, fewer than the persons on board.

Page 472
Cause and Effect
2. Effect—The steel became brittle from the cold, causing cracks to appear instantly in the hull of the ship and the seams to unrivet. Water poured inside, further weakening the hull.
3. Cause—The radio operator on the California was not on duty.

4. Effect—Accept all reasonable answers. Many passengers died and the *Titanic* went down. Help was too far away.
5. Effect—Water flooded through the hull to the ship's bow.
6. Effect—The passengers were encouraged.
7. Effect—Accept all reasonable answers such as:
   a. The ship's captain goes down with his ship.
   b. Many people died.
8. Cause—Accept all reasonable answers such as:
   a. The steel composition of the hull was faulty.
   b. The boat was traveling too fast.

Summary—Accept all reasonable answers.

Page 474
Vocabulary
1. gentleman's agreement   2. ban
3. immigrants   4. quota
5. excluded   6. restriction

Comprehension
1. The Chinese Exclusion Act was passed because people in the United States feared that Chinese laborers would work for less money.
2. American laborers were afraid they would lose their jobs to immigrants willing to work for lower pay. Others believed the newcomers were inferior to the people already living in the United States.
3. Prior to the 1880s—countries in Northern and Western Europe.
4. It sought to establish severe quotas for immigrants from southern and eastern European countries.

Page 475
5. Italy 5,082 people per year
   Russia 2,784 people per year
   Greece 307 people per year

Prefixes
(Sentences will vary.)
1. ex
2. in
3. pre
4. re
5. im
6. in

Page 477
Vocabulary
1. agriculture
2. resent
3. conserve
4. prosper

Cause and Effect
1. C
2. A
3. D
4. B
5. E

Answer Key *(cont.)*

Comprehension

1. A. They moved on to new land after depleting fertile soil.
    B. They plowed up natural grasses to plant wheat.
2. Californians called the people who migrated from the Great Plains region to California, "Okies," (derived from Oklahoma). It was used by some to mean dumb and lazy.
3. Some farmers, not wanting to share their surplus food with the Okies, destroyed it.
4. Labor camps in the San Juaquin Valley were created giving relief and education to the migrants.
5. A. Steinbeck wrote the novel, *The Grapes of Wrath*
    B. Lange photographed and documented the misery of the migrants.
    C. Guthrie sang songs about the lives and the problems of migrants.

Page 479

I. Pat Nixon
   A. renovated the White House
   B. made the White House into a Museum of American Heritage
   C. supported volunteerism in the community
   D. acted as the goodwill ambassador to Europe

II. Betty Ford
   A. public awareness of breast cancer
   B. supporter of Equal Rights Amendment
   C. made the public aware of alcohol and pain medication addiction
   D. founder of the Betty Ford Clinic for Substance Abuse

III. Rosalyn Carter
   A. presidential advisor
   B. official presidential representative to Central and South American countries
   C. took notes at cabinet meetings
   D. supported mental health reform, Society Security reform legislation, and the approval of the Equal Rights Amendment

Comprehension

1. Pat Nixon
2. Rosalyn Carter
3. A. Pat Nixon—community volunteerism
    B. Betty Ford—breast cancer/addiction
    C. Rosalyn Carter—mental health reform, Social Security reform, Equal Rights Amendment

Page 481

VCR video cassette recorder—taped programs when people were not at home

CD compact disc—enhanced sound for listeners of recorded music

PC personal computer—entertainment and productivity

Comprehension

1. A. Buy or rent video tapes of movies and watch whenever

    they chose.

B. Record a movie or show from television to watch at their leisure.
C. Watch a show on one channel while taping a show on another channel.
D. A new line of stores that sold and rented videos was the fastest growing 1980s industry.
2. Television studios recorded programs for viewing in different time zones or for repeat usage
3. A. Sony introduced the Betamax in 1975
    B. Matsushita released a VHS, video home system
4. Microchip technology, modems, and user friendly software

Page 482

VCRs

#7—It helped form a new line of business.
#8—It was the fastest growing industry in the 1980s.
#9—It was used in the entertainment industry.
#10—It is used for home entertainment.

Alike

#1—It is more affordable.
#3—Prices became lower.
#10—It is used for home entertainment.

Computers

#2—It is expensive.
#4—It advanced because of microchip technology.
#5—It was used by schools.
#6—It used a modem and software.
#10—It is used for home entertainment.

Page 484

Sequences

A. 9	F. 6
B. 3	G. 2
C. 1	H. 7
D. 4	I. 5
E. 10	J. 8

Sequence of Creating a Painting

A. He sketched a picture.
B. He made individual drawings of each element in each scene.
C. He made full-size charcoal drawings.
D. He made color sketches.
E. He painted the picture.

Paragraph (Accept all reasonable efforts.)

Page 486

Vocabulary

1. C
2. B
3. A
4. B
5. C
6. A

Complete the sentence

1. mother of the civil rights movement
2. Tuskegee, Alabama
3. NAACP (National Association for the Advancement of Colored People); Voters' League

Answer Key *(cont.)*

4. seamstress
5. vacate her seat on the bus for a white man
6. Edgar Daniel Nixon; Dr. Martin Luther King
7. A. Blacks were harassed, black leaders were arrested; many people lost their jobs.
   B. The United States Supreme Court ruled the Alabama bus segregation laws unconstitutional.
   C. The bus company lost $75,000 in revenues.

Page 487
8. A. walking
   B. carpooling
   C. riding bicycles
   D. riding mules
9. 381
10. Unconstitutional

Paragraph (Accept all reasonable answers.)

Page 489
True or False
1. True
2. False; Sweden
3. False; Brazilian and Swedish
4. False; Brazilian
5. True
6. True
7. False; junior league
8. False; knee

Fact or Opinion
2. Fact
3. Opinion
4. Fact
5. Opinion
6. Fact

Page 491
I. Early Life
  A. August 9, 1808
  B. Salem, Massachusetts
II. Education
  A. private school
  B. Public Latin School
  C. Harvard College
  D. Harvard Medical School
III. Places of Study
  A. Massachusetts
  B. France
  C. England
IV. Employment
  A. Pre-Civil War
    1. Boston Medical practice
    2. Worked for the abolitionists to help slaves escape to the North
  B. Civil War
    1. Doctor for the Union soldiers fighting in Virginia

2. Campaigned for and succeeded in having the Senate begin an army ambulance corps
V. Accomplishments
  A. improved public health by making people aware of how TB was spread.
  B. helped create health boards to monitor public health
  C. served on health boards
  D. in 1879 became the president of the American Medical Association
  E. spokesman for public health issues
  F. encouraged women to enter careers in medicine
Evaluation (Accept all reasonable answers)

Page 493
1. flour
2. five

Rhyming Patterns
Stanza 2
Line 1: fair, 3, wear, 4, there
Line 2: claim, 5, same
Stanza 3
Line 1: lay, 3, day, way
Line 2: black, 5, back
Stanza 4
Line 1: sigh 3, I, 4, by
Line 2: hence, 5, difference

Page 494
Line 3, Line 4
Line 5
Comprehension
1. nine
2. in a wooded area with two roads that diverged in different directions
3. the author, Robert Frost
4. Which road shall he take?
5. He took the road that was grassy and less traveled.
6. It has made all the difference in his life.

Page 495
1. It indicates that he is not afraid to explore a less familiar area
2. curiosity
   individuality
   confidence
   sense of adventure
3. It is easier, more accepted, and chosen by the majority.
4. a. Doing what is conventional does not always lead to the best outcome.
   b. You must make decisions for yourself and have the courage to carry them out.

Answer Key *(cont.)*

Page 497

Vocabulary

1. A
2. E
3. D
4. B
5. C

Comprehension

1. A. metaphor—*like* or *as* is not used
   B. Accept all reasonable answers, such as *a rock is strong and holds up well over time.*
2. simile—uses the word *like*, in *like a rock*
3. the poet, Edna St. Vincent Millay

Page 498

4. a brooch
5. It is not something she really needs, but she treasures it more than anything else she owns.
6. Accept all reasonable answers such as, it is not a necessary item in her life.
7. She wishes she had inherited her mother's courage.
8. Accept all reasonable answers.

Page 499

1. edge
2. divisor
3. quotient
4. product
5. sum
6. difference
7. dividend
8. addends
9. even
10. odd
11. fraction
12. numerator; denominator
13. estimate

Page 500

14. factors
15. mixed
16. prime
17. positive; negative
18. mean or average
19. median
20. range
21. capacity
22. mass
23. discount
24. mode
25. volume
26. variable
27. congruent
28. exponent
29. integers
30. multiple

Page 503

1. E
2. C
3. D
4. B
5. A
6. I
7. H
8. G
9. J
10. K
11. F
12. 7
13. 3
14. 6
15. Answers will vary.
16. 8
17. 0 + 6 = 6; 6 – 6 = 0
18. 4
19. 3
20. 7
21. 8 x (4 + 6)
22. (5 + 9)
23. n = 8
24. n = 8
25. n = 64

Page 504

1. 60
2. 3,700
3. 458,000
4. $3.00
5. $17.80
6. $351.70
7. 36,200
8. 460,000
9. $58.00
10. 74,500
11. 19,500
12. 52,500,000
13. 850,000
14. 36,499
15. 84,999
16. 37,499,999
17. 649,999
18. $73,900,000

Page 505

1. 389 389 + 359 = 748
2. 1,245 1,245 – 789 = 456
3. 12,164 12,164 – 3,489 = 8,657
4. 1,999 1,999 + 6,975 = 8,974
5. 1,919 1,919 + 13,989 = 15,908
6. 19,806 19,806 + 16,565 = 36,371
7. 40,000 + 90,000 = 130,000
8. 80,000 – 20,000 = 60,000
9. 40,000 + 40,000 = 80,000
10. 70,000 – 30,000 = 40,000
11. 90,000 + 30,000 = 120,000
12. 3,000 + 6,000 = 9,000
13. 6,000 – 2,000 = 4,000
14. 5,000 + 3,000 = 8,000
15. 6,000 – 4,000 = 2,000

Page 506

1. Est. Ans.—700 coins, Act. Ans.—621 coins
2. Est. Dif.—$6,000, Act. Ans.—$5,423
3. Est. Attend.—500 people, Act. Attend—431 people
4. Est. Mileage—1,200 mi., Act. Mileage—1,228 mi.
5. App. Profit—$50,000, Act. Profit—$49,499

Page 507

1. 3 + 7 = 10 9.63
2. 5 – 2 = 3 2.99
3. 10.00 + 0.00 = 10 10.01
4. 0.6 – 0.4 = 0.2 0.045
5. 7 + 3 = 10 9.57
6. 15 – 8 = 7 7.8
7. 19 + 40 = 59 55.7
8. 4 – 1 = 3 3.477
9. 27 – 23 = 4 4.4
10. >
11. <
12. overestimate
13. overestimate
14. No. Cindy will not have enough ribbon to wrap the gifts. She needs 6.65 meters, and she only has 5 meters.

Answer Key *(cont.)*

Page 508
1. 20.484
2. 20.924
3. 10.3
4. 38.85
5. $73.14
6. 12.496
7. 24.824
8. 41.266
9. 57.7037
10. 60.755
11. $93.36
12. 5,488.31
13. 3.5
14. 35.655
15. 6.25
16. 162.61
17. 71.082
18. 4.325
19. 57.68
20. 4.71
21. 72.146
22. 67.0242
23. 29.36
24. 362.13

Page 509
1. 22.2 inches
2. 25 yards
3. 4.50 miles per hour
4. $30.20
5. $202.14
6. $1254.46
7. 11.97
8. $2.80
9. $41.49

Page 510
1. 1 and 6; 2 and 3; composite
2. 1 and 8; 2 and 4; composite
3. 1 and 7; prime
4. 1 and 18; 2 and 9; 3 and 6; composite

Page 511
1. $3 \times 2 \times 3 = 2 \times 3^2$
2. $2 \times 2 \times 2 \times 2 = 2^4$
3. $2 \times 2 \times 5 = 2^2 \times 5$
4. $2 \times 2 \times 2 \times 3 = 2^3 \times 3$
5. $3 \times 3 = 3^2$
6. $2 \times 2 \times 2 \times 2 \times 2 = 2^5$
7. $5 \times 5 \times 3 = 5^2 \times 3$
8. $2 \times 2 \times 3 = 2^2 \times 3$
9. $2 \times 2 \times 3 \times 3 = 2^2 \times 3^2$
10. $(4 = 2 \times 2)$; $(12 = 2 \times 2 \times 3)$ GCF = 2
11. $(10 = 2 \times 5)$; $(30 = 2 \times 3 \times 5)$ GCF = 5
12. $(20 = 2 \times 2 \times 5)$; $(30 = 2 \times 3 \times 5)$ GCF = 5
13. $12 = 2 \times 2 \times 3)$; $(18 = 2 \times 3 \times 3)$ GCF = 3
14. $(12 = 3 \times 5)$; $(50 = 2 \times 5 \times 5)$ GCF = 5
15. $(18 = 2 \times 3 \times 3)$; $(20 = 2 \times 2 \times 5)$ GCF = 2

Page 512
Multiples of 4 (4, 8, 12, 16, 20, 24, 28, 32, 36, 40)
Multiples of 2 (2, 4, 6, 8, 10, 12, 14, 16, 18, 20)
Multiples of 3 (3, 6, 9, 12, 15, 18, 21)
Multiples of 5 (5, 10, 15, 20, 25, 30 35)
Least common multiple of 3 and 5 is 15

A. 6 and 12 B. 18 and 36 C. 40 and 80
D. 20 and 40 E. 24 and 48 F. 28 and 56
G. 4 yellow, 5 blue

Page 513
Estimations will vary. Accept reasonable responses.
1. <
2. <
3. <
4. B
5. B
6. A
7. 640
8. 25,000
9. 1,700
10. 2,500
11. 2,698
12. 4,984
13. 36,624
14. 634,150
15. 350,980
16. 2,226,566
17. 20,369,349
18. 24,180,052
19. 22,217,203
20. 23,908,653

Page 514
Estimations will vary. Accept reasonable responses.
1. 63.08
2. 31.62
3. 4.452
4. 0.4185
5. 181.764
6. 226.2
7. 4.3715
8. 22,174.6
9. 50.0208
10. $10.76
11. $184.48
12. $21.89
13. 0.28
14. 789.645
15. 4.4346
16. 129.708
17. $1,0222.76
18. 43,413.311
19. 153,000
20. 53,600
21. 2.5
22. 88.4
23. 9,287.5
24. 8,600

Page 515
1. $24.97
2. 12 cm
3. 392 miles
4. 1,275 miles
5. 6,548 miles
6. $258.38
7. $28.89
8. 504 pictures $141.12

Page 516
1. C
2. D
3. C
4. C
5. 9 or 10
6. 60
7. 800
8. 79
9. 431
10. 729
11. 8,162 r5
12. 5,758 r1
13. 4684 r1
14. 4,021
15. 5342 r4
16. 5,201 r4

Page 517
1. 2
2. 0.8
3. 4
4. 2
5. 3
6. 4
7. 784
8. 25.36
9. 46.2
10. 3.5
11. 72.14
12. 23.6
13. 45.7
14. 0.57
15. 0.03584
16. 0.752 = $0.75
17. 229.714 = 229.71
18. 7.461 = 7.5

Answer Key *(cont.)*

Page 518

1. 6	2. 5	3. 200
4. 500	5. 60	6. 700
7. 885 r14	8. 2052 r40	9. 7 r1
10. 1200	11. 173 r18	12. 86 r22
13. 3.6	14. 4.27	15. 5.896
16. 0.218	17. 0.606	18. 0.465

Page 519

1. 20 miles per minute
2. 29 trays
3. 40 class sets, 8 classes
4. 134 rooms
5. 42 rolls
6. $8.50/hour
7. 2,190 miles
8. $2.55

Page 520

1. A. 12, 25, 25, 35, 73
   B. 73 – 12 = 61
   C. (12 + 25 + 25 +35 + 73) ÷ 5 = 34
   D. 25
   E. 25
2. A. 23, 23, 30, 49, 51, 88, 100
   B. 100 – 23 = 77
   C. 52
   D. 49
   E. 23

Page 521

3. A. 18, 18, 24, 36
   B. 36 – 18 = 18
   C. 24
   D. 21
   E. 18
4. A. 22, 22, 36, 42, 70, 84
   B. 84 – 22 = 62
   C. 46
   D. 39
   E. 22
5. A. 170, 200, 305
   B. 135
   C. 225
   D. 200
   E. none
6. A. 22, 45, 66, 66, 69, 77, 89
   B. 67
   C. 62
   D. 66
   E. 66

Page 522

1. 120
2. 264
3. 1737.6
4. 66.24
5. 9
6. 37
7. 776.5
8. 15.5
9. 182
10. 31
11. 444
12. 13.78
13. 7.8
14. 3.5
15. a = 3: divide by 45
16. t = 30: divide by 35
17. m = 1600: multiply by 16
18. s = 215: multiply by 215
19. f = 9: divide by 81
20. p = 24: divide by 15

Page 523

1. 3/7	2. 6/8	3. 3/4
4. 7/10	5. 8/12	6. 52/100
7. 4/8	8. 3/9	9. 18/30
10. 10	11. 35	12. 21
13. 6	14. 24	15. 2/3
16. 40/100	17. 25	18. 1/3
19. 2/5	20. 1/3	21. 2/3
22. 2/7	23. 1/4	24. 9/10
25. 87/500		

Page 524

1. 4 1/6	2. 3 1/4	3. 8
4. 5 3/7	5. 3	6. 23/7
7. 28/5	8. 65/9	9. 35/8
10. 29/10	11. 2 1/5	12. 4 3/4
13. 9 3/5	14. 9 1/4	15. 0.25
16. 0.75	17. 6.20	18. 0.5
19. 0.25	20. 0.6	21. 3.6

Page 525

1. >
2. >
3. <
4. <
5. 2/8, 5/12, 3/6
6. 3/15, 2/3, 7/10
7. 2/9, 7/18, 4/6
8. 16/50, 10/25, 3/5
9. 5/16, 2/4, 5/8

Page 526

1. 1/3	2. 6/7	3. 1/4
4. 1/2	5. 17/20	6. 1 11/35
7. 5/18	8. 1/20	9. 1/5
10. 19/24	11. 11/20	12. 11/16
13. 10 7/12	14. 3 3/8	15. 3 2/9

Answer Key *(cont.)*

Page 528
1. 3 3/4
2. 13 3/5
3. 4/9
4. 20/77
5. 45/48
6. 25 3/5
7. 3
8. 27 1/5
9. 12
10. 13/180
11. 14 6/7
12. 11 29/36
13. 5 5/7
14. 42 2/3
15. 1/15
16. 2/81
17. 25/24=1 1/24
18. 3/8
19. 4 11/48
20. 16/25
21. 37/116
22. 1/44
23. 29/32
24. 56
25. 72 cupcakes
26. 8 fireflies left for himself

Page 529
1. 12 quarts; 24 pints; 48 cups; 384 ounces
2. 8 pints; 16 cups; 128 ounces
3. 1 cup, 2 ounces
4. 31 cups, 2 ounces
5. 10 cups
6. 6 tons
7. 3.75 tons
8. 5 pounds
9. 72 ounces
10. 48 ounces
11. 5000 pounds
12. 4.5 pints

Page 530
1. 84
2. 144
3. 108
4. 288
5. 4
6. 818
7. 600
8. 2
9. 45
10. 9
11. 18
12. 27
13. 122
14. 9
15. 305
16. 512

Page 531
1. 14 hours, 5 minutes
2. 27 hours, 7 minutes
3. 12 hours, 2 minutes
4. 14 hours, 9 minutes
5. 2 hours, 4 minutes
6. 6 hours, 37 minutes
7. 1 hour, 26 minutes
8. 0 hours, 59 minutes

Page 532
1. 6.67, 6.15, 5.71, 5.33, 5.00
2. .44 hours
   .33 hours
3. a, b, c (answers will vary)

Page 533
1. C
2. B
3. C
4. A
5. A
6. m
7. km
8. cm
9. cm or mm
10. mm
11. cm
12. m
13. km
14. B
15. A
16. C

Page 534
1. 1
2. 500
3. 3
4. 100
5. 5
6. 900
7. 6.5
8. 330
9. 1
10. 1
11. 6
12. 5
13. 8
14. 7
15. 7.53
16. 8.35
17. 400
18. 3,000
19. 700
20. 6,000
21. 900
22. 10,000
23. 680
24. 15,500
25. 0.004
26. 0.007
27. 65
28. 0.07
29. 0.65
30. 0.004
31. 6.5
32. 4,000
33. 0.004
34. 7,500
35. 4,000
36. 6.5
37. 0.225
38. 3,500
39. 225,00
40. 0.057

Page 535
1. 3, 500 mm, 3.5 m
2. 6,500 m
3. 1,525 m (second half)
4. 1.35 kg
5. 1.5 g
6. 410 mL
7. 0.6 m
8. 2,825 mL
9. 1,450 cm = 1.45 m

Page 536
1. H
2. A
3. F
4. G
5. E
6. C
7. B
8. D

Page 537
1. acute; 35°
2. obtuse; 100°
3. obtuse; 140°
Questions 4 through 8: accept all reasonable measurements.
9. angle BED
10. angle CED
11. angle BEC
12. angle AEB
13. angle AED
14. E

Answer Key *(cont.)*

Page 538

1. right
2. scalene
3. equilateral
4. isosceles
5. equilateral
6. isosceles
7. scalene
8. isosceles
9. 10 degrees
10. 77 degrees
11. 70 degrees
12. 47 degrees
13. 69 degrees
14. 30 degrees

Page 539

2. 5.38 centimeters
2. 358 millimeters
3. 24.2 meters
4. 33.6 inches
5. 126 meters
6. 210 feet
7. 38 inches

Page 540

1. 37.96 m^2
2. 24 in^2
3. 13.69 cm^2
4. 67.62 m^2
5. 101.2 m^2
6. 16 cm^2
7. 0.65 cm^2
8. 11.28 cm^2
9. 900 m^2
10. 64.8 in^2

Page 541

1. 46 in^2
2. 41.76 ft^2
3. 2,430 cm^2
4. 96 ft^2
5. 10,908 in^2 or 75.75 ft^2
6. 5 centimeters

Page 542

A. 3
B. 1
C. 2
D. 4
1. Line AB
2. E
3. EA; EI; EB; EF
4. DC; GH

Page 543

1. 25.12 millimeters
2. 4.71 centimeters
3. 37.68 inches
4. 9.42 feet
5. 12.56 millimeters
6. 62.8 inches
7. 81.64 centimeters
8. 81.64 centimeters

Page 544

1. 200.96 cm^2
2. 50.24 in^2
3. 78.5 mm^2
4. 55.39 cm^2
5. 28.26 m^2
6. 84.91 ft^2
7. 254.34 in^2
8. 360.32 ft^2

Page 545

1. 135 cm^3
2. 64 cm^3
3. 264 m^3
4. 24.24 in^3

Page 546

1. 1538.6 cm^3
2. 226.08 cm^3
3. 706.5 in^3
4. 50.24 m^3
5. 904.32 cm^3
6. 803.84 cm^3
7. 4,179.34 ft^3

Page 547

Draw the lines of symmetry for each figure.

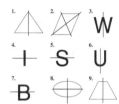

Page 548

1. translation
2. reflection
3. reflection
4. rotation
5. rotation
6. translation
7. rotation
8. reflection

Page 549

1. similar
2. congruent
3. similar
4. figure B
5. figure A

Page 550

1. A. 2 number sevens
   B. 2/6 or 2 out of 6
2. A. 1 number three
   B. 6
   C. 1/6 or 1 out of 6
3. A. 5
   B. 6
   C. 5/6 or 5 out of 6
4. 1 out of 10
5. 7 out of 10
6. 2 out of 10
7. 3 out of 10
8. 0

Answer Key (cont.)

Page 552

1. Fillings   Combinations
   Eggs   Ham
   Eggs   Bacon
   Eggs   Cheese
   3 Eggs x 3 fillings = 9 combinations
2. 2 shoes x 3 socks = 6 combinations
3. 1 x 3 x 2 = 6 choices
4. 5 x 7 = 35 combinations
5. 3 x 4 x 5 = 60 choices

Page 553

1. Celsius, Fahrenheit, Kelvin
2. a ruler or scale
3. degree
4. heat or cold
5. mercury or alcohol
6. Heat causes the molecules in the liquid to expand, and cold causes the molecules in the liquid to contract.
7. Fahrenheit, Celsius
8. water
9. 32 degrees Fahrenheit or 273 degrees Kelvin
10. 212 degrees Fahrenheit or 373 degrees Kelvin

Page 554

1. 212 degrees Fahrenheit and 100 degrees Celsius
2. 32 degrees Fahrenheit and 0 degrees Celsius
3. 20 degrees Fahrenheit; -10 degrees Celsius
4. 70 degrees Fahrenheit and 20 degrees Celsius
5. 80 degrees Celsius
6. Between 10 degrees and 15 degrees Celsius.
7. 80 degrees Fahrenheit; 30 degrees Celsius.
8. 98.6 degrees Fahrenheit or 37 degrees Celsius.

Page 555

1. 18 degrees
2. 52 degrees
3. 6 degrees
4. 25 degrees
5. 47 degrees
6. 7 degrees
7. -10 degrees
8. -16 degrees
9. -12 degrees
10. -20 degrees
11. -2 degrees
12. -5 degrees

Page 556

1. riders
2. pointer scale
3. beam
4. pan
5. object mass
6. Triple Beam Balance

7. pointer
8. left pan
9. standard weights
10. zero adjustment knob
11. right pan
12. object mass
13. scale
14. Double-Pan Balance

Page 557

1. 141 grams
2. 41.5 grams
3. 112 grams
4. 131.3 grams
5. 22.8 grams
6. 200.5 grams
7. 25 grams
8. 40 grams
9. 40 grams
10. 65 grams
11. 100 grams
12. 170 grams

Page 558

1. 30 ml
2. 18 ml
3. 55 ml
4. 50 ml
5. 30 ml
6. 50 ml
7. 20 ml

Page 559

1. 2 cm
2. 40 mm
3. 2 m
4. 800 cm
5. 5 km
6. 7000 m
7. A
8. A
9. B
10. C
Accept all reasonable answers
11. 42 mm
12. 75 mm
13. 27 mm
14. 58 mm
15. 6 cm
16. 5 cm
17. 6 cm
18. 7 cm